DORLING KINDERSLEY
MYTHS & FAIRY TALES
❖ COLLECTION ❖

❖ *Retold by* ❖
NEIL PHILIP

ILLUSTRATED BY NILESH MISTRY

DORLING KINDERSLEY
London • New York • Sydney • Delhi
www.dk.com

DK

A DORLING KINDERSLEY BOOK
www.dk.com

❖

Senior Art Editor Jacquie Gulliver

Senior Editors Alastair Dougall, Emma Johnson

Designers Lester Cheeseman, Sheilagh Noble, Robin Hunter

DTP Designer Nicola Studdart

Research Robert Graham, Natasha Billing

Picture Research Sharon Southren, Christine Rista, Kate Duncan

Production Josie Alabaster, Louise Barratt

Managing Art Editor Peter Bailey

Managing Editors Helen Parker, Anna Kruger

Consultant Sandra Dudley, Jesus College, Oxford

❖

First published in Great Britain in 1995
by Dorling Kindersley Limited, 9 Henrietta Street, London WC2E 8PS

This edition published in 1999

2 4 6 8 10 9 7 5 3 1

A CIP catalogue record for this book is available from the British Library

ISBN 0 7513 6209 3

Reproduced by Classic Scan, Singapore and Brightarts, Hong Kong
Printed and bound in Spain by Artes Graficas Toledo, S.A.
D.L. TO: 1281 - 1999

PART ONE
MYTHS
4-187

❖

PART TWO
FAIRY TALES
188-341

PART ONE
MYTHS

for
BRIAN HINTON

*Tezcatlipoca shows Quetzalcoatl his new, human
face and body in a smoking mirror, page 140*

CONTENTS OF PART ONE

Introduction   8

CREATION MYTHS

First Things • *Egyptian*   16

The Sweat of His Brow • *Serbian*   17

Out of the Ice • *Norse*   18

The Cosmic Egg • *Chinese*   22

The Floating World • *Japanese*   24

Izanami and Izanagi • *Japanese*   26

The Dreamtime • *Australian, Aboriginal*   28

An Earthly Paradise • *Iranian*   30

The Old Man of the Ancients • *Native American, Modoc*   32

Made from Mud • *Siberian*   34

Children of the Sun God • *Native American, Navajo*   36

The Food of Life • *Sumerian*   38

BEGINNINGS

The Sky World • *Indonesian*   42

Gilgamesh • *Sumerian*   44

The Great Flood • *Serbian*   49

The Origin of the Ox • *Chinese*   52

First Creator and Lone Man • *Native American, Mandan*   53

Vainamoinen • *Finnish*   54

The Gift of Fire • *Greek*   58

The Tree of Life • *Norse*   62

Loki the Trickster • *Norse*   64

Maui-of-a-Thousand-Tricks • *Polynesian*   68

Hunting the Sun • *Australian, Aboriginal*   69

The Sky God's Stories • *West African, Ashanti*   70

The Emperor of Heaven looks down on the poor people struggling to survive on earth and decides to help them, page 52

The abandoned babes Romulus and Remus are looked after by a she-wolf, page 138

The arrow refers you to related characters or stories ➤

The oracle of Apollo,
who tells mortals
of things to come,
page 96

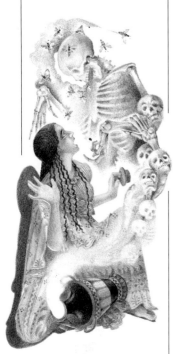

Pandora releases evils
into the world, page 60

The Apples of Youth • *Norse*   72

Earth-maker and Coyote
    • *Native American, Maidu*   74

Make Me a Man!
    • *East African, Baganda*   76

Why Do We Die?
    • *West African, Ibo*   77

FERTILITY AND CULTIVATION

Isis and Osiris • *Egyptian*   80

Persephone • *Greek*   82

World Without Sun
    • *Japanese*   84

The Sword in the Stone
    • *Celtic*   86

The Holy Grail • *Celtic*   89

Glooskap and the Wasis
    • *Native American, Algonquin*   92

Telepinu • *Hittite*   94

Cadmus and the Sown Men
    • *Greek*   96

Mother of Life and Death
    • *Indian*   98

GODS AND MORTALS

*The god Thor has
a drinking contest
with the giants,
page 122*

The Golden Touch • *Greek*   102

King Midas's Ears • *Greek*   104

Beowulf • *Anglo-Saxon*   106

Theseus and the Minotaur
    • *Greek*   108

The Fall of Icarus • *Greek*   112

Taliesin • *Welsh*   114

Going to the Palace
    • *Haitian*   117

Thor in the Land of Giants
    • *Norse*   118

Cuchulain • *Irish*   125

The Labours of Heracles
    • *Greek*   130

Thor tries to lift the giants' cat, page 123

GODS AND ANIMALS

Romulus and Remus
❖ *Roman*   138

The Plumed Serpent
❖ *Aztec*   140

The Elephant God ❖ *Indian*   144

The Cat Goddess ❖ *Egyptian*   146

King of the Birds ❖ *Indian*   147

The Winged Horse ❖ *Greek*   148

Benten and the Serpent King
❖ *Japanese*   150

The Phoenix ❖ *Chinese*   151

Enkidu and Gilgamesh grapple with the Bull of Heaven, page 45

VISIONS OF THE END

Aeneas in the Underworld
❖ *Roman*   154

The Death of King Arthur
❖ *Celtic*   156

The Voyage of Bran ❖ *Irish*   159

The Death of Balder ❖ *Norse*   162

Orpheus and Eurydice
❖ *Greek*   166

Sedna ❖ *Inuit*   168

How Big the World Is! ❖ *Inuit*   169

Atlantis ❖ *Greek*   170

The Death of Pan ❖ *Greek*   172

The Rainbow Serpent
❖ *West African, Fon*   173

Ragnarok ❖ *Norse*   174

The Purifying Stream
❖ *Iranian*   176

GODS AND PANTHEONS

Who's Who in Mythology   180

Index   342

A bee is sent to sting the angry weather god Telepinu into seeing sense, page 95

The rampaging Cretan bull, which Heracles captured as his seventh Labour, page 132

The funeral ship of Balder, Odin's son, page 163

INTRODUCTION

MYTHS ARE STORIES of the gods and of god-like heroes. They tell of beginnings and ends, creation and destruction, life and death. They explain the how and the why of life.

The word "myth" comes from the Greek *muthos* meaning a fable or a word. The Greek myths about the gods of Olympus are a major source for Western art and literature, providing a treasure-trove of stories and images that artists and writers even today – long after belief in the Greek gods has vanished – can make fresh, new, and meaningful.

But, of course, the Greek myths are only a part of world mythology. Wherever people have lived together, they have told stories about how the world came to be made, how people and animals came to live in it, and the characters and actions of the god or gods they worshipped.

A nature-spirit mask of the Inuit people

When a myth comes into existence, it is believed in a people's heart and soul. Because of this, myths are more than just stories: every myth is a shaft of human truth.

Myths and their associated rituals have often been seen as precious secrets. Even today we do not fully know what happened at the "mysteries" of Eleusis, the ancient Greek fertility cult. The cult centred on the myth of the corn goddess Demeter and her daughter Persephone, but no-one ever dared reveal its secret rites.

The Medicine Rite of the Winnebago Sioux was equally secret. It warned: "Never tell anyone about this Rite. Keep it absolutely secret. If you disclose it the world will come to an end. We will all die . . ." By the time a member of the tribe, Jasper Blowsnake, revealed the secrets in 1908, the ancient world of the Winnebago had come to an end.

Thor, Norse god of thunder, strikes the sleeping giant Skrymir with his hammer

Aztec deity Quetzalcoatl, the plumed serpent god, with his dog-shaped twin, Xolotl

One person's myth is another's religious belief; one person's truth, another's fiction. Paul Radin, to whom Jasper Blowsnake told the secret of the Winnebago Medicine Rite, quoted the words of an Inuit leader named Anarulunguaq, who, when standing on the roof of a New York skyscraper, declared: "I see things more than my mind can grasp; and the only way to save oneself from madness is to suppose that we have all died suddenly before we knew, and that this is part of another life."

Standing on the brink of this book, looking out over the myths of mankind, we too may feel lost. How can we begin to understand these stories, that meant so much to the people who told them and lived by them?

The best place to begin is at the beginning. All mythologies start by telling of the creation of the world. The Greeks, the Vikings, the Egyptians, the Chinese, the Japanese, all the peoples of Africa, and all the 500 nations of the Native Americans, each had their own version or versions of the creation. And when you begin to compare all these stories, a fascinating pattern begins to emerge.

Myths are the dreams of mankind. Like dreams, they are at once utterly strange and hauntingly familiar. The Aboriginal people of Australia, for whom myths are the true reality, call the time in which the world was created – and the ancestors shaped the land, created human beings and established their customs – the Dreamtime. However the Dreamtime is not an event in the long-distant past; it is an eternal present, part of the "dreaming", which forms a living tie between the people, the eternal ancestors, and the land. For Aboriginals, this living tie is illustrated by the "song lines", the paths that trace the Dreamtime wanderings of the eternal ancestors.

All these song lines converge at the most sacred place of all to the Aboriginals, Uluru, formerly known to white Australians as Ayers Rock. When an Aboriginal tells, enacts, or depicts the song lines, he or she actually enters the dreaming.

Persephone, daughter of the Greek goddess Demeter, pines in the Underworld

Outsiders can scarcely hope to have the same, intense experience of a myth that enables an insider to savour its full and true meaning. There will always be things we are unable to understand or appreciate, or which have been distorted in translation or retelling. But as with poetry, myths repel those who want to explain them away, and invite in those willing to listen and learn. As the ancient Greek writer Aristotle said: "The friend of wisdom is also a friend of myth."

Myths couch their wisdom, their inner meaning and mystery, in the form of stories. People everywhere love to tell and to hear stories, and that is why the myths came into being, and how they survived, and how they grew and changed. Teller and listener, when sharing a myth, are sharing a secret that will enrich them both. The poet W. H. Auden's translation of the Norse mythological poem "The Words of the High One" ends:

"Hail to the speaker, hail to the knower,
Joy to him who has understood,
Delight to those who have listened."

Joy, understanding, and delight; speech, listening, and knowledge. These are the essentials of a myth.

Norse mythology is recorded in poems that date back to when the Vikings worshipped the Norse gods, and also in prose versions written after the Vikings had converted to Christianity. At the changeover period, pagan and Christian stories often converged. Thus one side of a cross in Gosforth churchyard, Cumbria, England, shows scenes from Ragnarok, the Norse gods' final battle, and the other the crucifixion of Jesus. The Vikings were a warlike people, and when they developed their own myths from those of more peaceful Germanic tribes, they shifted the emphasis from agriculture to battle.

THE WESTERN HEMISPHERE

Kumush, the Old Man of the Ancients in the myths of the Maidu

NORTH AMERICA

Quetzalcoatl, creator god of the Aztecs

NATIVE AMERICAN
These myths have grown up from the hundreds of indigenous cultures that have evolved in North America.

AZTEC
This empire lasted from c.1200 BC to AD 1519, when it was crushed by Spanish invaders. This date had been accurately prophesied by Aztec myth.

❖ EUROPE
The conversion to Christianity of the Roman Emperor Constantine in AD 312 signalled the end for the mythologies of Greece and Rome as living religions, and also for Celtic and Germanic deities. In Scandinavia, however, the pagan Norse gods were worshipped until the 12th century.

❖ AFRICA
Many indigenous African gods and myths co-exist with Christianity and Islam. Some myths, transported to the New World by slaves, mutated into the Voodoo religion, based in Haiti.

❖ AMERICA
The Aztec and the Inca empires were destroyed by European invaders, and many of their myths were lost. The cost of recording the beautiful mythologies of native American tribes has been the destruction of their traditional culture.

The Norse giant
Hugi outruns the
mortal Thialfi

NORSE
The Norse myths were
not set down until the
13th century, after
Scandinavia had
converted to
Christianity.

*Merlin, the
enchanter of
Celtic myth*

EUROPE

GREEK
From c.800 BC to 330 BC,
belief in the Greek gods
was at its peak. Many
deities were adopted,
under different names,
by the Roman Empire.

*The oracle of
Apollo, Greek
god of the sun*

CELTIC
From c.750 BC to AD 100,
Celts occupied northern
Europe. Their myths were
set down by Roman historians and
Christian priests, and greatly
added to in the Middle Ages.

*Osiris, Egyptian
fertility god, and
Set, god of evil*

*Papa Ghede, Voodoo
god of death*

EGYPTIAN
The ancient Egyptian
religion was at its height
between c.3100 BC, when
the kingdom was united,
to about 30 BC.

HAITIAN
The myths of Voodoo, the
popular religion of Haiti
are a blend of West African
beliefs and Catholicism.

AFRICA

*A doll, made by
Kwaku-Ananse
the spider, to
catch Mmoatia,
the spirit*

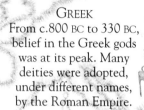

SOUTH
AMERICA

AFRICAN
Many native African
religions survive today,
occasionally spreading
to other parts of the
world, such as Haiti.

THE EASTERN HEMISPHERE

The dog – fated to serve people by Ulgan, the Siberian creator god

ASIA

Anu, the Sumerian sky god

The dragon and the unicorn are sacred animals in Chinese myth

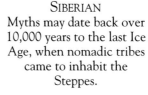

SIBERIAN
Myths may date back over 10,000 years to the last Ice Age, when nomadic tribes came to inhabit the Steppes.

The sandals of Ainu hero Aioina turn into squirrels

SUMERIAN
These myths date from at least 3500 BC. Elements from Sumerian mythology were absorbed into Christian traditions.

CHINESE
Folk myths and traditions date back to c. 2000 BC. Some were absorbed into the Taoist religion, which developed about AD 200. With Confucianism and Buddhism, Taoism is one of the main Chinese religions.

JAPANESE
The Shinto religion, which dates back to the 8th century and beyond to ancient traditions, has a rich mythology. The myths of the Ainu, Japan's first inhabitants, also survive.

Ganesha, Hindu god of wisdom

INDIAN
Hinduism, the dominant religion of India, dates back to at least 1200 BC, the date of the first Hindu texts, called the Vedas.

Bamapama, an Aboriginal trickster god

ABORIGINAL
Myths of the Dreamtime have evolved over 40,000 years, ever since the first people arrived in Australia from Asia.

AUSTRALASIA

A sea beast created from the fingers of Sedna, the Inuit goddess of the sea

INUIT
Belief in the nature spirits of Inuit mythology is alive. The Inuit have lived in the Arctic circle for over 10,000 years.

OCEANIC
Before the islanders of the South Pacific became Christians during the 19th century, they worshipped many different gods. Polynesia possessed the most organized mythology.

The sun, caught by Polynesian hero Maui

OCEANIA

❖ AUSTRALASIA AND OCEANIA
For the Australian Aboriginals, everything in the world is sacred because of its association with the Dreamtime ancestors. This makes their mythology absolutely central to their existence. In Polynesian mythology, too, life, belief, and the land are very closely linked.

❖ ASIA
These simple – though profound and wise – mythologies contrast with the complex Hindu mythology of India, which reflects its long smelting in the cultural melting pot of the Indian sub-continent. Similarly, the mythologies of China and Japan have developed in the light of sophisticated philosophies. Nevertheless, every mythology, like every religion, shares the same basic concern with the nature of the world, and the meaning of life and death.

All mythologies reflect the culture they serve. A farming people, such as the Chinese or the ancient Egyptians, especially venerated gods of agriculture and fertility. By contrast, the myths of Australian Aboriginals, who were hunter-gatherers not farmers, contain the sacred information of how to survive in Australia's vast, bare hinterland.

The stories in this book are just a fraction of the tales that make up world mythology, and some regions are better represented than others. The stories that have been written down are also just a fraction of those that have, throughout history, expressed the fears, hopes, and longings of humanity. Some myths have vanished almost without trace; others exist only as obscure fragments.

So we must be thankful to those who have recorded ancient myths for our delight and understanding. One such was Sandoval, Hastin Tlo'tsi hee, who told anthropologist Aileen O'Bryan the creation myth of the Navajo in November 1928. "I sit as on a mountaintop and I look into the future," he said. "I see my people and your people living together. In time to come, my people will have forgotten their early way of life unless they learn it from white man's books. So you must write down what I tell you; and have it made into a book that coming generations may know the truth."

Hail to the speaker, hail to the knower!

CREATION MYTHS

How did the world begin? How were people created, and why? And, when once we had been given life, why were we cursed with death? These are the first questions that the mythologies of the world attempt to answer.

Different cultures have found different solutions to these fundamental problems, but the stories in which those solutions are presented often follow a similar pattern. In the beginning, the world is in chaos, or covered in ice, or swamped with water.

A creator god comes and sets to work, separating the earth from the heavens, the sea from the land, and shaping the landscape. Then the creator peoples the earth, making human beings from drops of sweat, from plants and animals, from mud – or even from his own fleas. And then the real work starts.

Adapa breaks the South Wind's wing, and so incurs the wrath of Anu the sky god in The Food of Life – *a story that tells why mortals are "creatures of time"*

FIRST THINGS

A**T THE DAWN OF TIME**, Re gave birth to himself. Feeling that he was alone, Re spat, and from his spittle were born Shu, the air, and Tefnut, moisture. From the union of Shu and Tefnut came Geb, the earth god, and Nut, the sky goddess.

From Re's tears came the first human beings. He knitted together the mountains, he made mankind and the beasts, the heavens and the earth.

From his spittle, Re creates the universe

Each morning he rises and sails in his boat, Sektet, across the sky. At night, Nut swallows him, and in the morning she gives birth to him once more.

Nut swallows Re in his boat

THE CREATOR

Re (or Ra), the sun god, was the most important god of the New Kingdom period (1560-1070 BC) in ancient Egypt. Sometimes he was identified with Amun-Re, known as the "hidden" god because of his mysterious nature. Re was also believed to be the creator of the universe.

The serpent Apep is his foe, born from the spittle of the Great Mother, Neith. Re spends each night in combat with Apep, the chaos serpent.

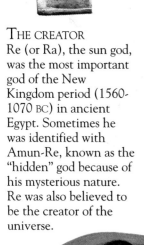

Some believe that one day, Apep may succeed in devouring Re, and then the world will end. Others say that Re will grow so old and tired that he will forget who he is. All that he has created will come to nothing.

And then, perhaps, Re will give birth to himself again.

Each night Re struggles with the serpent Apep

The Cat Goddess, page 146 ➤

THE SWEAT OF HIS BROW

God wakes up from a long sleep

I N THE BEGINNING THERE was nothing but God, and God slept and dreamed. For many ages, God dreamed. But at last he awoke.

Having roused himself from sleep, God looked around him, and every glance became a star. God was amazed. He began to travel, to see the universe he had created. He travelled and travelled, but wherever he went there was neither end nor limit.

At last he arrived on earth. He was weary and sweat clung to his brow. A drop fell to the ground, and became alive; thus the first man was made. He is God's kin, but he was not created for pleasure. He was produced from sweat and, from the beginning, he was doomed to a life of toil.

God travels the universe until he is weary and covered in sweat

A drop of sweat falls from God's brow and becomes the first man

OUT OF THE ICE

NORSE WARRIOR
This 12th-century
Swedish wall-hanging
of a warrior or king is
often thought to be of
Odin, the chief god of
Norse mythology. It is
said that Odin knew
everything that went
on in the world.

❖

THE FROST GIANTS
All of the frost giants
were descended from
the first giant, Ymir.
They were constantly
at war with the gods, of
whom they were jealous.
Often they tried to steal
the gods' treasures or
gain power over them.

ODIN IS THE ALL-FATHER. He is the oldest and most powerful of the Norse gods. Through the ages he has ruled all things. He created heaven and earth, and he made man and gave him a soul. But even the All-Father was not the very first. Listen!

In the beginning, there was no earth, no sea, no sky. Only the emptiness of Ginnungagap, waiting to be filled. In the south, the fiery realm of Muspell came into being, and in the north, the icy

As the ice melts, it shapes itself into the giant Ymir

realm of Niflheim. Fire and ice played across the emptiness. And in the centre of nothingness the air grew mild. Where the warm air from Muspell met the cool air from Niflheim, the ice began to thaw. As it dripped, it shaped itself into the form of a giant. His name was Ymir, and he was evil.

As Ymir slept, he began to sweat. There grew beneath his left arm a male and a female, and from his legs another male was created. These were the first frost giants, all descended from Ymir.

Then the ice-melt formed a cow, named Audhumla. Four rivers of milk flowed from her teats and fed Ymir. Audhumla nourished herself by licking the ice. She licked the salty blocks of ice and by the end of the first day she had uncovered the hair of a head. By the end of the second day the whole head was exposed, and by the end of the third day there was a complete man. His name was Buri and he was strong and handsome. Buri had a son named Bor, who married Bestla, the daughter of one of the frost giants. Bor and Bestla had three sons: Odin, Vili, and Ve.

The cow Audhumla licks the salty ice until she uncovers the head of a man

LAND OF FIRE
It is not hard to see where the inspiration for the fiery realm of Muspell came from. Iceland is a country of volcanoes and bubbling geysers, as well as icy glaciers. The fountain of Strokkur, shown above, is Iceland's most impressive geyser. The tranquil surface of the pool is suddenly broken as the geyser swells, creating a dome that bursts explosively. This dramatic eruption occurs roughly every nine minutes.

From the sweat beneath Ymir's left arm, a male and a female frost giant grow; from his legs, a male giant emerges

Four dwarfs, one at each corner, secure Ymir's skull in the sky

The moon is made from sparks of fire from Muspell

The Earth is surrounded by an ocean of blood

Clouds are made from Ymir's brains

Odin and his brothers make the earth from Ymir's flesh, and rocks and stones from his teeth and bones

ROCKY GIANTS
Weathered by wind, water and ice, rocks like this one in Sweden look like giant mythological figures.

Odin and his brothers hated the brutal frost giant Ymir, and they slew him. So much blood flowed from the slaughtered giant that it drowned all the frost giants save Bergelmir and his wife, who escaped in a boat made from a hollowed tree trunk.

From Ymir's flesh, Odin and his brothers made the earth, and from his shattered bones and teeth, they made the rocks and stones. From Ymir's blood, they made the rivers and lakes, and they circled the earth with an ocean of blood.

Ymir's skull they set in the sky, secured at four points by the four dwarfs named East, West, North, and South. They flung sparks of fire from Muspell high into the sky to make the sun, the moon, and the stars. From Ymir's brains, they shaped the clouds.

The earth was made in the form of a circle, and around the edge of it lay the great sea. Odin and his brothers gave Utgard to the giants as their citadel. And for themselves they established the kingdom of Asgard, protecting it from the giants with fortifications made from Ymir's eyebrows.

As they walked along the shore of the great sea, Odin and his brothers came across two logs. Odin gave them breath and life; Vili gave them brains and feelings; and Ve gave them hearing and sight. These were the first man, Ask, and the first woman, Embla, and Midgard was their home. From them, all the families of mankind are descended.

Below Midgard is the icy realm of death, Niflheim. Above it is the realm of the gods, Asgard, where Odin sits on his throne and watches over all the worlds. Asgard and Midgard are linked by the rainbow bridge, Bifrost.

At the centre of all the realms is the great ash tree, Yggdrasil, whose branches shade the world, and whose roots support it.

The land of Midgard is protected by Ymir's eyebrows

BIFROST
The way into Asgard, home of the Norse gods, was over a fiery rainbow bridge called Bifrost. Only the gods could cross this bridge, which was intended to keep mortals and giants out of Asgard. Bifrost was guarded by the god Heimdall.

ASK AND EMBLA
In Norse myth the first people were Ask and Embla. They were made by the gods from two logs, one thought to be an ash (Ask).

Ask

Embla

Odin and his brothers create the first man and woman from two logs on the shore

21

The Tree of Life, page 62 ➤

THE COSMIC EGG

YOUNG MOUNTAINS
The sharp limestone peaks of this landscape in southeastern China have been created comparatively recently by the erosive power of wind and water. They form a fitting backdrop to this story, which describes a world where humans are just insignificant fleas compared to the majesty of nature.

❖

YIN AND YANG
In ancient Chinese philosophy, all things are believed to combine the two opposites, Yin and Yang. Yin is negative, cold, dark, heavy, and feminine, while Yang is positive, light, bright, warm, and masculine. The symbol for Yin and Yang is a diagram of an egg divided into yolk and white, dark and light – Yin and Yang.

AT THE BEGINNING of time, all was chaos, and this chaos was shaped like a hen's egg. Inside the egg were Yin and Yang, the two opposing forces of which the universe is made. Yin and Yang are darkness and light, female and male, cold and hot, wet and dry.

One day, the warring energies inside this egg rent it apart. The heavier elements sank, to form the earth, and the lighter ones floated, to form the sky. And between the earth and the sky was P'an-ku, the first being. Every day for eighteen thousand years, the earth and the sky separated a little further, and every day P'an-ku grew at the same rate, so that he always filled the space between them.

*P'an-ku, the first being, bursts out of the cosmic egg
and keeps apart Yin and Yang, earth and sky*

P'an-ku's body was covered with thick hair, and he had two horns thrusting from his forehead and two tusks from his upper jaw. When he was happy, the weather was fine, but if he grew troubled or angry, it rained or a storm blew up.

People tell two different stories about the great P'an-ku. Some say that, exhausted by the labour of keeping earth and sky apart while the world took shape, he died. His body split asunder, so that his head became the mountain of the north, his stomach the mountain of the centre, his left arm the mountain of the east, his right arm the mountain of the west, and his feet the mountain of the south. His eyes became the sun and moon, his flesh the land, his hair the trees and plants, and his tears the rivers and seas. His breath became the wind, and his voice the thunder and lightning.

When he dies, P'an-ku's eyes become the sun and moon

❖

SPECIAL ANIMALS
In one of the stories about P'an-ku, he goes about the world accompanied by four imaginary animals that were highly symbolic to the ancient Chinese: a dragon, the chief of all scaly creatures; a tortoise, the chief of all creatures with shells; the phoenix, the most important of feathered creatures; and the unicorn, chief of all animals with hair.

P'an-ku's fleas became mankind. However, others say that P'an-ku, in company with the first tortoise, the first phoenix, the first dragon, and the first unicorn, wrought the universe into shape with his hammer and chisel. He ruled mankind in the first epoch of history. Every day he instructed them from his high throne, until they knew all about the sun and the moon and the stars above, and the four seas below. Listening to him, people lost their tiredness.

One morning, though, when the great P'an-ku had passed on all his wisdom to mankind, he disappeared and was never heard of again.

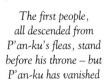

The first people, all descended from P'an-ku's fleas, stand before his throne – but P'an-ku has vanished

IMPERIAL DRAGON
This 14th-century imperial seal features a five-toed dragon, the symbol of the Emperor of China. Dragons represented wisdom, strength and goodness, and the life-giving power of water.

The Phoenix, page 151 ➤

THE FLOATING WORLD

JAPANESE WAGTAIL
This pied wagtail ranges widely over Asia and is popular in Japanese as well as Ainu myth. A wagtail made the Shinto gods Izanami and Izanagi fall in love. Wagtail bones and feathers are still used as love charms.

IN THE BEGINNING, the world was nothing but a slushy quagmire. The water and the earth were all mixed up and there was nothing but a great swamp. Nothing could live there. But in the six skies above and in the six worlds below dwelt gods, demons, and animals.

In the fog skies and hanging skies of the lower heavens, demons lived. In the star-bearing skies and the high skies of the clouds lived the lesser gods. In the skies of the most high lived Kamui, the creator god, and his servants. His realm was surrounded by a mighty metal wall and the only entrance was through a great iron gate.

Kamui made this world as a vast round ocean, resting on the backbone of an enormous trout. This fish sucks in the ocean and spits it out again to make the tides; when it moves it causes earthquakes.

One day, Kamui looked down on the watery world and decided to make something of it. He sent down a water wagtail to do the work. When the poor bird arrived and saw what a mess everything was

When the enormous trout spits, it creates the ocean tides

in, it was at its wits' end to know what to do. However, by fluttering over the waters with its wings and by trampling the mud with its feet and beating it with its tail, the wagtail at last created patches of dry land. In this way islands were raised to float upon the ocean in this, the floating world. Even today, the faithful wagtail is still carrying on its work, still beating the ground with its tail.

When Kamui created the world, the devil tried to thwart him. One morning, the devil got up and lay in wait with his mouth gaping wide to swallow the sun. But Kamui sent a crow to fly down the devil's throat and make him choke and cough. That is why the crow is such a bold bird. Because a crow once saved the world, all crows think they can act as they like, even stealing people's food.

When the animals who lived up in the heavens saw how beautiful the world was, they begged Kamui to let them come and live here, and he did. But Kamui also made many other creatures especially for this world.

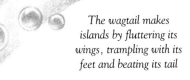

The wagtail makes islands by fluttering its wings, trampling with its feet and beating its tail

ISLAND PEOPLE
The Shiretoko peninsula is a long finger of land that reaches out into the Sea of Okhotsk from a "floating world" – the northern Japanese island of Hokkaido. The island is still home to the people who tell this story, the Ainu, Japan's first ever inhabitants.

The first people, the Ainu, had bodies of earth, hair of chickweed, and spines made from sticks of willow. That is why when we grow old, our backs become bent.

Kamui sent Aioina, the divine man, down from heaven to teach the Ainu how to hunt and to cook. When Aioina returned to heaven after living among people and teaching them many things, the gods all held their noses, crying, "What a terrible smell of human being there is!"

They sniffed and sniffed to find out where the stink was coming from. At last they traced the smell to Aioina's clothes. The gods sent him back to earth and refused to let him back into heaven until he left all his clothes behind. Down in the floating world, Aioina's cast-off sandals turned into the first squirrels.

Aioina's old sandals turn into the world's first squirrels

IZANAMI AND IZANAGI

BRIDGE OF HEAVEN
This sandbar, covered
with pines, runs right
across Japan's Wakasa
Bay. Its name,
Amanohashidate,
means "Bridge of
Heaven", recalling
the myth of Izanami
and Izanagi.

*Izanagi stirs the ocean
with a spear to create
the first island*

IN THE BEGINNING, HEAVEN and earth were not divided. Then, from the ocean of chaos, arose a reed, and that was the eternal land ruler, Kunitokotatchi.

Then came the female god, Izanami, and the male, Izanagi. They stood on the floating bridge of heaven and stirred the ocean with a jewelled spear until it curdled, and so created the first island, Onokoro. They built a house on this island, with a central stone pillar that is the backbone of the world. Izanami walked one way around the pillar, and Izanagi walked the other. When they met face to face, they united in marriage.

Their first child was named Hiruko, but he did not thrive, so when he was three, they placed him in a reed boat and set him adrift; he became Ebisu, god of fishermen.

Then Izanami gave birth to the eight islands of Japan.

And finally Izanami began to give birth to the gods who would fashion and rule the world – gods of the sea and gods of the land, gods of wind and rain. But when Izanami gave birth to the god of fire, she was so badly burned that she died.

Izanagi was furious with the fire god and cut him into three pieces. Then he set out to search for Izanami. He went right down into the Land of Gloom looking for her. He called her, saying, "Come back, my love. The lands we are making are not yet finished!"

She came to him, saying, "You are too late. I have already eaten the food of this land. But I would like to return. Wait here for me, and I will ask permission from the spirits of the underworld. But do not try to look at me."

At length, Izanagi got tired of waiting, so he broke off a tooth from the comb he wore in his hair to use as a torch and followed her. When he found her, he saw that she was already rotting, and maggots were swarming over her body. She was giving birth to the eight gods of thunder.

Izanagi drew back, revolted. Izanami called after him, "Shame on you." She commanded the foul spirits of the underworld to slay him.

While the spirits of the Land of Gloom devour bamboo shoots, Izanagi escapes

The spirits pursued Izanagi, but he managed to escape. He threw down his headdress and it turned into grapes, which the spirits stopped to eat. Then he threw down his comb, which turned into bamboo shoots, and once again the spirits stopped to eat.

By the time Izanagi reached the pass between the land of the dead and the land of the living, Izanami herself had nearly caught up with him. But Izanagi saw her coming and quickly blocked the pass with a huge boulder that it would take a thousand men to lift, so making a permanent barrier between life and death.

Standing on the other side of the boulder, Izanami shouted, "Every day I will kill a thousand people, and bring them to this land!"

THE KOJIKI
The story of Izanagi and Izanami forms part of Shinto, Japan's oldest religion. Along with many other tales, this story was preserved by storytellers, who sang them at religious festivals. The stories were not written down until the 8th century, when the Empress Gemmyo had the Shinto legends collected in a book called *Kojiki* or "Record of Ancient Things".

To escape Izanami's fury, Izanagi blocks the pass to the Land of Gloom with a huge boulder

Izanagi replied, "Every day I will cause one thousand five hundred babies to be born."

Then Izanagi left Izanami to rule the Land of Gloom, and returned to the land of the living.

Izanagi came to a grove of orange trees on a plain covered with bush clover. There he bathed at the mouth of a clear stream and, as he washed the filth of the underworld from his face, more gods were born. He wiped his left eye, and created Amaterasu, goddess of the sun. He wiped his right eye, and created Tsuki-yomi, god of the moon. He wiped his nose, and created Susanowo, god of the tempest.

When Izanagi wipes his right eye after washing in a stream, he gives birth to the moon god, Tsuki-yomi

World Without Sun, page 84 ➤

THE DREAMTIME

BURNING WILDERNESS
The vast Simpson Desert of central Australia is one of the hottest places in the world. But, to Aboriginals, even this forbidding landscape has meaning, and bears the traces of the eternal ancestors.

❖

ALCHERA
The story of the Dreamtime told here belongs to the Aranda Aboriginals of central Australia. Their name for the Dreamtime is "Alchera". A huge number of myths associated with the Dreamtime are told by Aboriginal peoples. These myths tell how the landscape was shaped and explain the characteristics of animals and birds. For Aboriginals, the Dreamtime becomes part of the present when its myths of creation are relived by being acted out in holy ceremonies.

IN THE BEGINNING the earth was a bare plain. All was dark. There was no life and no death. The sun, the moon, and the stars slept beneath the earth. All the eternal ancestors slept there too, until at last they woke themselves out of their own eternity and broke through to the surface.

When the eternal ancestors arose, they wandered the earth, sometimes in animal form – as kangaroos, or emus, or lizards – sometimes in human shape, sometimes part animal and human, sometimes part human and plant.

Two such beings, self-created out of nothing, were the Ungambikula. Wandering the world, they found half-made people. They had been created out of animals and plants, but were shapeless bundles, lying higgledy-piggledy, near where water holes and salt lakes could be made. The people were all doubled over into balls, vague and unfinished, without limbs or features.

The eternal ancestors awake and wander the earth both in human shape and in the forms of animals

With their great stone knives, the Ungambikula carved out heads, bodies, legs and arms. They made the faces, and the hands and feet. At last the human beings were finished.

Every man and woman was transformed from a plant or an animal, and each person owes allegiance to the totem of the animal or the plant that they were made from – the plum tree, the grass seed, the large and small lizards, the parakeet, the rat.

TOOL OF LIFE
This stone knife (on right) was made by the Aranda Aboriginal people and found by a European expedition in 1906. The sheath is made of bark. In this story, the eternal ancestors, the Ungambikula, use similar knives to create humans in the Dreamtime.

One of the Ungambikula frees the limbs of a human being

Their sacred work done, the ancestors went back to sleep. Some of them returned to underground homes, others became rocks and trees.

The trails the ancestors walked in the Dreamtime are holy trails. Everywhere the ancestors went, they left the sacred traces of their presence – a rock, a waterhole, a tree.

For the Dreamtime does not merely lie in the distant past, the Dreamtime is the eternal Now. Between heartbeat and heartbeat, the Dreamtime can come again.

SACRED PLACE
This Aboriginal painting is on Uluru (formerly known as Ayers Rock), a huge rock in central Australia. It is sacred to the Anangu people, who have lived in the region for over 20,000 years.

Hunting the Sun, page 69 ➤

AN EARTHLY PARADISE

THE WISE LORD
An Assyrian king,
Shalmaneser II, pays
homage to the "Wise
Lord", Ahura Mazda
(left), in a relief from
the 8th century BC.
The winged disc in the
centre symbolizes Ahura
Mazda's power.

AT THE BEGINNING, the wise lord Ahura Mazda lived in the light; his twin, Angra Mainyu, known as Ahriman, lived in the dark. Between them there was only air.

Then Ahura Mazda created time, and the world began. He brought the sunlit days and set the stars to glitter in the sky; he made the moon wax and wane and yoked the swift lightning and loud thunder to the wind and clouds. He created the Good Mind, that works within man and all creation for the best; Love is his daughter.

Ahriman came to him, set about with demons, in anger and spite. Ahura Mazda welcomed his brother with words of peace, but Ahriman spurned him. So Ahura Mazda sent Ahriman back into the darkness whence he had come. He said, "Neither our thoughts, teachings, plans, beliefs, words, nor souls agree."

Ahura Mazda created the first man, Gayomart, from the light. For three thousand years Gayomart did not move or speak, but stayed in rapt contemplation of the wisdom of the creator and the perfection of the earthly paradise he had made. Then Gayomart became the first fire-priest, tending the flame that is the sign of Ahura Mazda.

Ahura Mazda creates Gayomart, who worships his maker as a fire priest

Ahriman, banished by prayer to the outer darkness, attacked creation furiously. He broke through the sky in blazing fire. He brought many things with him: lust, starvation, disease, pain, and even death, to spoil the world. He defiled everything he touched, and rejoiced as he did so. "My victory is perfect," he crowed. "I have fouled the world with filth and darkness, and made it my stronghold. I have dried up the earth, so that the plants will die, and poisoned Gayomart, so he will die."

Ahura Mazda saw that it was safer to shackle Ahriman than to let him roam free, so he set a limit to time and trapped Ahriman inside creation. Ahriman struggled as furiously to get out of the world as he had to get in, but he could not. And so he has remained in the world, doing evil until the end of time.

Ahura Mazda sent plentiful rain to end Ahriman's drought, and the rain brought forth, from Gayomart's seed, the first human couple, Mashya and Mashyoi, from whom we are all descended.

Ahriman sends demons of suffering and death to spoil Ahura Mazda's paradise on earth

At first, Mashya and Mashyoi praised Ahura Mazda for the beauty and bounty of his creation, but then they became confused and began to praise Ahriman, even hailing him as their creator. For Ahura Mazda left all men and women free to make their own choice between what is good and what is evil.

All men are born good and the earth is happiest where one of the faithful is standing. When one of the faithful sows corn, he spreads the word of Ahura Mazda.

THE LAND OF IRAN
The continuing battle between the wise Ahura Mazda and the cruel Ahriman is reflected in the landscape and climate of Iran, from where this story originates. Barren, harsh, mountainous regions, as shown above, contrast sharply with highly fertile, coastal areas.

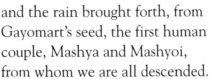

The first couple, Mashya and Mashyoi rejoice in earth's beauty – but become confused about which god created it

Mashyoi

Mashya

Therefore, Ahura Mazda made every land dear to its people and he made the lands beautiful, longing for the good and the bright. But Ahriman infected the people with sin, with disease and with sorrow.

❖

THE FIRST MAN
Gayomart, the first man, whose name meant "Dying life" in Persian, was created by Ahura Mazda. In Persian myth, Gayomart was a spirit for 3,000 years, then took human form. He died young, however, aged only 30, poisoned by Ahriman, Ahura Mazda's evil twin.

The Purifying Stream, page 176 ➤

THE OLD MAN OF THE ANCIENTS

THE CREATOR
Kumush, the Old Man of the Ancients, is the supreme god of the Modoc tribe. He created the whole world, made the Modoc's land especially for them, his chosen people, and scattered seeds over it. Modoc myth tells that Kumush could bring a man back to life if he had only so much as a single hair left on his head.

Kumush created the world. It was Kumush, the Old Man of the Ancients, who scattered seeds over the land, and asked the mountains, hills, rivers, and springs to care for them for ever. Kumush will never die. Nothing can kill him, for the bright disc he wears on his back always brings him back to life. Now he lives in the sky, but once he lived here, on earth.

One day, Kumush left his lodge and went wandering to the edge of the world. When he came back, he had a daughter with him. No one knows where she came from. He was away so long that, by the time he returned, all the people he had known had died.

He made his daughter ten fine dresses – one for each stage of her life. The tenth one was her burial dress. It was the most beautiful of all, made of buckskin and covered with bright shells.

Kumush makes his daughter a dress for each stage of her life

Kumush returns from the edge of the world with a daughter

A few days before she became a woman, she went into Kumush's lodge to dance. Afterwards, she fell asleep and dreamed that she was soon to die. When she awoke, she asked her father for her burial dress. He offered her each of the others in turn, but she refused them. She would only have the shroud.

As soon as she put it on, she died, and her spirit set out for the west. The sorrowful Kumush said, "I know all things above, below, and beyond. Whatever is, I know. I will follow her spirit down into the caverns of the House of Death."

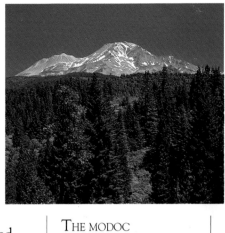

Kumush's daughter puts on the most beautiful dress of all, her burial dress

The House of Death was beautiful and full of spirits. There were so many that if every star in the sky and all the hairs of every man and every animal were counted, they would not equal the number of spirits in that house. There Kumush stayed, dancing with the spirits.

At length, he grew weary of the House of Death, and determined to return and people the earth again. He took with him a basketful of bones, but the bones shouted and dug into him, making him stumble. Twice he fell, and twice the bones leapt out of the basket and back into the caverns below.

Kumush spoke angrily to them, saying, "Bones, be quiet! Life is good!"

At last, Kumush reached the sunlight. He took the bones from the basket and sowed them in the soil. First one tribe sprang up, then the next. Last of all were the Modocs, Kumush's chosen people. "You will be a small tribe; your enemies will be many," he said. "But you will be the bravest of all."

The bones leap out of Kumush's basket and back into the caverns of the dead

Then Kumush took leave of his daughter and journeyed to the edge of the world. He took the sun's road until he came to the middle of the sky. There he built his house, and there he lives still.

THE MODOC
A small tribe, living on the California-Oregon border, the Modoc were forced from their homelands in 1864. The Modoc War followed between 1872 and 1873, when for six months around 60 Modocs kept over 1000 US troops at bay – fulfilling Kumush's prophecy of the tribe's great bravery.

PRECIOUS SHELLS
Several tribes in western North America used abalone shells to decorate clothes (such as the burial dress in this story), to wear as jewellery, and to trade as money.

MADE FROM MUD

I**N THE BEGINNING** there was no earth, only ocean. Ulgan, the great creator, came down to make the earth, but he could not think how to do it. He saw some mud that looked as if it had a body and a face floating on the surface of the water. Ulgan brought the mud to life, called the creature Erlik, and made it his friend and companion.

One day, Ulgan and Erlik, in the shape of two black geese, were flying over the water. Erlik, who was always full of pride and boastfulness, flew too high and, exhausted, fell into the water.

Erlik began to sink. Drowning, he called out for help, and Ulgan raised him up, and also commanded a stone to rise to the surface for Erlik to sit on.

THE FROZEN NORTH
This story comes from Siberia, a vast region of Russia covering about 7,511,000 sq km (2,900,000 sq miles). Parts of it, such as Kamchatka in the east (shown above) contain treeless tundra, where the subsoil is permanently frozen. In the brief summer, the tundra has numerous mosquito-infested bogs – all, according to this tale, created by the devious Erlik.

❖

WHITE CREATOR LORD
Another name for Ulgan, used by the Yakuts who live near the river Lena in Siberia, is Yryn-ai-tojon, which means "White Creator Lord".

Ulgan

Erlik, in the form of a goose, crashes into the water

Ulgan

Erlik

Newly created out of mud by Ulgan the creator god, the evil Erlik rises up out of the mire

Then Ulgan asked Erlik to dive down and fetch up some mud, to make the earth. Erlik did as he was asked, but, each time, he kept some mud in his mouth, hoping to make his own world when he had seen how it was done.

Ulgan commanded the mud to expand, and the mud in Erlik's mouth obeyed. Erlik nearly choked. He spat out the mud, and that is the reason why the earth has boggy places.

Ulgan created the first man, using earth for flesh and stone for bones. Then he made the first woman out of the man's rib. But the man and woman as yet had no living spirit. Ulgan went off to look for one to give them, leaving the first dog to guard their lifeless bodies.

Erlik came and, seeing that the dog was shivering because it had no hair, he bribed the dog to look away by offering it a warm coat. Then Erlik took a reed and blew life into the bodies of the first man and woman. Thus Erlik, and not Ulgan, became the father of mankind.

When Ulgan returned and saw what had happened, he didn't know what to do. He wondered whether he should destroy the man and woman and start again. However the first frog saw Ulgan pondering this problem and told him not to worry. "If they live, let them live. If they die, let them die." So Ulgan let them live.

As for the dog, Ulgan told it that from now on it would always have to guard humankind and live out in the cold, and if it was ill-treated by humans, that was its own fault.

SIBERIAN HUSKY
Large and powerful, with great powers of endurance, the Siberian husky is used in teams for hunting and pulling sledges. This tale tells how the close partnership between dog and humans came to be forged.

Erlik bribes the first dog to look away by giving it a furry coat

Erlik

Ulgan

The frog watches as sly Erlik blows life into the first people

❖

MYTHICAL TREE
The Yakuts believe that a mythical tree (similar to Yggdrasil, the Tree of Life in Norse myth), connects the upper world where the good Ulgan rules, the world of human beings, and the underworld, where Erlik holds sway.

Ulgan never forgave Erlik for breathing life into people. Ulgan had had enough of Erlik's sly ways, so he banished him to the underworld. There Erlik sits on a black throne, surrounded by evil spirits, who he sends out each night to carry off the souls of the dead.

CHILDREN OF THE SUN GOD

SANDPAINTING
This Navajo blanket is decorated with a sand-painting design. It shows two Holy People – perhaps White Corn Boy and Yellow Corn Girl – with the sacred maize plant, their gift to mortals. The Navajo create sandpaintings to invoke the Holy People to cure sickness among the tribe. There are over 800 different designs. Every detail of the pattern has to be correct for the sandpainting's healing power to work.

❖

SPIDER WOMAN
This wise woman teaches weaving. Spiders are protected by the Navajo, and spiders' webs are rubbed on the arms of girl babies, so that they will grow up to be tireless weavers.

THIS IS THE FIFTH WORLD. The ancestors of mankind were living in the fourth world, below this one, when a great flood came, with waves as high as mountains. The ancestors made a hole in the sky, and escaped into the world we live in now.

One day, the people heard from afar the faint "Wu'hu'hu'ú" of Hastseyalti, the talking god. Slowly the noise grew louder, until they could hear his moccasined tread, and at last he stood before them. From a piece of turquoise, he made Estsánatlehi, Changing Woman. From two ears of corn he made White Corn Boy and Yellow Corn Girl.

Changing Woman married Tsohanoai, the sun god, who carries the sun on his back and hangs it on the west wall of his house at night. He built her a home on an island far to the west, where she now lives. It is from there that the fresh breezes of spring blow and the rains come to water the Navajo country.

Changing Woman had two fine sons, Killer of Enemies and Child of Water. However, their father, the sun god, refused to have anything to do with them.

When they had grown into two strapping lads, Killer of Enemies and Child of Water decided to set out one day to find

Changing Woman grows old in the winter and young again in the spring

their father and seek his help in overcoming the many evil spirits that were tormenting mankind.

They saw a plume of smoke rising from a hole in the ground, and climbed down a ladder into a chamber. There they found Spider Woman, an old crone of great wisdom. She told them how to find the sun god's house; she also gave them a special charm to keep them safe from evil, and life-feathers from the high-flying eagle.

The brothers came to the sun god's house, on the shores of a lake. The sun god was away, so they decided to surprise him. Guarding the door were two fierce bears, but the brothers spoke the Spider Woman's charm, and the bears let them pass. The brothers hid among some rugs. The rug they chose was the rug of darkness.

As soon as the sun god returned home, he sensed someone was there. He took down the rugs. First he unrolled the rug of dawn, then the blue rug of the sky, the yellow rug of the evening light, and finally, the blue-black rug of darkness.

The boys fell out. The furious sun god threw them east against the rocks of white shell; south against the rocks of turquoise; west against the rocks of mother-of-pearl; north against the black rocks. But the brothers clutched their life-feathers and were unharmed. At last the sun god's anger cooled, and he accepted the boys as his children. He gave them magic arrows to fight evil spirits – Teelget, the man-eating antelope, the Tsenhale, huge birds of prey, and Yeitso, the scaly one.

But though Killer of Enemies and Child of Water have done mighty deeds against these evil spirits, others survive. Old Age, Cold, Hunger: these can never be slain.

Bears guard the turquoise door of the sun god's house

CULTURE OF BEAUTY

As well as being superb silversmiths and makers of jewellery, the Navajo are famous for their fine rugs and blankets, woven using wool from their own sheep. Weaving is more than just a useful skill to the Navajo; the discipline, thought and controlled breathing required is a reflection of cosmic harmony.

The sun god shakes the blue-black rug of darkness and out tumble Killer of Enemies and Child of Water, his children

THE FOOD OF LIFE

CUNEIFORM TABLET
The Sumerians invented a written language called cuneiform, which means wedge or nail-shaped. This tablet dates from 2100 BC.

A DAPA, THE INVENTOR OF LANGUAGE, was the first of the Seven Sages sent by their father, Ea, god of wisdom, to teach people the art of living. Ea gave Adapa understanding beyond that of ordinary mortals, but only a mortal span of life.

Adapa lived with the people of the city of Eridu and taught them how to worship and to pray. He baked bread for the city and set the offering table with bread and water; it was Adapa, also, who fished the waters around the city.

Each day Adapa set out from the quay in his rudderless fishing boat. With no way of steering, he was at the mercy of the winds. One day the South Wind rose against him, threatening to overturn his boat and drown him. But Adapa said, "Strong as you are, South Wind, I am stronger!"

And Adapa cursed the South Wind and broke its wing.

For seven days the South Wind did not blow. The sky god Anu, eldest and greatest, asked, "What has happened to the wind?"

His servant Ilabrat answered, "My lord, Adapa, son of Ea, has broken its wing."

Adapa, who is out fishing in his boat, curses the South Wind and breaks its wing

Anu the sky god rose in anger from his throne and ordered Adapa to be brought before him.

Ea advised his son Adapa to approach Anu in full mourning, with his hair straggling loose and his clothes torn. "When you get to the gate of heaven," Ea added, "Tammuz will be guarding the way. He will ask you why you are in mourning. You must answer, 'I am mourning for you.' He will laugh and let you through. But do not accept any bread or water that you are offered, for they will be the bread and water of death."

Adapa followed his father's advice. Tammuz brought Adapa before Anu the sky god and spoke a word on his behalf; Adapa humbled himself before the great god, and explained that he had only broken the wing of the wind when he was threatened by a storm.

Anu listened to him, and forgave him. But still Anu's heart was heavy. "Why did Ea send you to wretched mankind, to teach them the ways of the gods? Why trouble yourself with human beings? For the life of a man is but the wink of a god's eye. Come Adapa, eat and drink the bread and water of eternal life." But Adapa refused the bread and water of life, thinking that Anu was playing a trick on him.

Adapa humbles himself before the great god Anu

"Well," said Anu, "you have made your choice. You could have lived for ever, but now you will one day die."

So Adapa returned to Eridu, full of the knowledge of death. It was his father, Ea, who had really tricked him out of eternal life, for Ea knew that mortals are creatures of time, while the gods carry on forever.

The bread and water of life

❖

ANU
The Sumerian god Anu was the first and most important god, the god of heaven, and ruler of the universe. He lived in the third highest heaven, far removed from mortals, but he was respected for his wise judgement and sense of justice. He was also the keeper of the bread and water of life.

Gilgamesh, page 44 ➤

BEGINNINGS

Once given life, human beings must be taught, and their immortal teachers may be wise and helpful, or mischievous and cruel. But the price of wisdom can be great, even for the gods – as Odin discovers when he gains knowledge through suffering on Yggdrasil, the Tree of Life.

Having passed on vital knowledge to humankind, creator gods and other beings may retire to homes in the sky, or mysteriously disappear. But sometimes they become angry at people's wrongdoing and decide to destroy their own creation. Myths of a great flood, such as the one Noah survived in the Bible, are found worldwide – here, in the Sumerian story of *Gilgamesh* and the Serbian tale entitled *The Great Flood*.

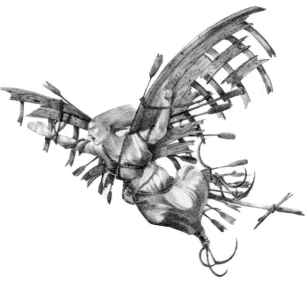

The hag Louhi turns herself into a hideous bird-woman in Vainamoinen, *a story that tells of an epic struggle to obtain a magical mill of plenty*

THE SKY WORLD

PUPPET MYTHS
Indonesia has a centuries-old tradition of shadow-puppet shows, called *wayang*. Puppets like the one above are used to dramatize all kinds of mythological tales.

HERE ONCE WERE THREE BROTHERS and two sisters who lived up above, in the sky world. One day, Parpara, the youngest brother, went out fishing and lost a fish hook that he had borrowed from his brother Hian, who was the eldest of the three.

Hian was furious with his little brother. "I must have that fish hook!" he shouted. "Go and look for it!"

So Parpara dived into the water to search for the fish hook. After a long while, he came upon a fish, which asked him what he was looking for. Parpara explained, and the fish promised to help him. Eventually, they came across another fish, which was choking in its death-throes. Something sharp was stuck in its throat – the missing fish hook.

Parpara returned the hook to Hian, but that wasn't the end of the matter. Parpara was very angry about the bossy way his big brother had spoken to him. He decided to get his own back.

Hian knocks into Parpara's jug of wine

A fish helps Parpara find Hian's fish hook

Parpara

Fish choking on hook

ISLAND FISHERMAN
This story begins with an argument over a fish hook – in former times a valuable possession. Fishing is still carried out all around the islands of Indonesia, often by fisherman using traditional outrigger canoes.

Parpara hung a jug of palm wine above Hian's bed, just where Hian was bound to knock into it when he got up.

Sure enough, Hian fell into the trap. As he got out of bed, his head smacked into the jug, which fell on to the floor, spilling its contents everywhere.

"Now look what you've done," shouted Parpara. "You've spilled all my palm wine. I want it back!"

So Hian began to scrape and dig, trying to stop the palm wine seeping into the earth. He dug so furiously that he made a hole right through to the world below.

When the brothers saw the hole, they forgot about their quarrel.

"I wonder what could be down there?" said Parpara.

"Let's see," Hian replied.

They tied a dog to a rope, and lowered it down. When they pulled it up again, the dog had pure white sand on its paws.

Intrigued, the brothers decided to discover for themselves what the world below was like. All three brothers and one of their sisters climbed down,

The brothers and sisters climb down a rope leading from the sky world into the world of human beings

each person taking a dog with them. Finally, it was the turn of the second and younger sister. As she began to descend, her brothers looking up at her made her feel nervous. She made the rope shake so much that it attracted the attention of the other people who lived in the sky world. As soon as they saw what was going on, they pulled her back up into the sky world, and the rope with her.

So Parpara, Hian, their brother and sister, and their four dogs, were trapped for ever on the world below, the world that we now live in, and they became our ancestors.

WHITE SANDS
This tale comes from the Kai Islands in southeastern Indonesia. It is not surprising that, in the story, the brothers' dog had white sand on its paws, for the islands are famous for their white sand beaches.

❖

THE FIRST MEN
The mythology of Oceania is rich and varied. Another myth from the Kai Islands relates that the first men emerged from the ground. In other Oceanic myths people are born from birds' or turtles' eggs, from a clot of blood, or from stone or wood carvings.

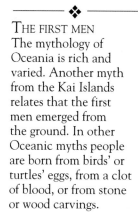

GILGAMESH

EPIC HERO
Gilgamesh was the hero of an epic poem first written down between 1800 and 1600 BC. This carving shows him with a lion.

GILGAMESH, LORD OF URUK, was shaped by the gods to be a king among men. Two-thirds divine, he had perfect beauty, courage, and wisdom. He was as proud as a young bull.

Gilgamesh crossed the ocean to the edge of the sunrise. He journeyed far to find out the secrets of the world, and to bring back the story of the time before the Flood. He built the city of Uruk, where the story of Gilgamesh is carved in tablets of stone.

Now Gilgamesh was so fine in his glory that no man could stand against him, and no woman could resist him.

Aruru, the goddess of creation, decided to create a comrade for Gilgamesh. She spat into her hands, took a pinch of clay, and threw it down into the wilderness. In this way she created Enkidu, the warrior, the child of silence, the strong. His body was covered in hair like an animal; he knew nothing of mankind.

A woman from the temple of Ishtar, the goddess of love, tamed him, wild Enkidu, who was born in the hills like a falling star. She woke in his heart the thoughts of a man. She took him to Uruk, to challenge great Gilgamesh. "I am the strongest," cried Enkidu. They fought like two bulls, but at last Gilgamesh overpowered him. From struggle came friendship, closer than the love of man for woman.

Gilgamesh

Ishtar

Ishtar, the goddess of love, wants Gilgamesh to be her husband

Together, Gilgamesh and Enkidu roamed the world, for Gilgamesh had a restless heart.

Ishtar desired Gilgamesh. "Be my husband," she said, "and I will set the world at your feet." But the hero refused, saying to her, "To which lover have you ever been faithful?"

Ishtar's desire turned to hatred. She went to her father Anu and her mother Antum. "Gilgamesh has scorned me," she said. "Father, make me a Bull of Heaven to destroy Gilgamesh. If you do not, I will break open the doors of hell and let the dead eat with the living."

Anu replied, "If I make the Bull, it will cause a seven-year drought." Ishtar told him, "Make the Bull."

Ishtar took the reins of the Bull of Heaven in her hands, and guided it to Uruk. It landed by the river, and with a snort opened up a chasm into which a hundred young men fell. It snorted again and opened up another chasm, which swallowed up another hundred young men. It snorted a third time and opened up yet another chasm. One hundred, two hundred, three hundred young men of Uruk fell into it.

Enkidu seized the Bull by its horns. As it frothed spittle into his face, he called out, "Gilgamesh, brother, strike with your sword!" Gilgamesh thrust his sword into the neck of the Bull of Heaven. He slew the Bull, and gave its heart to Shamash, the sun god.

Ishtar gave a great cry of grief at the death of the Bull and called down her curse on Enkidu and Gilgamesh. She summoned all the women of her temple to mourn over the body of the Bull of Heaven.

The next day, Enkidu told Gilgamesh, "Brother, I have had a dream. I saw the gods sitting in council. Anu and Shamash were there with Enlil of the earth and air and Ea, god of water. Anu said that, because we have killed the Bull of Heaven, one of us must die. Anu, Enlil, and Ea argued that my life should be forfeit. Shamash tried to save me, but he was only one against three. So I must die." And that very day, Enkidu fell sick.

Gilgamesh stayed at Enkidu's side during his long illness, as he wavered between life and death. One day Enkidu told Gilgamesh, "I have dreamt my death. The Black Bird of Death seized me in his talons and carried me to the House of Dust, the palace of Erkalla, Queen of the Dark." With these words, Enkidu died.

Enkidu holds the bull while Gilgamesh kills it

THE BULL OF UR
One of the treasures found at the ancient Sumerian city of Ur was this bull's head made of gold and lapis lazuli, which dates from about 2500 BC. Originally, the head decorated the sound box of a lyre.

THE GODDESS ISHTAR
This alabaster figure of the 3rd century BC represents Ishtar. As star of the morning, she was the goddess of war; as star of the evening, she was the goddess of love.

At the gate of Mashu, Gilgamesh faces the Scorpions, who can kill a man at a glance

Headdresses symbolizing the sky gods, Anu and Enlil

BOUNDARY STONE
In Sumeria and Babylonia, boundary stones were set up in temples or fields to record land and tax agreements. These stones were carved with symbols of the gods and goddesses who witnessed the contracts. This stone shows Anu and Enlil, the sky gods.

Still weeping for Enkidu, Gilgamesh roamed far and wide. "Why must we die?" he asked. "The gods live for ever, but we mortals come and go in a single breath. I will ask my ancestor Utnapishtim, whom the gods saved from the Flood, and gave eternal life."

Gilgamesh journeyed over plains and mountains, until he came to the twin peaks of Mashu, guardians of the rising and setting sun. At the gate of Mashu stand the terrible Scorpions, half man and half dragon, whose glance is death to man. But Gilgamesh was two-thirds divine. "Why have you come to this forbidden place?" they asked.

"I have come in search of my ancestor, Utnapishtim," he replied. "I have questions for him, concerning life and death."

"No human being, or mortal thing, has trodden this road," they said. "It is the road of utter darkness. Are you not afraid?"

"Although I am afraid, still I must go in," said Gilgamesh.

And the Scorpions opened the gate.

Gilgamesh entered the dark. Dark filled his mouth and his eyes. He reached out and clutched at the dark, but it slipped through his fingers. He kept walking, while outside the sun rose and set.

And at last, Gilgamesh walked into the light, into the garden of the sun. There, by the edge of a bitter sea, Gilgamesh found the goddess of wisdom, Siduri.

Siduri told him, "You are weary, despair is in your heart. You will never find eternal life." But Gilgamesh replied, "Though I am tired, I will speak with Utnapishtim."

"No mortal has crossed this sea of death," said Siduri. "Only Shamash, the sun, can cross the ocean. Do not try. Go home. Eat, drink, rejoice. Man must die, but life is sweet."

"Where is life's sweetness, when Enkidu is dead?" asked Gilgamesh.

"Go into the forest then," said Siduri, "and seek Urshanabi, the ferryman, who will take you across the sea to Utnapishtim. But do not touch the waters of death."

Gilgamesh came last to the home of Utnapishtim, his forefather. "I am Gilgamesh, Lord of Uruk," he said. "Far have I come, through the empty dark and across the bitter water, to ask you why men die. Enkidu, my friend, is dead, and the fear of death is upon me. Must I join him in the House of Dust? You were once a man like me. Tell me your story, Forefather."

Utnapishtim replied, "What grows, decays. The wise man and the fool both die. The dragonfly lives for the glory of the sun, then it is gone. A man grows like a reed in the river, and is cut down. Death is just like sleep, it comes to all. The gods give out the days of life, and the day of death. But I will tell you my tale."

"I lived in the city of Shurrupak, by the banks of the Euphrates, a faithful servant of the wise god Ea.

"The city grew old, and the gods grew old – Anu, the father, and his children, Enlil, Ea, Ninurta, Ennugi, Ishtar, and the rest.

"Ishtar caused trouble among men: war and unrest. The gods could not sleep for the tumult. And at last Enlil, the warrior, said to the gods, 'Let us loose the waters of the world, and drown this rabble that disturbs our rest.' And the gods agreed.

"Even Ea was bound by the gods' decision. He could not warn mankind of the flood, but he whispered the secret to my house of reeds, and the wind in the reeds whispered it to me in my sleep: 'Man of Shurrupak, tear down your house, and build a boat.'

"Obedient to the god, I built a boat, long and wide, and roofed, and took into the boat the seed of all living things. I took my family and possessions, and a male and a female of all the living creatures in the world, both wild and tame.

"For six days and six nights the tempest raged, drowning the world in a fury of wind and rain. On the seventh day, the storm calmed. I looked out from the boat, and there was nothing but water on the face of the earth. And then I wept, but that was just more water.

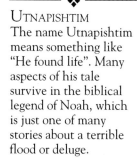

Utnapishtim builds a boat large enough to take his family and a male and female of all the creatures in the world

❖

UTNAPISHTIM
The name Utnapishtim means something like "He found life". Many aspects of his tale survive in the biblical legend of Noah, which is just one of many stories about a terrible flood or deluge.

CYLINDER SEAL
Before cuneiform writing, a method of recording information was to use a seal, or stamp. The cylinder seal, shaped like a cylindrical bead, was decorated with scenes that, when rolled on a piece of wet clay, produced a frieze. This cylinder seal, which dates from 2300 BC, shows the goddess Ishtar and the god Ea.

Utnapishtim gives Gilgamesh a secret to take home

While Gilgamesh washes himself in a pool, a snake eats the magic plant of youth

"Finally, the boat ran aground on the top of Mount Nisir. Eager to find out whether the flood was going down, I loosed first a dove, then a swallow, then a raven. The dove and the swallow both returned, exhausted, but the raven did not – it had found a resting place. In my joy, I made a sacrifice to the gods.

"As soon as Enlil smelled the sweet-scented smoke from my sacrifice, he was furious. 'Have some of these troublesome mortals escaped? All should have died. Someone must have warned them!'

"But wise Ea replied, 'The flood was too hard a fate for all humankind. This man, at least, did not deserve to die. However, I sent him no warning; the man had a dream.'

"At that, Enlil's anger cooled. He took me by the hand and set my wife by my side. We knelt, and he touched our foreheads. 'Until now, Utnapishtim was mortal. Now he and his wife shall be as the gods.' "

Utnapishtim looked hard at Gilgamesh. "Now, Gilgamesh, how will you persuade the gods to grant you eternal life?"

"I shall not give up," said Gilgamesh.

"Then first, you must stay awake for six days and seven nights."

As Utnapishtim spoke, sleep breathed over Gilgamesh like a fog. He slept for six days and seven nights. Each day Utnapishtim's wife placed a fresh loaf by his side. At last, Utnapishtim woke him.

"I have only been sleeping a minute," protested Gilgamesh.

"Lying man," said Utnapishtim. "Look at these loaves by your side. Today's is fresh-baked, but the others are stale and dry."

"Is there nothing I can do to become immortal?" cried Gilgamesh. "Death is stealing over me like sleep."

"You have worn yourself to nothing by journeying here," Utnapishtim replied, " so I will give you a prize to take home. On the far shore of the sea of death there grows a plant with sharp thorns like a rose. Once eaten, it will restore lost youth to a man."

Gilgamesh soon found the plant, which he called, "The Old Man Made Young Again". He took it back to Uruk, determined to try it on the old men of the city, and then on himself. But as he stopped at a pool to wash, a snake ate the plant.

Ever since, snakes have been able to shed their skins and become young again. But mankind, having once lost the plant of eternal youth, has never found it again.

THE GREAT FLOOD

ONCE, MEN LIVED IN paradise on earth. They worked only for pleasure, for everything they needed was provided for them. But they ignored the commands of God, and because of their folly he flooded the valley in which they lived, and they were drowned.

Only one man survived the terrible flood, having been set as a lookout on top of a mountain. His name was Kranyatz and he was a giant of immense strength.

Kranyatz fled higher and higher from the flood, until the water rose to the top of the highest mountain.

All there was for Kranyatz to cling on to was a vine, which was the walking stick of Kurent, the trickster god. Now although Kurent liked to play mischievous jokes and tricks on people, he had a kind side to his nature and was happy to help Kranyatz. So for nine years, until the flood receded, Kranyatz hung on to the vine and survived on its grapes and juice.

At the end of nine years, Kranyatz thanked Kurent for preserving him, but Kurent said, "It's not me you should thank, but the vine. Swear that you will always praise it, and love its juice more than any other food or drink." And Kranyatz swore.

After the flood, Kurent and Kranyatz argued about who should rule the earth. At last Kurent said, "Let us have a contest. Whoever can jump across the broad sea shall rule the earth, both on this side and the other." Kurent jumped first, and just wetted one foot on the other side of the ocean. But Kranyatz, who was far bigger and stronger than the feeble folk we see today, stepped easily across the sea, winning the first round.

Then Kurent said, "Let us see who will rule below the earth. It shall go to the stronger." And he stamped his foot and split the earth to reveal a great cavern beneath. But when Kranyatz stamped, the earth split open right to the bottom, where pure gold flows like a river.

For nine years Kranyatz clings to the vine that is Kurent's walking stick

Kranyatz the giant jumps over the sea and splits the earth to defeat his rival, Kurent

BLACK HELLEBORE
Known as Christmas rose because it flowers in winter, this plant grows wild in central and southern Europe. The root was formerly used to cure cattle "troubled with cough or any poisonous thing".

"Third time pays for all," said Kurent. "Let us shoot an arrow into the sky. The one who shoots highest will rule the earth and all that is above and below."

Kurent shot, and his arrow did not come back for eight days. When Kranyatz shot, his arrow did not return for nine days, and, when it fell, the rooster who guarded God's provisions was skewered on it.

"You are emperor of the world," said sly Kurent. "I am your subject." But Kurent was thinking all the while how he could win by cunning what he had lost in the trial of strength.

Kurent squeezed his vine walking-stick and pure red juice burst out of it. He went to find Kranyatz, who was enjoying being emperor of the world, and offered him some. "Very refreshing," said Kranyatz.

Kurent went away and squeezed juice from the vine again, but this time he mixed some hellebore in with it, a plant that, when plucked by moonlight, gives visions. He found Kranyatz by the river of gold. "I'm very thirsty," said Kranyatz, "for there's no water here, only gold, and it's a seven-year walk back to the world."

Kurent collects drops of red wine from his stick

Kranyatz shoots an arrow so high in the air it takes nine days to come down

"Have some of this, my lord," said Kurent, and Kranyatz drank. But one cup of wine was not enough to make big Kranyatz drunk, and he did not want to drink a second cup.

A third time Kurent squeezed the vine, and this time he added some of his own trickster blood to the juice. He went looking for Kranyatz once more, and found him sitting on the top of the highest mountain at God's own table, eating God's food. "If you are eating God's food, you really deserve a divine drink to accompany it," said Kurent. "Try this wine, it's the best there is."

Kranyatz drank and immediately his senses began to dim. He called for more wine and Kurent poured it, like an obedient servant. Kranyatz's head began to swim and he forgot where he was. And so God came back and found Kranyatz sitting at his table, having eaten his meat, lolling drunk amid the grease and bones.

God became angry and struck Kranyatz with his mighty hand. Kranyatz rolled down the mountain and lay there for many years, all bruised and broken. When he got well again, he was no longer strong. He could not step across the sea, or climb down to the bottom of the earth or up to heaven.

So Kurent the trickster ruled the world after all, and mankind has been feeble and weak ever since. Through the vine we were saved, and through the vine betrayed.

MOUNTAIN COUNTRY
The rugged landscape of Serbia, with its deep gorges and fast-flowing rivers, makes a suitable setting for this story of towering strength brought down to earth by low trickery.

Kurent fills Kranyatz's drinking horn with wine mixed with blood to put him into a drunken stupor

THE ORIGIN OF THE OX

THE SAGE'S MOUNT
The renowned Chinese sage Lao-Tzu, founder of Taoism, one of China's religions, began his wanderings riding upon an ox, as shown in this bronze.

❖

THE OX
The ox has a special place in Chinese myth. It is the second sign of the zodiac; people born under this sign are thought to be reliable and considerate. At various times in history, the ox has been protected by law. Many Chinese still feel that eating beef is a shameful way to repay an animal that puts its strength at the service of humans.

LONG AGO, LIFE was very hard – even harder than it is today. People had to struggle in the fields with their bare hands to grow enough food to feed themselves. They rarely had enough to eat – even though they worked day and night.

The Emperor of Heaven saw the poor people toiling on the earth and took pity on them. He summoned the Ox star from the sky, and sent it down to tell the people that if they worked hard, they would be able to eat well every third day.

The Ox rushed down to pass on the news. But it was a stupid creature, and so proud of being the Emperor's messenger, that it muddled the message. The Ox told the people that if they worked hard the Emperor of Heaven said they could have three meals a day!

The Emperor of Heaven did not want the people on earth

The Emperor of Heaven

to think that he broke his promises, so the Ox found itself yoked to the plough to till the fields. People just couldn't have done the work by themselves.

The Ox finds itself yoked to the plough to help mankind till the fields

FIRST CREATOR AND LONE MAN

IN THE BEGINNING, the surface of the earth was covered with water, and everything was dark. The First Creator and Lone Man were walking upon the surface of the water when they saw something move – a little duck.

They sent the duck diving right down to the bottom of the ocean, and it brought back some sand. First Creator and Lone Man used this sand to make the earth.

Lone man tells the tribe that the totem pole will protect them when he is gone

First Creator took the south and made the hill country, full of valleys and mountains and flowing streams. Lone Man took the north and made the plains, flat land with lakes and ponds. First Creator filled his land with game: buffalo, deer, and antelope. Lone Man made the cattle and sheep.

First Creator was not very impressed with the land Lone Man had made. "There's nowhere to hide!" he said.

But Lone Man just shrugged his shoulders. "Well, it's done now," he replied. "It's too late to change it."

Men and women peopled the land. When hard times came, Lone Man saw the people's suffering and wanted to share it. So he entered into some corn that a young girl was eating and she gave birth to him as a human being.

Lone Man was born as a man and lived with the girl's tribe. He was pure and good, and always the peacemaker in every quarrel. He never married, but the children loved him and followed him everywhere.

He taught the people many important things, but eventually it was time for him to leave them. So he instructed the tribe to set up a cedar trunk as a totem pole in the centre of the village, paint it red, and burn incense to it. "This cedar is my body," he said, " which I leave with you to protect you from all harm." And then he departed.

As for First Creator, he turned into a coyote.

CORN ON THE COB
The Mandan used to hunt buffalo and grow corn in the plains and fertile valleys of what is now North and South Dakota. Some cobs were braided into strings (as above) and dried.

VAINAMOINEN

❖

AGED HERO
Vainamoinen is born old. In another story, a girl, Aino, chooses to become a mermaid rather than marry him.

A wild duck makes its nest on the air-girl's knee

FINNISH FATHERLAND
Vainamoinen is credited with transforming barren ground to create the tree-covered landscape of the legends of the Kalevala, which means "Fatherland of Heroes".

A LONG TIME THIS TALE has lain in the cold, waiting to be sung: the tale of Vainamoinen, the eternal singer. Once there was a girl made of air, nature's daughter, who lived in the empty skies. She grew bored, and went down to the blue rolling sea. The wind whipped up; the waves grew fierce. And wind and wave together made the air-girl conceive a child, Vainamoinen.

Seven hundred years she carried her unborn child. Bitterly she called out to the Old Man, who holds up the sky, to deliver her from the birth-pangs.

One day, there came a wild duck, flying here and there looking for a nesting place. It landed on the air-girl's knee, jutting out of the water. There it built its nest and laid seven eggs: six of gold, and one of iron.

As the eggs hatched, the air-girl felt as if she was on fire. She shook them off, and they smashed as they fell into the sea. From the eggs came mother earth, and the heavens above; the sun, the moon, the stars, and the clouds.

Ten summers passed; the air-girl made the islands and the mainlands; but still her child was not born.

For another thirty summers, Vainamoinen wondered what awaited him in the world outside his mother's womb. Then, calling on the sun and moon for strength, he forced his way free, and his mother the air-girl returned to the skies. Eight years the sea rocked Vainamoinen before he reached land.

The bare earth gave birth to a son, Pellervoinen, whom Vainamoinen asked to sow the land with trees and flowers. When the trees grew into forests, Vainamoinen took his axe and cleared the land to plant the first barley; however he left one birch tree for the birds to rest in. Vainamoinen prayed to the Old Woman underground to nurture the seeds, and to the Old Man in the heavens to water them. And the crops grew.

Now Vainamoinen longed for a wife and he decided to search for one in the northlands. An eagle carried Vainamoinen across the sea, but the winds battered him so severely that, when he arrived, he was so exhausted he could only lie on the ground and cry for his home.

Louhi, gap-toothed mistress of the north, heard him. "What would you give me, Vainamoinen," the hag asked, "to send you home again?"

He offered her gold, he offered her silver, but she would take only one thing. "I will bring you to your own land, where the cuckoo sings, if you can forge the Sampo, the mill of plenty. Beat it out of a swan's feather and a cow's milk, from a grain of barley and a sheep's wool. I will give you my beautiful daughter in return."

"I cannot forge the Sampo," said Vainamoinen, "but Ilmarinen the smith could."

"Then fetch him," grinned Louhi eagerly, "and he shall have my daughter for his wife."

Vainamoinen sang up a wind to whisk Ilmarinen the smith to the northlands, so that he could forge the magical Sampo. Three days Ilmarinen worked at his forge. He hammered and tapped, until the Sampo was made. On one side of it was a corn mill, on the second, a salt mill, and on the third, a money mill.

The hag Louhi refuses gold and silver to allow Vainamoinen to return to his homeland. Her price is far higher – the magic mill of plenty called the Sampo

Vainamoinen whistles up a wind to blow Ilmarinen the smith to the northlands, so he can forge the Sampo

Ilmarinen begins to forge the Sampo from a swan's feather

F OLK ART
This 19th-century relief sculpture from the Old University of Turku, Finland, shows Vainamoinen playing the kantele.

T HE KANTELE
Vainamoinen created miraculous music from this harp-like instrument. His own kantele had a frame made from the jawbones of a horse; its strings were hairs from the horse's tail.

The hag Louhi was pleased with his work. She locked the Sampo behind nine locks and rooted it in the earth by magic. However, she sent Ilmarinen back home over the seas, in a ship of copper, without her daughter.

Determined to be revenged on Louhi, Ilmarinen and Vainamoinen decided to steal the Sampo; Lemminkainen, a resourceful young friend, returned to the north with them. Vainamoinen played sweet music on his kantele to lull Louhi to sleep and Ilmarinen smeared the nine locks with butter to ease them open. Lemminkainen then tried to pull out the Sampo, but its magic roots would not break. So he borrowed a northland ox and plough,

The monstrous whale

The Sampo

The mist-daughter shrouds Vainamoinen's ship in fog

cut through the Sampo's roots and stole away with it.

As the three comrades sailed homewards, Lemminkainen began to bellow out a song of triumph. Louhi awoke, heard his song and called on the mist-daughter to shroud the ship in fog. But Vainamoinen cut a way through the fog with his bright sword.

Louhi called up the monstrous whale to rise from the deep, but Vainamoinen sang it back down again. Then Louhi called on the Old Man in the heavens to summon up a storm. As Vainamoinen's ship struggled in the raging seas, Louhi came upon it in a ship filled with vengeful men. But into the sea Vainamoinen threw a piece of tinder that quickly grew into a hidden reef, and Louhi's ship foundered.

Louhi fastened scythes to her feet to act as claws, tied timbers from her ship's wreck to her arms to make wings and, using the ship's rudder as a tail, turned herself into a woman-bird, a mighty eagle. She flew after Vainamoinen and settled on the mast of his ship.

Vainamoinen cried, "Mistress of the North, will you not share the Sampo with us?"

"Never," she screamed.

Vainamoinen struck her with an oar, knocking her off the mast. But as she fell, she grabbed hold of the Sampo, pulling it after her.

Louhi and the Sampo hit the water and the Sampo fell to pieces.

❖

THE *KALEVALA*
The ancient legends of Vainamoinen were first collected and written down, in the form of a narrative poem called the *Kalevala*, in the early 19th century. By the time the editor, a Finnish scholar named Elias Lönnrot, had finished, the poem had over 22,000 verses. The *Kalevala* was the basis for the poem *Hiawatha*, by Longfellow.

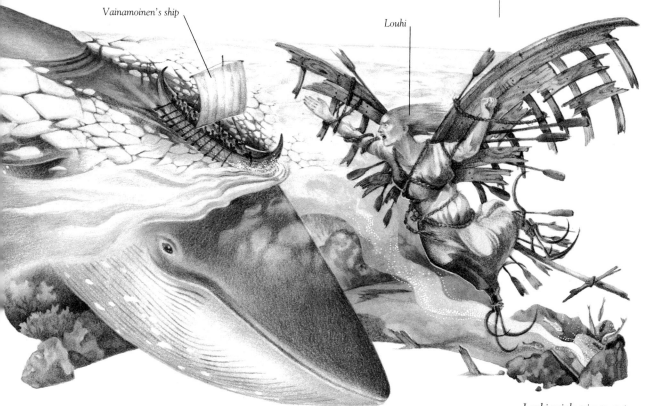

Vainamoinen's ship

Louhi

Louhi vainly tries to stop Vainamoinen's ship with fog, a whale, and by force. When her boat sinks, she becomes a terrifying eagle-woman

The corn mill and the money mill were smashed. Louhi was left with just one piece – the bare inheritance of the frozen northlands. Others, Vainamoinen gathered to enrich Finland's land. But the salt mill still rests on the sea bed, grinding out salt until the end of time.

THE GIFT OF FIRE

✦

TITANIC STRUGGLE
The Titans were the
children of Uranus and
Gaia. After a 10-year
battle, Zeus, the son of
Titans Cronus and
Rhea, overthrew the
Titans and imprisoned
them. Prometheus, also
the son of a Titan,
fought on Zeus's side.

✦

THE OLYMPIANS
The Greek gods, led by
Zeus, were known as
the Olympians after
their home on Mount
Olympus. Zeus was
married to Hera, and
was the father of many
of the Olympian gods.

WHEN GREAT ZEUS overthrew his father, Cronus – as Cronus in turn had overthrown his father, Uranus – he turned against mankind. He intended to destroy the human race and start again. But he was foiled by quick-witted Prometheus.

Now the name Prometheus means "forethought", and of all the immortal Titans, Prometheus was the most clever. This was why he sided with deep-thinking Zeus against brutal Cronus and the other Titans. Although Prometheus was immortal, he was the champion of mankind; some say he even created humans from clay and water.

Prometheus gave human beings the precious gift of thought and taught people many crafts and skills, such as how to study the stars in their orbits, and how to use them to navigate the seas.

Chariot of the sun

Prometheus tricks Zeus into taking the wrong portion of ox

Prometheus teaches mankind how to study the stars

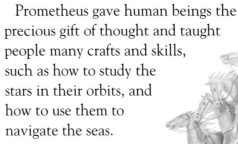

This championship of mankind angered Zeus, and his anger came to a head when Prometheus cheated the gods out of their rightful sacrifice, giving it to mankind instead. Prometheus slaughtered an ox, and divided it into two portions, wrapped in hide. The large portion was just fat and bones; the small one contained the meat. Prometheus allotted the small portion to the gods, whereupon Zeus complained. Prometheus smiled and said, "Zeus, most glorious of the gods, choose whichever you like." Of course Zeus chose the large portion. When he saw that he had been tricked, he withheld fire from mankind. "Let them eat their meat raw," he cried.

But Prometheus outwitted him. He entered Olympus, the home of the gods, stole fire from the chariot of the sun, and carried it back to earth in a fennel plant. Then he showed mankind how to use fire to cook and keep warm. When Zeus looked down on earth and saw the glow of fires, he fell into a deadly fury.

Zeus is angry when he sees fires burning on earth

HOME OF THE GODS
Mount Olympus in northern Greece soars to a height of 2,917 m (9,596 ft). The Greeks believed that this mountain was the home of the immortal gods, because it was so high that it seemed to touch the heavens.

SWEET FENNEL
Prometheus is said to have hidden fire in a fennel stalk. Sweet fennel is popular in Greece. The leaves are used as a herb and the fleshy stalk and root is eaten as a vegetable.

Prometheus shows mankind how to use fire to cook and keep warm

With the fire hidden in a fennel stalk, Prometheus steals away from Mount Olympus

PANDORA'S JAR
The scene on this Greek vase shows Pandora receiving gifts from the gods. Athena breathed life into her, Aphrodite gave her beauty, Apollo made her musical, Hermes taught her deceit. Pandora possessed all the contradictions of human nature.

Zeus took a terrible revenge on Prometheus and mankind for stealing the gift of fire. He ordered the lame smith Hephaestus to make a woman out of clay who would possess the beauty of an immortal goddess but would bring misfortune to the human race. All the gods showered her with personal gifts, and they named her Pandora, which means "all gifted".

Zeus sent Pandora as a present, not to subtle Prometheus, but to his slow-witted brother, Epimetheus, whose name means "afterthought". Prometheus had warned his brother not to accept any gift from Zeus, but Epimetheus was so enchanted by Pandora's beauty he took her for his wife.

Now Epimetheus had helped his brother distribute many gifts to mankind, and in his house he had a sealed jar that contained all the ills of disease, old age, and vice. Prometheus and Epimetheus had kept these from mankind.

Pandora couldn't help wondering what was in this jar, and one day her curiosity was too much

Pandora's curiosity gets the better of her and she opens the jar, freeing all the ills of mankind

for her. She opened the seal. Out flew all the curses of mankind, which fill our lives with suffering and misfortune. When Pandora, in her panic, replaced the lid of the jar, one thing was trapped at the bottom: Hope, who called out to her. Pandora heard the faint, sad cry and released Hope into the world to comfort mankind.

Meanwhile Zeus was planning an even crueller revenge on Prometheus. Zeus condemned him to be chained to a rock in the mountains, to endure blazing sun and freezing cold. Furthermore, each day a long-winged eagle came to gnaw at his liver. His liver grew back again during the night, so the torment was never-ending.

But Prometheus did not give in. Although wracked with agony, he mocked Zeus, saying, "I am the only god who knows the secret that will hurl you into oblivion, like your father before you. You must release me if you wish to save yourself."

For Prometheus knew that if Zeus made love to the sea nymph Thetis, as he intended, she would bear a son stronger than his father, and Zeus's reign would end. To discover this secret, Zeus eventually allowed his own son, Heracles, to free Prometheus. In return for his freedom, Prometheus warned Zeus about Thetis, and she was married instead to a mortal, King Peleus. Their son was Achilles, a hero of the Trojan War.

ZEUS AND HEPHAESTUS This detail from a Greek cup depicts a scene from a famous Greek myth: to cure Zeus of a terrible headache, his son, Hephaestus, struck him with an axe; Athena sprang, in full armour, from his head.

Each day a long-winged eagle comes to gnaw at Prometheus's liver, which renews itself at night

Persephone, page 82 ➤

THE TREE OF LIFE

Huginn

O DIN THE ALL-FATHER sometimes wanders Midgard, the middle-earth, among men. He comes disguised as an old man, leaning on his staff, and he repays kindness with riches, courtesy with wisdom, and ill-treatment with vengeance.

Each morning his two ravens, Huginn and Munnin, fly forth across the world, bringing news to Odin about mankind. Odin himself can change his shape, and while his body lies as if asleep, he can travel far in the form of a bird or beast, unknown to men.

Many stories are told of how the All-Father gained his great wisdom and his magical powers. But for every gain, there was a price to pay.

Munnin

The world tree, Yggdrasil, is a gigantic ash that towers over the world. One root is in the dread realm of Niflheim, where the serpent Nidhogg feeds on corpses, and gnaws at Yggdrasil itself. A second root is in the gods' realm of Asgard, and here dwell the Norns, three old women who rule the destinies of men. Their names are Fate, Being, and Necessity, and they keep Yggdrasil alive by sprinkling the root with pure water from the well of fate. The third root lies in Jotunheim, the land of the giants. Beneath this root is the well where the severed head of wise Mimir speaks hard words. Odin paid with one of his eyes to drink insight and knowledge from that well.

But it was on Yggdrasil itself that the High One, the All-Father, the Hooded One, the terrible Spear-Shaker, Odin of the many names, gained the secret of the runes, magic symbols by which men can record and understand their lives. For nine long nights Odin hung on the windswept tree, pierced with a spear, offering himself in sacrifice. Not even Ratatosk, the squirrel that runs up and down the tree carrying insults from the eagle at the top to the serpent Nidhogg at the bottom, offered him food or drink. At the end of his ordeal, Odin gave a great cry and, seizing the runes, fell from the tree.

When he rose again from death, Odin knew many things hidden from man. He knew how to heal the sick; he knew how to blunt his enemy's blade, and how to catch an arrow in its flight.

ONE-EYED GOD
This one-eyed figure is thought to be Odin, god of war and wisdom, and the most powerful god of Norse myth. Odin wanted to know all things, so he exchanged one of his eyes for knowledge. Then he offered himself as a sacrifice to gain the secret of the runes, or magic spells.

❖

HUGINN AND MUNNIN
Odin's constant companions were two ravens, Huginn and Munnin, whose names mean "thought" and "memory". These two birds, who fed off the bodies of the dead on the battlefield, brought information to Odin, whispering it in his ear.

◀ *Out of the Ice, page 18*

Eagle

Ratatosk

Yggdrasil

TREE ARMLET
This 10th-century gold armlet from Rabylille in Denmark is engraved with the tree of life, Yggdrasil. This giant ash tree had three roots, each one in a different world. The highest, Asgard, was where the gods lived; on the next level was Jotunheim, the realm of the giants; at the bottom was Niflheim, the land of the dead.

Nidhogg, in Niflheim   _The Norns, in Asgard_   _Mimir, in Jotunheim_

For nine nights Odin hung on the tree of life, pierced through with a spear, until, at long last, he gained the secret of the runes

God of gods, god of battles, Odin holds mankind in his care. To poets he gives sips of the mead of poetry brewed long ago by the dwarfs; to warriors slain in battle, he gives a lordly welcome in the golden halls of Valhalla.

Loki the Trickster, page 64 ➤

LOKI THE TRICKSTER

FREYJA THE BEAUTIFUL
The Norse goddess of magic, fertility, and love, Freyja was so beautiful that all ornaments were named after her. This Viking pendant representing Freyja shows the necklace Brisingamen, around her shoulders.

THE NORSE GODS were troubled in the high realm of Asgard. Their home had no wall to protect them from enemies. So when a horseman came and offered to build a wall, they listened eagerly.

"It will be a great wall," he said, "a barrier to all your foes. In eighteen months from now, all your worries will be over."

"And what is your price?" asked Odin the wise.

"Nothing less than the goddess Freyja as my wife," replied the stranger. "And the sun and moon, too."

The gods were furious, and would have thrown the man out of Asgard for daring to think that the beautiful Freyja could be bartered for building work. But cunning Loki said, "If you can build the wall in six months, it's a deal." To the other gods, he whispered, "In six months he can only build half a wall, but at least that'll be free."

The builder took one more look at Freyja, as she wept tears of gold, and agreed, as long as his horse was allowed to help him.

All through the winter the stranger worked. With the help of his horse he managed to quarry the stone for a massive wall around Asgard.

As Loki plots and Freyja weeps, the builder starts to make a wall around Asgard

Odin

Thor

Loki

Freyja

As summer approached, disaster stared the gods in the face. For, against all odds, the builder had nearly completed the wall.

"You think you're so clever, Loki," said Odin. "You got us into this; you must get us out. We cannot let Freyja marry this stranger, who must be a giant in disguise. And without the sun and moon, life will scarcely be worth living. Do something!"

So Loki thought hard, and finally he said, "Without the horse, the builder could not haul the rocks to complete his work."

Now Loki was able to change his shape, and that night, disguised as a pretty mare, he lured away the builder's horse.

VIKING SLEDGE
This sledge is part of Viking burial treasure found at Oseberg in Norway. It has curved oak runners and a decorated open box. This type of sledge was used by the Norse people for transporting goods over ice or snow.

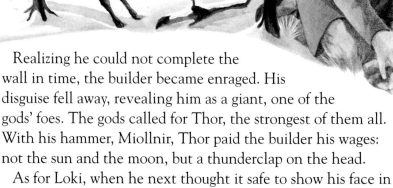

The builder's horse is lured into the woods by Loki, disguised as a mare

Thor strikes the builder with his hammer, Miollnir

Loki and Sleipnir

Realizing he could not complete the wall in time, the builder became enraged. His disguise fell away, revealing him as a giant, one of the gods' foes. The gods called for Thor, the strongest of them all. With his hammer, Miollnir, Thor paid the builder his wages: not the sun and the moon, but a thunderclap on the head.

As for Loki, when he next thought it safe to show his face in Asgard, he was leading a strange horse with eight legs, whose name was Sleipnir. Loki gave Sleipnir to Odin, saying, "No horse will ever keep pace with this one. He will bear you over the sea and through the air, and to the land of the dead and back." As Loki promised, Sleipnir never failed his new master, Odin.

Not all of Loki's offspring are like Sleipnir. Loki himself is half giant, and he has three children by a giantess. The first is the Fenris-wolf, who at the end of the world will devour Odin. The second is the Midgard serpent, and the third is the mistress of death, Hel, who feasts on hunger and thrives on sickness.

The Midgard serpent is so enormous that it encircles the world and bites its own tail

Hel, one of Loki's terrible children, feasts on hunger and thrives on sickness

FROZEN LANDSCAPE
The Norse people lived in lands of glaciers and icefields, and these features are reflected in their myths and sagas.

When Odin realized that these terrible children were loose in the world, he had them brought to him. The serpent he threw into the ocean; it was so huge it encircled the world and bit its own tail. Hel he banished to Niflheim, the Land of the Dead, and gave her power over all who die of illness or old age.

However, the Fenris-wolf was not so easily managed. Only the god Tyr was brave enough to feed it, and even he could see that the Fenris-wolf would soon grow strong enough to do terrible harm. So the gods made a strong chain and tied the wolf up. But with one kick it smashed the links. They tried again with an even stronger chain. Once again the wolf broke free.

Finally Odin asked the dwarfs for help, and they made the fetter called Gleipnir. Silky soft, Gleipnir was made of special ingredients: the sound of a cat's footfall; a woman's beard; a mountain's roots; a bear's sinews; a fish's breath; and a bird's spittle.

The gods took the Fenris-wolf to a lonely island, and challenged it to break Gleipnir. Sensing a trap, the wolf agreed to be bound only if one of the gods would put a hand in its mouth, as a token of good faith. So brave Tyr thrust his hand into the wolf's fearsome jaws.

They bound the wolf with the silken fetter, and this time

✦

TYR THE BRAVE
The god Tyr was courageous and daring, which is why he agreed to put his hand into the Fenris-wolf's mouth. He was also a war god and helped establish basic rules for fighting. Swords were often marked with a T for Tyr, which was said to bring victory in battle. Tuesday is named after the god Tyr.

The Fenris-wolf

Tyr

The gods bind the Fenris-wolf with the magic fetter, and Tyr puts his hand into its mouth

when he kicked, the fetter only tightened. Furious, the Fenris-wolf clamped its great jaws together, and bit off the god Tyr's right hand.

Even though they knew that the time would come when the Fenris-wolf would break free and bring death and destruction to them all, the gods did not kill it. "What must be, will be," they said.

✦

GLEIPNIR
The magic fetter Gleipnir was as soft as a silk ribbon, but it was much stronger than any metal chain.

The Apples of Youth, page 72 ➤

MAUI-OF-A-THOUSAND-TRICKS

MANY ARE THE STORIES of Maui-of-a-Thousand-Tricks, who fished up the islands of the South Seas from the bottom of the ocean. Maui also went down into the Underworld and brought back the secret of fire for mankind.

One day Maui said, "The days are too short – there's no time to get anything done!"

Maui set to thinking how the sun could be made to move more slowly across the sky. From coconut-shell fibres, he made a great noose with which to catch the sun, but the sun burned it up.

Then Maui cut off the sacred tresses of his wife, Hina, and wove them into a rope, fashioning the end into a noose. He travelled to the eastern edge of the sea and waited for the sun to rise.

Maui fishes up islands from the sea bed

With a rope made from his wife Hina's tresses, Maui lassoes the sun

MAUI
The trickster hero of Polynesian culture was born a premature weakling. His mother, Taranga, threw him into the sea, but he survived and grew to be a hero. This story tells of just two of his many feats of cunning and strength: fishing up islands from the sea and slowing down the sun to make daytime last longer.

At dawn, Maui flung his rope and caught the sun by the throat! The sun struggled and pleaded, but Maui refused to let it go. Eventually the sun grew so weak it could no longer run across the sky, but only creep. In this way Maui brought humans more hours of light.

HUNTING THE SUN

Bamapama was a crazy man in the Dreamtime. He was a robber and a no-good, always getting into trouble – usually for chasing after girls. He used to live underground, in the country where the sun never goes down but just hangs in one place.

One time, he decided to go above ground, saying, "I think I'll go hunting." When he got to the surface he saw a beautiful, big kangaroo. Bamapama took his spear and gave chase but the kangaroo ran off towards the west. As the kangaroo ran away, so, little by little, the sun went down.

At last the kangaroo stopped running and Bamapama took aim with his spear. But just as he was about to throw it, the sun disappeared completely and night fell. Never having known darkness, Bamapama was very afraid and began to cry. He climbed a tree to see if he could get above the darkness, but to no avail. He climbed down and, tired out, fell asleep on the ground. When he awoke next morning, to his joy he found that it was light again.

When he saw the sun, he said, "This is a good way they do things up here – sleeping at night and getting up with the sun."

When he got home, everyone asked him, "What happened to you?"

"I was chasing this big kangaroo," he said, "and then everything went dark. Come up with me and see. Everything is different up there. The sun comes up in the day, but at night you sleep. It's a good way."

He took all the people up to the surface. When it grew dark, they too were afraid and climbed up trees, but he coaxed them down. "Don't be afraid," he said. "I know what I'm doing."

In the morning the sun rose, and they stretched in the warmth. "This is good!" they said. "This is better than living down below, where it is so hot all the time. And there's wood to make fires if we get cold. Let's stay."

So Bamapama's people stayed on the surface. But they are not like us. They have no mouths, just an opening in the top of their heads. One of them once went to look for a honey bees' nest. He filled a basket with the honey, then put it on his head. He made a hole in the bottom of it so that the honey would drip down into his stomach. They're all like that.

KANGAROO
This was one of the main animals hunted for food by Aboriginals and is the subject of many paintings. The stripes on the kangaroo represent different clans.

Bamapama ventures above ground to hunt

THE SKY GOD'S STORIES

KWAKU-ANANSE the spider once went to the sky god Nyankonpon to try to buy his stories. The sky god said, "What makes you think you could buy my stories? The richest villages have all tried, and have all failed."

Kwaku-Ananse asked, "What is the price?"

"The price is Onini the python; Osebo the leopard; Mmoboro the hornet swarm; and Mmoatia the spirit."

The spider replied, "I will bring you all these things and my mother Nsia, too."

The spider went home and told his mother, Nsia, and his wife, Aso, what the sky god had said. "How can I catch Onini?" he asked.

"Go and cut a branch from a palm tree and some creeper, and bring them to the stream," said Aso.

Kwaku-Ananse did as he was told, and then he and Aso began to argue over the branch. "It's longer than he is," said Aso.

"You lie," replied Ananse. "He is longer."

The python overheard and, overcome with curiosity, asked what the quarrel was about. Ananse replied, "My wife, Aso, says that this palm branch is longer than you and I say it is not."

So Onini the python stretched himself full length along the branch and, as he did so, Ananse trussed him tight with the creeper, all the way up to his head.

PLANTAIN
Larger than a sweet banana, a plantain, or cooking banana, is popular in African and West Indian cooking. The large leaves of the plantain are often used to protect food when it is steamed. In this story, Ananse the spider pretends to shelter from the rain under a plantain leaf.

As the python stretches himself along the branch, Ananse ties him to it with creeper

Then they turned their attention to Mmoboro the hornet swarm. Aso told Ananse what to do. He cut a gourd and filled it with water, and carried it to where he could see the swarm hanging from a

Ananse shelters under a plantain leaf

branch. He spilled half of the water on the hornets, and half on himself. Then he cut a plantain leaf and put it on his head, calling out, "Hornets! It is raining! I am sheltering under this leaf, but you have no protection. Why don't you come into this gourd to keep dry?"

So the hornets flew into the gourd, and Ananse slapped the plantain leaf over the opening and trapped them inside.

Then Aso told Ananse to dig a pit, and he did so. He dug it on the path between Osebo the leopard's lair and the stream, and covered it with leaves. At first light he went to the pit and there, helpless inside, was the leopard.

There remained the spirit, Mmoatia, to catch. Aso and Ananse carved a doll from wood and plastered it with sticky gum from a tree. Then they set the doll down where the tree spirits play, with a brass basin beside it containing an appetizing mash of yams. When the spirits came, Mmoatia saw the doll, and asked it, "Can I have some yams?" The doll did not reply. So the spirit slapped the doll's cheek, and her hand stuck fast. She slapped it again; her other hand stuck, too.

Then Ananse went to the sky god with Onini the python, Osebo the leopard, Mmoboro the hornet swarm, Mmoatia the spirit, and Nsia, his old mother. The sky god called all the other gods to him, saying, "See! Great kings have come seeking my stories, but were not able to buy them. But Kwaku-Ananse has paid the price and added his mother, too. Therefore, today and forever I make a gift of my stories to Ananse the spider, and now they shall be known as Spider Stories!"

The hornets fly into the gourd

The leopard is caught in the pit

Ananse carves a doll from wood

The sky god gives his stories to Ananse the spider

GOURDS
These fleshy fruits with hard skins come in many shapes and sizes, the most common being the bottle gourd. Gourds can be hollowed out and used as containers.

71

THE APPLES OF YOUTH

GOLDEN EAGLE
In this story the giant Thiassi disguises himself as an eagle in order to eat the ox, and then carry off Idun and her apples. Loki disguises himself as another bird of prey – a falcon – to rescue Idun and bring her back to Asgard. The golden eagle, above, is the largest bird of prey in Northern Europe. It is a strong and skilful flier, with a wingspan of over 2 m (over 6 ft). It swoops down on its prey and carries it off in its powerful talons.

❖

THIASSI
The giant Thiassi took great pleasure in teasing and tormenting the gods. Like most giants in Norse myths, he was a master of deception and disguise, but in the end he could not get the better of mighty gods such as Odin.

LOKI'S CAPACITY FOR getting into trouble, and then getting out of it with his quick wits, means no one can feel really safe when he is around. He is easily bored, and so is always making mischief. Once, he nearly cost the gods their youth. It was like this.

One day, he and Odin were travelling through the wilderness. They were hungry, and so they killed an ox and made an oven in the earth to cook it in. But however long they waited, getting hungrier and hungrier, the meal just would not cook. They heard laughter above them, and when they looked up they saw a great eagle sitting in a tree. The eagle told them it was to blame for their trouble. "If you let me eat my fill of the ox, then it will cook." The gods agreed. The eagle dropped down from the tree just as the smell of cooked meat began to fill the air, and started to devour the ox. Loki and Odin could see that soon there would be nothing left. So Loki, in a temper, picked up a pole from the ground and struck the eagle with it.

The pole stuck fast to the eagle – and also to Loki's hands. When the eagle flew away, it dragged Loki into the air behind it.

Odin and Loki look up to see an eagle in the tree, laughing at them

Loki pleaded to be let go, but the eagle – who was the giant Thiassi in disguise – said, "I'll only release you if you promise me the goddess Idun and her Apples of Youth, which keep the gods forever young." Loki agreed.

Loki returned to Asgard and told Idun that he had found some wonderful apples in the forest, better even than the Apples of Youth.

The eagle drags Loki behind it

"Bring your apples with you, and come and compare them to the ones I've found," he said. So he lured Idun out of Asgard, in order that the giant Thiassi could come in eagle shape and steal her away.

Without Idun and her apples the gods became grey and old. "What has become of her?" they asked. And then someone remembered seeing her outside Asgard with Loki.

Loki tricks Idun into leaving Asgard with the Apples of Youth

So the gods brought Loki before them, and threatened him with a thousand painful deaths if he didn't bring Idun back.

"I can do it," he said, "if I can use Freyja's falcon shape."

So Loki flew in the shape of a falcon to Thiassi's mountain, where he found Idun alone.

MAGIC APPLES
Idun, the wife of Bragi, was the keeper of the Apples of Youth, which kept the gods from growing old. Idun was the personification of youth and beauty. Her trusting nature made it easy for Loki to trick her into taking the apples out of Asgard. In both Norse and Greek mythology, apples are associated with eternal youth.

The gods, who have grown old and grey, question Loki about Idun's disappearance

He changed Idun into a nut and, holding her in his falcon's claws, flew back to Asgard as fast as he could. But Thiassi followed him in eagle shape, and the beating of his great wings whipped up a fierce storm behind them.

The gods saw the storm and knew that Thiassi was on his way. They prepared a bonfire inside the wall of Asgard, and as soon as Loki had landed, they set light to it. Thiassi flew straight into the fire and burned his feathers. Then the gods killed him, for daring to steal Idun. Odin threw Thiassi's eyes into the sky, where they still shine as stars.

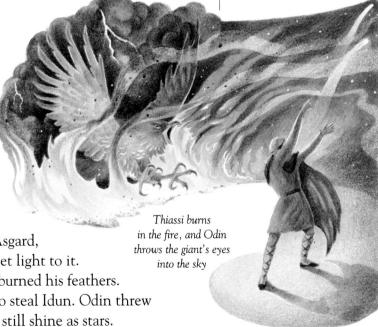

Thiassi burns in the fire, and Odin throws the giant's eyes into the sky

Thor in the Land of Giants, page 118 ➤

EARTH-MAKER AND COYOTE

THE COYOTE
A relative of the jackal family, the coyote ranges widely over North America. Smaller than a wolf, it is adaptable and cunning. Attempts to eradicate it, by poison, shooting, or trapping, have been largely ineffective. The coyote seems indestructible – just like the character in this story.

❖

TRICKSTER GOD
Coyote is the trickster god of the tribes of the southwestern USA. In this myth, from the Maidu of California, Coyote is cunning and destructive, a bringer of sickness, sorrow, and death. Sometimes, however, Coyote is a bringer of benefits. For example, the Lakota Sioux have a story about him creating the horse.

WHEN THIS WORLD was just covered water, Earth-maker floated on the surface. Coyote was with him; they were the first two chiefs. When Earth-maker sang this world into being, he said, "Let the world be good!"

But Coyote replied, "No!"

Every good thing Earth-maker said, Coyote contradicted. For instance, after he had made men, Earth-maker said, "When they die, they shall come back to life."

But Coyote said, "Why? When they are dead, they should stay dead. I am the oldest, and what I say goes."

Now Coyote had a son, a good boy, who had never left the house. One day, Coyote said to him, "Go to the stream and fetch some water." When the boy got to the stream, the rushes turned into rattlesnakes and bit him, and he died.

"What have I done?" moaned Coyote. "I take it all back. Death was

By the stream, the rushes turn into rattlesnakes and kill Coyote's son

a bad idea." He pleaded with Earth-maker, "Make him come alive again, and I will agree with everything you say."

But it was too late, Earth-maker could not undo what had occurred. Angry and bitter, Coyote started to travel around the world, and everywhere he went he made mischief, scratching up the soil and causing havoc. Earth-maker said, "People, if you see Coyote, kill him. He is bad all through. I wanted to make the world good, but he has thwarted me."

The people, heeding Earth-maker, went in search of Coyote. Eventually they cornered him on a little island. "You can stay there and starve," they said. Earth-maker told them that if after four days they heard no howling, then Coyote was dead.

But Coyote escaped by making himself like fog and drifting across the water to land. Then he howled fit to make the people's hair stand on end. So they knew he was not dead.

Every time the people tried to kill him, Coyote escaped. So Earth-maker told them to make a big canoe and get in it, and then he flooded the world. At the last minute, Coyote slipped into the canoe.

DANCE PLUME
The Maidu are very skilled at creating garments, such as headbands, cloaks, and blankets, from feathers. These are often used in ceremonial dances.

To avoid being starved to death on an island, Coyote makes himself like fog and drifts away

After the flood, Coyote escapes from the canoe on to a mountain peak, becoming an everlasting trouble to humankind

He was disguised, and no one knew he was there until they sighted land – the peak of Canoe Mountain, poking out of the water. Coyote leapt from the boat, bold as brass, saying, "This land is mine."

Earth-maker said, "Brother, you are too powerful. I can't kill you. You have won."

And Coyote is still in the world, causing trouble wherever he goes.

MAKE ME A MAN!

MAN OF IRON
The king asks the smith Walukaga to make him an iron man, perhaps similar to this statue of the war god Ebo, made by the Fon tribe of Bénin, West Africa.

The king orders his people to shave their heads and burn their hair, and to collect 100 pots of their tears, so that Walukaga can create a living man from pieces of iron

LONG, LONG AGO there was a king who called Walukaga, chief of the metal smiths, to him. "Make me a man!" the king commanded.

Walukaga said, "But –"

"But me no buts," interrupted the king. "Here is all the iron you'll need. But mind, it must be a real, living, breathing man, with blood in his body and brains in his head."

Walukaga took the iron and went sorrowfully home. He asked all his friends, but none of them had the slightest idea how to make a real man. But Walukaga knew that, if he failed to create a man, he and his whole family would be severely punished – even killed.

One day, as he walked along pondering this hopeless situation, Walukaga met an old friend who had gone mad and lived alone in the wilderness. Walukaga told this madman his troubles, and the madman – who was not as crazy as he seemed – told Walukaga what to do.

With the madman's wise words ringing in his ears, Walukaga went to the king and said, "I've gone into this business of making a man and it can be done. But first, your majesty, you must order all the people to shave their heads and burn their hair, to make a thousand loads of charcoal. Then you must make them collect one hundred large pots full of tears to quench the fire while I am forging the man. For, of course, ordinary charcoal from wood and ordinary water from a stream are no use at all for making a man!"

The king did as Walukaga asked. All the people had to shave their heads and burn their hair, but all their efforts only produced one load of charcoal. They all wept until their eyes were dry, but they only produced two pots of water.

So the king had to send once more for Walukaga. "Do not trouble to make the man," he said, "for I cannot supply the charcoal or the water."

"Your majesty," replied Walukaga, "I am glad that you could not find enough hair or enough tears, for, to tell the truth, I could not make you a man!"

WHY DO WE DIE?

CHUKU, THE GREAT SPIRIT, created the world and humankind. He sent a dog to the first people to tell them that, if anyone died, they should lay the body upon the earth and sprinkle it with ashes, and then the person would come back to life. But the dog dawdled on the way, so Chuku sent a sheep with the same message.

When the sheep arrived, it had forgotten what it was supposed to say. It got the message all muddled, and said that if anyone died, the body should be buried in the earth.

When the dog eventually arrived, it was too late. No one would believe him. "We have been told to bury the dead, and that is what we shall do," the first men said. So death came to humankind.

❖

THE GREAT SPIRIT Chuku, whose name means "Great Spirit", is the supreme god of the Ibo of southeastern Nigeria, West Africa. Chuku is the creator of all things, and all good things flow from him. His daughter is Ale, the goddess of the earth.

Chuku, the Great Spirit, sends a dog with a vital message: how to bring a dead person back to life

When the dog is late, Chuku sends a sheep. But the sheep gets the message wrong

CULTURAL CENTRE
A large country with great contrasts in landscape, ranging from tropical rainforest to grasslands, Nigeria has been a centre of African culture since 500 BC. There are four main tribes. The Ibo, who tell this tale, live in the southeast; the Hausa and Fulani live in the north, and the Yoruba in the south.

FERTILITY AND CULTIVATION

Many myths seek to explain the everyday miracles of life: the rising and setting of the sun, the growth of crops, the births of babies. Sometimes a god of fertility or farming may become angry, like Telepinu, and require appeasing, or, like Osiris, be sacrificed to enrich the land. A nervous sun goddess, Amaterasu, may have to be enticed out of a dark cave so that crops will grow, or an act of great courage may be required to bring fertility to a blighted land.

The medieval tales of King Arthur touch on these themes. Arthur inherits a riven land, and unites it. His knights then have to embark on a spiritual quest in search of a lost Christian relic, the Holy Grail. Only when the purest of Arthur's knights, Sir Galahad, has found the Grail can the wasteland kingdom bloom again.

A cow shows Cadmus where to build a great city in Cadmus and the Sown Men, *which also tells of warriors springing up from the earth and founding a proud race*

ISIS AND OSIRIS

THE SKY GODDESS NUT and her husband, the earth god Geb, were so close that nothing could exist between them; nor could Nut's children be born. So Shu, their father, separated them, holding Nut's body aloft so that living things could exist on the earth. Nut brought forth two sets of twins: Osiris and Isis, and Set and Nepthys. Isis and Osiris loved each other, but Nepthys hated Set; she, too, loved Osiris.

At the birth of Osiris a voice was heard all over the world, saying, "The lord of all the earth is born!" Osiris became King of Egypt and ruled wisely with Isis as his queen. He established the laws, taught the people how to grow food and how to worship the gods.

Osiris had only one enemy: his jealous brother, Set. Set secretly measured Osiris's body, and made a painted coffin to fit him exactly.

SPIRIT OF CREATION
Osiris, god of the Underworld, was tall, handsome and dark-skinned. His followers looked forward to a life of eternal bliss. He was also the god of creation and the fertile earth.

Shu holds the body of Nut the sky goddess aloft so that life can exist on earth

Geb

Osiris fits perfectly into the coffin that his brother Set has made for him

SPIRIT OF DECAY
According to myth, Set had pale skin and red hair – which indicated an evil character to the Egyptians. Set is the eternal enemy of the life-affirming Osiris.

Then he gave a feast, to which he invited his brother. He showed off the magnificent coffin and said that he would give it as a present to whoever fit inside it.

All the guests took turns to lie down in the coffin, but they were all too small. At last Osiris himself lay down; his body fit perfectly. Then Set and his friends nailed down the lid, poured boiling lead over it to seal it, and set the coffin adrift on the River Nile.

When Isis heard what had happened to her husband, she was stricken with grief. She cut off her long hair, dressed in mourning, and set off in search of the coffin. No one she asked could tell her what had become of it; but at last some children playing by the river told her where it lay.

Isis brought the coffin back to her palace, and summoned the jackal-headed god Anubis to embalm Osiris's body. But first she turned herself into a sparrowhawk and, hovering over Osiris, fanned breath into his body with her wings. She revived him for long enough to conceive a son, Horus. Then she hid the child from the wrath of Set.

Set, hunting in the moonlight, came upon the opened coffin and, in his rage, tore the body of Osiris into fourteen pieces, which he scattered all over the country.

Isis travelled all over Egypt in a boat of papyrus reeds, gathering up the corpse of Osiris and burying each piece where she found it.

ANUBIS
This Egyptian god with the head of a jackal presided over funerals and was known as "Lord of Mummy Wrappings".

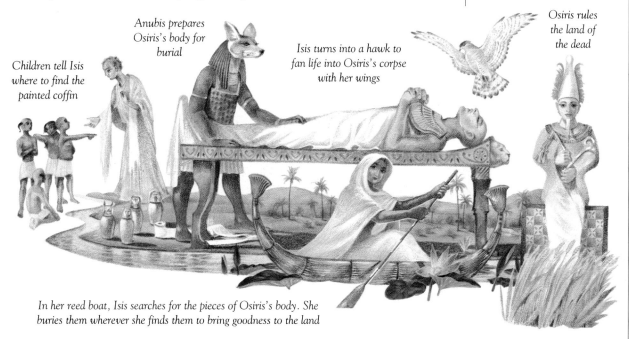

Children tell Isis where to find the painted coffin

Anubis prepares Osiris's body for burial

Isis turns into a hawk to fan life into Osiris's corpse with her wings

Osiris rules the land of the dead

In her reed boat, Isis searches for the pieces of Osiris's body. She buries them wherever she finds them to bring goodness to the land

Osiris went to rule the other land, where he judges the souls of the newly dead. But when his son Horus grew to adulthood, Osiris momentarily returned to ask him to avenge his death. So Horus and Set began their eternal struggle of good and evil. Sometimes one seems to win and sometimes the other, but neither can be vanquished. It is said that when Horus finally overcomes Set, Osiris will return to the land of the living to rule as king once again.

❖

GOD OF THE SKY
Horus, the sky god, is depicted with a falcon's head. Many Egyptians believed the sky was a vast falcon; its two eyes were the sun and moon.

PERSEPHONE

P ERSEPHONE IS THE daughter of Demeter, goddess of the cornfield. As a young girl she was known as Core, the maiden, but now she is called Persephone, Queen of the Underworld, and each time she cuts a hair from her head, someone dies. This is what happened.

One day, Core was picking flowers in a meadow, when the ground opened up at her feet. Out of the gaping earth drove fierce Hades, King of the Underworld, in his great chariot drawn by four jet-black stallions. Hades had loved Core from a distance, and had brooded in his dark kingdom over her bright beauty. In an instant he seized her, pulled her into his chariot, and dragged her down with him.

Her screams still echoed in the air above the chasm, but Core was gone.

Core scatters her flowers in terror as the earth opens

Hades, King of the Underworld, seizes Core and pulls her into his chariot

THE SEASONS
Demeter, the goddess of the cornfield, was responsible for the harvest of all crops, flowers, and plants. When she lost her daughter, she forbade anything to grow on the earth. Winter fell when Persephone was in the Underworld; when she came back to earth, it was summer again.

Hades's chariot disappears into the depths of the dark Underworld

Demeter, her mother, heard her cries. Dressing herself in mourning, she lit two torches at fiery Mount Etna and, with one in each hand, she wandered the world for nine days and nights, neither eating nor drinking, calling for her daughter. But no answer came.

At last Demeter came to Helios, the sun, who had seen everything. "It is no use calling," he said. "Your daughter Core is now the bride of Hades. She is no longer a maid; her new name is Persephone."

Demeter had been the gentlest of all gods and goddesses, but at this news she let out a terrible cry. She turned her anger on the world, and forbade the flowers to bloom or the crops to grow. Soon the earth became a wasteland. The gods begged Demeter to relent, but she would not. At last Zeus ordered Hades to give up the girl, provided she had not eaten the food of the dead. Persephone had eaten nothing but six pomegranate seeds given to her by the gardener Ascalaphus, so Hades was forced to agree.

*Demeter wanders the world
calling for her daughter*

*As Demeter
greets her long-lost
daughter, winter fades
and the world becomes
green again*

*In her underground prison,
Persephone eats six pomegranate seeds*

Ascalaphus

POMEGRANATE SEEDS
Persephone could not leave the Underworld forever because she had eaten the pomegranate seeds from Hades's garden. Some say it was Hades's gardener, Ascalaphus, who saw Persephone eat the seeds. The pomegranate is a thick-skinned fruit with seeds floating in a juicy pulp. The tree grows in Mediterranean countries, and in other parts of the world that have a hot, dry climate.

When Persephone reached the upper world, she ran to embrace her mother. Demeter's anger melted, and the world became green again.

Zeus told Persephone that each year she must spend six months in the Underworld, as the bride of Hades, one winter month for each seed that she had eaten. But for the other six months, of spring and summer, she could return to the living world, to be with her mother.

Cadmus and the Sown Men, page 96 ➤

WORLD WITHOUT SUN

SWORD GUARD
This 19th-century Japanese sword guard, made of silver inlaid with gold, shows the Buddhist god Kannon riding on the back of a carp. Kannon is a merciful god, who sailors believe protects them from shipwreck.

UZUME
The goddess of mirth lures Amaterasu the sun goddess from her cave, restoring light to the world. This figurine stands just over 13 cm (5.2 in) high and is made of wood with an ivory face.

WHEN THE GOD IZANAGI gave birth to the sun goddess Amaterasu, the moon god Tsuki-yomi, and the storm god Susanowo, he was so pleased with his offspring that he divided up the world between them. To Amaterasu he gave the rule of the High Plains of Heaven. To Tsuki-yomi he entrusted the realms of the night. And to Susanowo he gave the rule of the oceans.

But while Amaterasu and Tsuki-yomi were pleased, Susanowo screamed and howled, and complained that he did not want to rule the oceans. "I'd rather have been given charge of Yomi, the Land of Gloom," he said. But that was the province of Izanami, goddess of death and decay.

So instead of looking after the oceans, Susanowo just hung around in heaven and on earth, causing trouble wherever he went. He uprooted trees, destroyed rice paddies, and knocked down buildings. Finally he skinned a dappled pony in the heavens, and dropped it through the thatched roof of the sacred weaving hall, where Amaterasu and her maidens were at work, weaving the world into pattern and order.

Amaterasu was so shocked and terrified that she fled. She shut herself inside a cave and wouldn't come out. The whole world, both heaven and earth, was plunged into darkness. Nothing would grow, and soon chaos reigned.

The gods decided that they would have to lure Amaterasu from her hiding-place. They trooped to the entrance of the cave and hung a magic mirror from the branches of a sakaki tree. Then they caused roosters to crow constantly, as if it were dawn.

Disgusted at only being given rule over the sea, Susanowo, the storm god, wreaks havoc

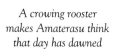

A crowing rooster makes Amaterasu think that day has dawned

They lit bonfires, and, while some of the gods provided the music, a young goddess called Uzume climbed on to an upturned tub and began to dance. She shimmied and pranced – in a way that was at once so seductive and so funny that all eight million gods laughed and laughed until the heavens shook.

Amaterasu was so intrigued that she opened the cave door a crack and called, "What's going on?"

"We're celebrating," replied Uzume, "because we've found a goddess who shines even more brightly than you!"

Uzume's comic dancing lures Amaterasu out of the cave

Amaterasu

The gods bar the cave entrance and hang a mirror in a tree to make Amaterasu believe they have found a more radiant goddess

Amaterasu looked out, and the gods turned the magic mirror towards her, so that she saw her own reflection. As she gazed in wonder at her own radiant beauty, one of the gods seized her hand and pulled her from the cave, and another stretched a rope of straw across the entrance, saying, "This is as far as you may go."

So Amaterasu was tricked back into the world by the laughter of the gods and the beauty of her own reflection, and since that time the sun has never again failed.

As for Susanowo, the gods punished him for his part in the affair by cutting off his beard, and his fingernails and toenails, and banishing him from the High Plains of Heaven. But he and his powerful storms are still causing mischief on earth.

SUSANOWO

There are many stories linked with Susanowo the storm god, some of which show him as good, some evil. In one, he rescues a goddess from being eaten by a dragon with eight heads. In another, his sister Amaterasu gives him jewels which he uses to make lightning and hail.

THE SWORD IN THE STONE

❖

WHO WAS ARTHUR? The first mentions of Arthur are in the Latin works of Celtic monks and in a Welsh poem written around 600 AD. Many tales about him come from *The History of the Kings of Britain*, written by Geoffrey of Monmouth in 1138. According to legend, Arthur was a noble Celtic ruler who fought the Anglo-Saxon invaders. The magician Merlin, who helped find King Uther's true heir through the sword in the stone, became Arthur's counsellor.

IT WAS CHRISTMAS. The squabbling barons and knights who had been fighting and feuding ever since the death of old King Uther Pendragon were gathered together in London's great church. They had been summoned by the enchanter Merlin, a wild figure who had been King Uther's chief advisor. No one knew why they were there.

When they came out of the church, they saw in the churchyard a mighty sword, sticking through a metal anvil into a huge block of marble. On the stone were the words: "Whoever pulls this sword from this stone is the rightful king of all England."

Every one of the barons and knights thought he should be king. They all tugged and wrenched at the sword, but none of them could budge it. At last, they all gave up.

It was announced that on New Year's Day, a tournament would be held. There would be jousting and feasting. Afterwards, anyone with a claim to the throne could try again to pull the sword from the stone.

People came from all over the country to take part in the tournament. Among them were a north-country knight, Sir Ector, and his sons: proud Sir Kay and his young brother Arthur.

Not one of the knights or barons can pull the sword from the stone

Sir Kay   Sir Ector

Merlin

Kay was so excited about taking part in his first tournament that he forgot his sword. He did not realize his mistake until they had arrived at the jousting-field. "Go and fetch my sword from our lodgings," he told Arthur, "and look lively!"

Arthur rode as fast as he could back to the lodging house, but everyone was out and it was locked up. Kay had a nasty temper, and Arthur didn't want to have to tell him that he could not find his sword. So when he saw a sword sticking out of a stone in the churchyard, he decided to borrow it. He quickly pulled out the sword and took it with him.

As soon as Sir Kay saw the sword, he knew at once that it was the sword from the churchyard. He took it to Sir Ector, saying, "Father, look! I have pulled the sword from the stone. I must be the rightful king."

Sir Ector took Sir Kay and Arthur back to the churchyard. "Now," he said, "tell me again, Kay, how you got this sword."

Kay could not look his father in the eye. "Father, my brother Arthur brought it to me."

Then Sir Ector asked Arthur, "How did you come by this sword?"

"I hope I haven't done wrong," said Arthur. "Kay had forgotten his sword, and this one was sticking out of the stone. I only borrowed it. Let me put it back." And Arthur pushed the sword back through the anvil into the stone.

Sir Ector seized the hilt and pulled with all his strength. The sword resisted him. Then Sir Kay tried, and still the sword would not move. But when Arthur took hold of the sword, it answered to his hand and slid out of the stone like silk.

Sir Ector knelt down.

"Father, why are you kneeling?" asked Arthur.

The tournament gets under way on the jousting-field

Sir Ector and Sir Kay kneel before Arthur, the true king

◆

JOUSTING
By the 13th century, jousting had become part of the tournament – a series of mock battles for entertainment. In a joust, two knights on horseback charged towards one another and tried to unseat each other with a wooden spear, called a lance.

Pommel ———

Crossguard ———

Fuller ———

KNIGHT'S SWORD
The sword was a knight's most prized weapon: a symbol of knighthood itself. This sword has a double cutting edge, and a groove, called a fuller, running down the centre of the blade to make it lighter.

NOBLE KING
Arthur ruled his kingdom with justice and honour, and his knights of the Round Table were expected to uphold these virtues. In this 13th-century carving, Arthur looks wise and thoughtful.

King Arthur's Round Table seats more than one hundred of the noblest knights that ever lived

THE ROUND TABLE
Arthur's table was round so that everyone who sat at it was of equal importance. The Winchester Table, above, dates from around 1300. It may have been made for the medieval pastime called Round Tables, at which nobles dressed up as Arthur's knights.

"I am not your father," confessed Sir Ector, "though I love you like a son. You were brought to my door one stormy night, a little squalling baby in the arms of Merlin, the wizard, the dream-reader. And now I understand that you must be the son of King Uther Pendragon, and the rightful king of all England."

And so it was that the boy Arthur, who was not even yet a knight, was acclaimed King of England by the people; for try as they might, no one else could ever shift the sword from the stone.

King Arthur, with Sir Kay at his right hand and Merlin at his left, set about bringing peace to the country. He married the beautiful Guinevere, and founded the order of the Knights of the Round Table. There were one hundred and fifty seats at that table, and whenever a knight was worthy to sit there, his name would appear, by Merlin's magic, on his seat.

Many famous knights came to sit at the Round Table in Camelot, including Sir Gawain, Sir Perceval, Sir Lancelot and Sir Galahad, the most perfect knight of them all. Their adventures in the cause of good will be told and retold forever, because these were the finest of all the noble knights who ever lived.

The Holy Grail, page 89 ➤

THE HOLY GRAIL

KING ARTHUR FILLED his Round Table with the best knights in all the world. But for many years, one seat remained empty. No one could sit on it and live, which is why it was called the Siege Perilous, or seat of danger. Merlin prophesied that when a knight came to claim the Siege Perilous, the days of the Round Table would be drawing to their close.

One day a young knight appeared at court, in red armour and without weapons. He bowed to King Arthur, walked straight to the Siege Perilous, and sat down. The knights gasped. But behind the young knight appeared in letters of gold, "Galahad, the High Prince".

"Welcome," said King Arthur. "Please tell us who you are."

"I am Sir Galahad, and my mother Elaine is the daughter of King Pelles, the Maimed King."

"I have heard of King Pelles, who lies crippled at the castle of Carbonek. But I did not know he had a grandson. And yet, Sir Galahad, I feel I know you. You look like Sir Lancelot as a young man."

"This is not surprising," said Lancelot, "for he is my son."

KNIGHTS ON A QUEST
This 13th-century French manuscript illustration shows Galahad, Perceval, and Bors with the Holy Grail. These three knights went in search of the Grail, and were the only ones to find it.

Sir Galahad

The Siege Perilous

The Knights of the Round Table stare in amazement as the young knight walks straight to the Siege Perilous

◄ *The Sword in the Stone, page 86*

The maiden lifts the cloth just enough to allow each knight to drink

THE ARDAGH CHALICE
The Holy Grail was thought to be a lost chalice, or cup, that contained Christ's blood. The sacred vessel may have been similar to this 8th-century Irish chalice from Ardagh.

That night, as the knights feasted, there was a tremendous storm outside. Thunder crashed overhead and lightning flooded the hall with light. The knights were silenced, and into that silence and strange light came a maiden bearing a vessel covered with a white cloth. And from that vessel each knight drank. And then the maiden left, and the unearthly light disappeared.

"What can this mean?" asked King Arthur.

Sir Galahad replied, "That vessel was the Holy Grail. I will not rest until I have seen it uncovered." The other knights agreed, "We must find the Grail, which has been lost for so long."

King Arthur was reluctant to let them go, for he foresaw that this was no ordinary quest, and that many of his knights must fail, and perhaps die along the way. He knew now why Merlin had told him that the day the Siege Perilous was filled would be the day that the Fellowship of the Round Table would begin to crumble. But once the knights had sworn to search for the Grail, they had to do so.

King Arthur's knights set out in all directions, each following his own way. Their adventures on this, the greatest of all quests, would easily fill a book on their own. But most of these tales tell of knights who lost their way and became embroiled in fights and love affairs. The quest for the Holy Grail was not for worldly men such as these, but only for the pure in heart.

Of all the knights of the Round Table, three rode together, free from rivalry, greed, or ambition, searching for the Grail with all their hearts and minds. They were Sir Perceval, Sir Bors, and Sir Galahad. And behind them rode Sir Lancelot, begging God's forgiveness for falling in love with Guinevere, Arthur's queen.

Sir Perceval, Sir Bors, and Sir Galahad arrived at a seashore and found a magic ship waiting for them. They stepped on board, and at once the ship set sail. It took them to the castle of Carbonek, where Sir Galahad's grandfather, King Pelles, ruled over a blighted kingdom from his bed of pain.

In King Pelles's bedchamber, the strange, intense light appeared again. Two maidens appeared. The first was carrying the Holy Grail, as before, but this time it was uncovered, and it was clear that it was the source of the light. The other maiden carried a spear that seemed to weep blood from its tip in great drops, which the first maiden caught in the Grail.

"What does this mean?" asked Sir Galahad.

"The spear is the weapon that pierced Our Lord's side as He hung on the Cross. The vessel is the Holy Grail, in which were caught the drops of His blood that fell from the wound."

Sir Galahad took the spear and touched King Pelles with its tip. At once the King was made well again, and his blighted kingdom began to bloom once more. Then they all went into the chapel and celebrated Mass, but this time only Sir Galahad saw the Holy Grail uncovered, for he alone of all the Knights of the Round Table was utterly pure in thought and deed. When he had done so, he seemed to

❖

THE CRUSADES
The Grail myth may have been inspired by the Crusades, holy wars fought in the Middle East (then known as the Holy Land) between Christians and Muslims. Unlike Arthur's knights, however, the Christian Crusaders were more interested in power and plunder than religion.

Sir Galahad

Sir Perceval

King Pelles

Sir Bors

Sir Galahad touches King Pelles with the spear, making him well again and bringing renewed life to his kingdom

fill with light, until he became one with it. Then he, the maidens, the spear, and the Grail itself disappeared from the world of men for ever.

Sir Bors and Sir Perceval came out of the chapel and found Sir Lancelot lying exhausted on the ground. Strength of will had carried him thus far, but, despite repenting all his sins, he was not worthy to enter the chapel and see the Grail uncovered – even though he was the greatest knight who ever bore arms.

❖

SIR LANCELOT
Lancelot was the most splendid of Arthur's knights, but his chivalrous reputation was ruined by his love affair with Queen Guinevere. Because of this, Lancelot was not able to see the Grail.

The Death of King Arthur, page 156 ▶

GLOOSKAP AND THE WASIS

GOLDEN HOMELAND
Many of the Algonquin tribes are from the densely wooded northeast of North America. This may help to explain their belief that when Glooskap fired arrows at some birch trees, the first people appeared from their bark. Birch bark was used for canoe building and for making bowls and other utensils. It is a sacred material for some tribes.

❖

A GOD SAILS AWAY
Glooskap taught mankind many things, but at last lost patience with people's sinfulness and ingratitude. He sailed away in a canoe, but one day he will return to save his people from evil.

GLOOSKAP WAS THE MIGHTIEST WARRIOR of all. He was the Lord of Men and Beasts. He had mastered the ghosts of the night and the spirits of the day. At last, having achieved many great feats during his wanderings, Glooskap decided to return home. But when he entered his house, his wife barely gave him so much as a glance.

She was looking at a creature on the floor. Glooskap had battled ghosts, and devils, and wild animals of every kind, but he had never seen anything like it.

"What is it?" he asked.

"It is the mighty Wasis," she replied. "And I warn you, if you meddle with him, you will be in trouble. I must serve him night and day."

"I wouldn't put up with such a tyrant," said Glooskap.

"You would have no choice," said the woman. "The mighty Wasis holds the past in one hand, and the future in the other. He is master of all the world."

"Not of me," cried Glooskap. "I am Lord of Men and Beasts. Nothing can defeat me!"

He walked right up to the mighty Wasis.

"I am not afraid of you," he said.

The Wasis gurgled.

Glooskap took up his fighting stance. "I am the strongest," he said.

The Wasis sat and sucked on some maple-sugar.

"I am Lord of Men and Beasts," thundered Glooskap. "Come here!"

But the Wasis howled back. He screamed and screamed and screamed until Glooskap thought his head would split.

Having mastered wild beasts and ghostly spirits, Glooskap returns home

"Stop that!" he shouted.

But the mighty Wasis just kept on screaming.

Desperate to quiet him, Glooskap danced his ghost dance and sang the songs that raise the dead.

Then Glooskap danced his spirit dance and sang the songs that scare away devils.

And, at long last, the Wasis stopped screaming, looked at Glooskap, and smiled, a big smile as wide as the world. "Goo!" he said.

Totally exhausted by his heroic efforts to stop the Wasis screaming and howling, Glooskap collapsed in a dead faint.

So whenever you see a baby sitting on the floor with a big smile all over its face, chuckling "Goo! Goo!" for no reason at all, you may be sure it is remembering the day it defeated the great Glooskap, the Lord of Men and Beasts, who had conquered the whole wide world.

MEDICINE BAG
Among the tribes of northeastern America, bags such as this are used to hold medicinal charms and herbs. They are made of otterskin (the otter symbolizes healing power). At one time, when a healer died, his bag was often buried with him. However medicine bags now tend to be passed on from father to son or otherwise kept within the tribe.

For of all the beings that have ever been created since the Beginning, a baby is the only one that nobody has ever got the better of – nor ever will, until the End of Time.

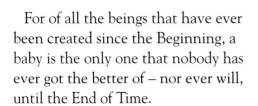

Despite all Glooskap's strength, he is no match for the mighty Wasis and its terrible bellowing

TELEPINU

The ancient people from whose mythology this story comes established a powerful empire in Anatolia (in modern-day Turkey) around 1590 BC. The Hittite Empire collapsed in about 1200 BC, but aspects of the Hittite civilization lived on for several centuries in parts of Anatolia and what is now Syria.

THE WEATHER GOD
This relief shows the Hittite weather god wearing distinctive Hittite clothing – a pointed hat and a short tunic tied with a sash. In the Hittite family of gods, the weather god was important, but not as powerful as the mother goddess.

TELEPINU, GOD OF FARMING, grew angry with the world; no one knows why. He was in such a rage that, in his haste to depart, he put his left boot on his right foot and his right boot on his left foot.

Without him, the world grew covered with mist. Logs in the fire refused to burn; the gods could not hear the prayers of men. Both men and gods began to starve.

The weather god hammers on his son Telepinu's door

Angry with the world, Telepinu, god of farming, pulls on his boots

Telepinu's father, the weather god, grew worried. Hannahanna, the mother goddess, implored him to find his son before everything died.

They sent out an eagle to search for Telepinu, but it could not find him. Then the weather god himself went to Telepinu's house and battered on the gates with his hammer, but to no avail.

So Hannahanna said, "Let us send a bee to look for him."

"Don't be ridiculous," said the weather god. "A bee is too small to be of any use." But Hannahanna sent it anyway.

"Let us send a bee to look for Telepinu," says Hannahanna, the mother goddess

The bee searched far and wide, and eventually found the god asleep in the wilderness. As Hannahanna had instructed it, the bee stung Telepinu on the hands and on the feet, and smeared wax on Telepinu's eyes.

At last the bee finds Telepinu

Hannahanna thought this would bring Telepinu to his senses; but it only made him angrier still. His renewed rage caused floods to rise, and houses, men, and animals were swept away.

At last Kamrusepas, the goddess of healing and magic, was called. She stood on a mountainside, with twelve rams as a sacrifice to appease Telepinu's anger.

Kamrusepas cried, "Doorkeeper of the Underworld, open the seven doors, unlock the seven bolts. Into your cauldrons of bronze, receive Telepinu's rage, his malice, his fury. Let them not come back!"

Telepinu returns on the back of an eagle

Kamrusepas, goddess of magic, asks the Doorkeeper to receive Telepinu's anger

A ram's fleece, corn, wine, and oxen are offered to Telepinu on his return

Then, with a loud roll of thunder, and streams of lightning, Telepinu returned, riding on the back of an eagle.

The people set up a pole before him, hung with the fleece of a ram, and placed offerings of corn, wine, and oxen around its base.

Telepinu was pleased with these things, for they spoke to him of growth, and plenty, of long life and children. His anger was gone.

TELEPINU
The myth of Telepinu has parallels in other cultures. When the god of agriculture disappears, the earth dies; when he returns, everything begins to grow again.

HATTUSHASH
The imposing ruins of the ancient Hittite capital city of Hattushash (present day Bogazköy in Turkey) are still guarded by the massive stone lions of the Western Gate (above). Hattushash was a thriving city from about 1650 to 1200 BC, owing mainly to the Hittites' military strength and to their silver and iron mines, which were the richest in Asia Minor. When Hattushash was excavated, over 10,000 cuneiform tablets, containing myths – such as this tale of Telepinu – literature, and historical records of the Hittites were found.

CADMUS AND THE SOWN MEN

ATHENA
The goddess Athena, depicted on this coin from the 5th century BC, was a warrior and favourite daughter of Zeus. She was known for her good sense, and is associated with the owl, an ancient symbol of wisdom. Athena was also the patron goddess of Athens.

WARRIOR
This detail from the "Warrior Vase" shows a Greek soldier carrying a shield and a spear. The vase, which comes from Mycenae in southern Greece, can be dated to c.1200 BC.

C ADMUS HAD A SISTER named Europa. She was carried off by Zeus, who was disguised as a bull, and became the mother of King Minos of Crete. When Europa disappeared, Cadmus went in search of her. For many months he scoured the lands around his home, but could find no sign of his sister. At last he went to Delphi to consult the oracle, where the advice and prophecies of the god Apollo were revealed. Cadmus asked the oracle what he should do.

"Your sister is safe. Search for her no more," said the oracle. "Your destiny lies elsewhere. When you leave here, you will see a cow. Follow it, and when it falls to the ground, exhausted, there you must build a great city."

Outside Delphi, Cadmus saw a cow, just as the oracle had promised. With a group of men he followed it for many miles until at last it sank to the ground. "Here we will found our city, and call it Thebes," said Cadmus. "But first, we must sacrifice this cow to the goddess Athena. Go and fetch some water from the spring to honour the goddess."

The oracle of Apollo tells Cadmus that a cow will show him where to build a new city

Cadmus sees the cow and follows it

◄ *Persephone, page 82*

When the men took water from the spring, they disturbed a terrible serpent, which killed them all with its fearsome, snapping jaws. In fury, Cadmus slew the serpent with a blow from a huge rock.

No sooner had Cadmus sacrificed the cow than the goddess Athena appeared. She told him not to worry about the loss of his men. "I will supply you with better men than any king can command. Just take the serpent's teeth and sow them in the soil."

❖

THE FIRST THEBANS
The "sown men" were known as the *spartoi*, from the Greek "to sow". The five who survived were the first inhabitants of the city of Thebes, of which Cadmus was king.

*When Cadmus sows the serpent's teeth,
an army of warriors bursts from the earth*

Cadmus did as he was told, and from the soil sprang fully grown men, warriors all. Before the men could turn on him, Cadmus threw a stone amongst them, and they fought so fiercely about who had thrown it that in the end only five survived. Cadmus made peace with them, and these warriors, the strongest and the fiercest of all the sown men, helped him establish the great city of Thebes.

Theseus and the Minotaur, page 108 ➤

MOTHER OF LIFE AND DEATH

MOTHER OF DEATH
This relief from the
8th century AD shows
the goddess Durga
killing the demon
Mahisha who has taken
on the form of a giant
water buffalo.

❖

THE GODDESS DEVI
Devi, whose name
means "goddess", is the
Divine Mother of the
Hindu religion. She has
many forms. As well as
the warlike Durga and
the terrifying Kali, who
both appear in this
story, she can be gentle,
as the beautiful Parvati
and the religious Uma.

THE GODDESS DEVI is the consort of Shiva, god of generation and
destruction. She is the mother of all, holding in her hands both
joy and pain, life and death. She is known under many names, in
many forms.

As mother of life, Devi brings the rain and
protects against disease. She is mild and loving.

As mother of death, she is terrible.

As Durga, the yellow-haired warrior goddess,
she is frightening enough. She has eight arms,
and rides into battle against her foes.

But when Durga is enraged, the goddess Kali
springs from her forehead, and then it is not only
the wicked who must cower in fear, but the good also. For Kali is so
deadly and furious a fighter that she becomes entirely consumed with
bloodlust. If she is not stopped, she will rampage through the world,
fighting until no one is left alive.

Durga herself is a fighter almost without equal. She came into being
to protect the gods against the demon Mahisha, who, in the form of a
huge water buffalo, had been terrorizing them with its deadly hooves
and horns, and with the hurricane of its breath. Neither Vishnu,
the protector, nor, Shiva, the destroyer, could defeat it.

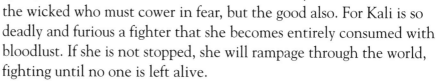

*Devi holds life and
death in her hands*

Durga

*The warrior goddess Durga attacks
the demon Mahisha*

Mahisha

Durga rode against the buffalo on her lion and caught it in a noose. Then Mahisha changed himself into a lion. Durga cut off the lion's head, but the demon became a man armed with a sword and shield. Durga shot the man with an arrow, and Mahisha turned into a huge elephant, trumpeting defiance. Durga cut off the elephant's trunk with her sword, and Mahisha turned once more into a monstrous buffalo. The buffalo charged at her, but she leapt first, red-eyed and laughing in her battle-fury.

She mounted the buffalo and kicked it in the neck. As she did so, Mahisha's spirit was driven half out of the buffalo's mouth. Durga swung her sword and cut off the demon's head. When the buffalo fell, all the gods cried, "Victory!" All the demons wailed in anguish.

Once, however, Durga was hard pressed in battle with the demon lords Chanda and Munda, and the demon Raktabija. The reason was this: every time a drop of Raktabija's blood touched the ground, a replica of the demon instantly arose. The harder Durga fought against him, the more replicas of him there were to fight.

So Durga summoned Kali, and she came. Her tongue lolled from her fanged mouth to savour the blood in the air. In one of her four hands she held a bloodstained sword.

First, with a roar, she slew the demon lords. Then she attacked Raktabija himself, swiping off his head with one stroke of her sword. Her tongue shot out and caught his blood as it fell, and then she drained his body dry. The few little demons that sprang up where droplets of the demon's blood touched the ground, she swallowed whole.

Such is the wrath of Devi, the mother, who holds the universe in her womb.

DEVI AS KALI
This 18th-century painting shows Kali, the most bloodthirsty form of the goddess Devi, whose long tongue laps blood. In her left hands she holds tokens of death – a sword, and a severed head. However in one right hand she carries a holy book, and with the other she blesses her followers. The Indian city of Calcutta is named after the goddess Kali.

SHIVA
Shiva, an important Hindu god, has a third eye that flashes fire in the middle of his forehead. He was roused from life as a religious hermit by an arrow of desire fired by Kama the god of love. This caused Shiva to fall in love with a beautiful mountain girl, Parvati, one of the forms of the goddess Devi. Shiva is both terrifying and gentle, destructive and merciful.

Kali beheads Raktabija

Kali

Raktabija's head

Demons spring from Raktabija's blood

The Elephant God, page 144 ➤

GODS AND MORTALS

While creator gods may choose to leave the world once their work is done, other gods and goddesses find men and women endlessly fascinating.

Not content with merely looking on, these immortals cannot resist meddling directly in the lives of human beings, leading to all kinds of extraordinary adventures and happenings. Some gods even fall in love with mortals, and from such unions come many of the heroes of mythology. These semi-divine beings possess remarkable qualities, usually great strength or cunning. Sometimes a gift from the gods may come by accident, as in the tale of Taliesin, an ordinary boy who is transformed into Wales's greatest poet. And sometimes, as King Midas discovers, a gift from an immortal may turn out to be a terrible curse, not a blessing.

Hugi the giant outruns Thialfi in Thor in the Land of Giants, *in which giants hoodwink gods and men alike*

THE GOLDEN TOUCH

◆

SATYRS
The satyrs were woodland gods; often the lower parts of their bodies resembled horses or goats. Silenus was older but, like the other satyrs, was a companion of Dionysus.

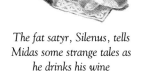

The fat satyr, Silenus, tells Midas some strange tales as he drinks his wine

GOLDEN TREASURE
This jug with coins, dating from 650-625 BC, was found in Ephesus, Turkey. The coins are made of electrum, an alloy of gold and silver used in ancient times.

THE GIFTS OF THE gods are not always what they seem. Take warning from the tale of King Midas, who thought himself wise. Midas had been tutored in the mysteries of the god of wine, Dionysus, by the poet Orpheus. So when one day some peasants brought before him an old, drunken satyr, bound with chains of flowers, Midas recognized him as Silenus, a companion of Dionysus.

Midas feasted Silenus for ten days and nights and, in return, Silenus told him many strange things. He told of a terrible whirlpool beyond which no traveller may pass. Beside it, two streams flow. By the first grows a tree whose fruit causes those who eat it to waste away. By the second grows a tree whose fruit will make men young again. One bite takes an old man back to middle age; two bites and he is a young man again; in three bites he is back in adolescence; in four he is a child; in five, a baby. Take a sixth bite, and he will disappear altogether.

At length, Midas took Silenus back to Dionysus, by the banks of the River Pactolus. The god had been missing his companion, and by way of gratitude for Silenus's safe return, he offered to grant Midas any wish he might ask for.

Midas first thought of Silenus's tale, but then he remembered a story that when he was a baby, some ants had been seen carrying golden grains of wheat and placing them between his lips – a sign of great wealth to come. So, instead of choosing youth, Midas said, "Grant that whatever I touch will turn to gold."

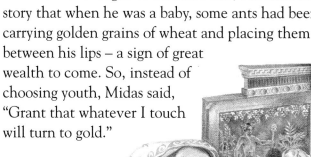

As a baby, Midas is fed by ants on golden grains of wheat

The god granted Midas's wish, and the king went away, delighted with his good fortune. He broke a twig from a low-growing branch of oak, and it turned to gold. He touched a stone and a clod of earth, and they, too, turned to gold. He gathered an ear of corn and it turned to glittering metal in his hand. He picked an apple, and it became as golden as the fabled apples of the Hesperides.

He touched the pillars of his palace doorway, and they turned to gold. Even the water in which he washed splashed golden over his hands. He called for food and wine. But when he reached for a piece of bread, it too turned to gold; when he bit into some meat, it turned to metal where his teeth touched it. Even the wine, Dionysus's discovery and gift to men, turned to liquid gold as it passed his lips.

Midas could neither eat nor drink, and soon he was in a torment of hunger and thirst. Gold, which had once been his heart's desire, was now hateful to him. He begged Dionysus to free him from his gift.

Dionysus took pity on the wretched man, and told him, "To cancel the gift, you must go to the source of the River Pactolus. Bathe in the spring there, and wash away your greed." Midas did as he was told and, as he bathed, his golden touch washed away into the river. The waters ran with gold, and even now the soil along the riverbank has a golden gleam.

WINE VESSELS
In Ancient Greece wine was a popular drink. It was believed to be the gift of the god Dionysus to mankind. Wine was often diluted, and the larger of these two bronze wine vessels would have held water for this purpose. The mixture was poured into a jug and the ladle used to fill the cups.

Midas washes away his golden touch in the river

Everything Midas touches turns to gold, including his food and wine

King Midas's Ears, page 104 ➤

KING MIDAS'S EARS

APOLLO
This statue of Apollo, with a smile on his face, dates from 575-550 BC. Apollo, who was the god of music and light, had beautiful long, curling hair.

THERE IS ANOTHER STORY of Midas, which shows that although he freed himself from the desire for gold, he did not rid himself of foolishness. For he became a worshipper of Pan, the god of pastures and wild places and, by taking Pan's side, he offended great Apollo.

Now Pan enjoys playing simple country tunes on his wooden pipes, and because everyone always likes what they hear, he began to boast that he was a better musician even than Apollo, the god of music. He went so far as to challenge Apollo to a contest, to be judged by the river god Tmolus.

Tmolus dressed himself as a judge, with an oak wreath in his hair and bunches of acorns hanging by his brow, and sat down to listen to the music. Pan played first, and his merry piping charmed everyone. But then Apollo took up his lyre, and the notes he plucked rippled on the breeze like waves across the ocean, liquid and delicious.

Tmolus and Midas judge the music contest between Pan and Apollo

Pan

Midas

Tmolus

Apollo

Midas is horrified to find that he has ass's ears

DONKEY CUP
The painted pottery of ancient Greece often features figures and scenes from Greek mythology. Less common are the cups and jugs shaped as animals. This unusual two-handled drinking cup has a donkey's head as a spout for pouring.

———— ❖ ————

Tmolus had no hesitation in awarding the prize to Apollo, but Midas objected. "I preferred Pan's playing," he said.

"You can't have heard properly," said Tmolus.

"There's nothing wrong with my ears," said Midas.

At that, Apollo's anger overflowed. "You are not fit to have human ears," he said, "if that is the use you make of them." And he gave Midas, instead, a pair of ass's ears: long, grey, and hairy. "Now you look the donkey you are," he said.

King Midas was ashamed of his new ears, and tried to hide them from the world by wrapping them up in a turban. However his barber eventually discovered his embarrassing secret.

The barber did not dare tell anyone about the king's strange deformity, but he could not keep such an extraordinary thing to himself. So he went out into the country, dug a hole, and whispered the secret into the ground. Then he buried it underneath the earth.

But all secrets will out. A clump of reeds grew where the barber had dug his hole, and as the wind whistled through them, they sighed, and seemed to call, "King Midas has ass's ears! King Midas has ass's ears!"

When he learned that his secret was common knowledge, Midas died of shame.

THE PAN PIPES
King Midas is said to have invented the pipes that Pan played in the music contest. This is perhaps why he preferred Pan's playing to Apollo's.

————————

Everyone hears the reeds whisper, "King Midas has ass's ears"

The Death of Pan, page 172 ➤

BEOWULF

❖

EPIC POEM
The poem of Beowulf was sung or recited long before it was written down. The version we know today originated in the 8th century, though the only surviving manuscript dates from the 10th.

HROTHGAR, KING OF THE Danes, built a great feasting hall at Heorot. There he gave arm rings of gold and other gifts to reward his followers; there mead was drunk, boasts were made and bards sang of all the wonders of the world. The sound of merrymaking rang from the rafters.

Outside, lurking in the brackish fens, was an evil creature, Grendel by name – a vile monster that stalked the borderlands. The sound of bright laughter caused it pain. Night after night it endured the torment. Then, driven beyond endurance, it ventured to Heorot. The men in the hall were slumbering, their heads full of ale and their bellies full of food. Grendel broke their necks and dragged them off like slaughtered meat to its lair.

The monstrous Grendel drags a victim to its lair in the fens

THE ANGLO-SAXONS
After the Romans left Britain, around AD 400, the Britons asked north European tribes – the Angles, Saxons, Jutes, and Frisians – to help them fight the Picts and Scots. These "Anglo-Saxons" defeated the Britons' enemies, but then began waging war on the Britons. By AD 600 they had conquered large parts of Britain.

Grendel visited Hrothgar's hall each night for twelve years. In all that time, no songs or laughter were heard there. But at last a hero came, Beowulf of the Geats, who declared, "I will kill this monster, or die."

"No one can stand against it," jeered Unferth, one of Hrothgar's men, "still less a lad like you."

Beowulf vows to kill the monster with his bare hands

"I will kill it with my bare hands," replied Beowulf.

That night Grendel broke into the hall once more. Beowulf seized the monster and wrestled with it. And with a horrible, wet, tearing sound, he pulled its mighty arm clean from its body. The monster howled and, moaning pitifully, fled into the dark.

The next night, all rejoiced. But they celebrated too soon. For in the dark, an even viler creature came, and killed Aeschere, the king's great friend. It was Grendel's mother, come to avenge her offspring.

Beowulf tracked her across the moors to the lake where she lurked.

"I am sorry for what I said," said Unferth. "Here, take my sword, Hrunting. It never fails."

Beowulf dived into the lake. Down and down he swam, till he reached the monster's lair. She clawed at him, but his corslet of metal rings protected him. He swung at her, but Unferth's sword could not pierce her tough hide. Then he saw, lying on the bottom, a great sword, made for a giant. Beowulf alone of mortal men could have lifted it. He seized it, and struck.

The waters of the lake boiled with blood.

The men watching ashore said, "Beowulf is dead." But suddenly he surfaced, holding the heads of both Grendel and Grendel's mother.

LAND OF MONSTERS
The Anglo-Saxons did not find it hard to believe that hideous monsters lurked in the mists, marshes, and stagnant pools of fenlands, such as these in Cambridgeshire, England.

The young warrior seizes the great sword from the bottom of the lake and strikes at Grendel's mother

WINGED DRAGON
This bronze, winged dragon, part of the decoration on an Anglo-Saxon chief's shield, is just one of the many treasures that were found in the burial ship at Sutton Hoo, Suffolk, England, in the late 1930s.

Then there was feasting and giving of gifts, until Beowulf and his men took ship once more on the gull's path, the whale's way, back to the land of the Geats, where Beowulf was to be king.

THESEUS AND THE MINOTAUR

MOUNTAINOUS CRETE
The Greek island of
Crete is a place of
contrasts: snow-capped
mountains as well as
fertile valleys. Between
2500 and 1100 BC, Crete
was occupied by the
Minoans, named after the
legendary King Minos.

G REAT ZEUS HAS HAD many human lovers, whom he attracts
using different disguises. Many of these lovers have borne him
children upon whose fates the whole world has turned. One such
lover was Europa, whom Zeus saw walking by the shore. He disguised
himself as a snow-white bull and approached her. Amazed at seeing a
bull at once so fine and so tame, Europa petted him and hung flowers
from his horns. Then, suddenly bold, she jumped on to his back and
let him carry her down to the sea.

Once in the water, Zeus swam away with Europa across the ocean to
the island of Crete, where, disguised as an eagle, he lay with her. She
bore him three sons: Minos, Rhadamanthys, and Sarpedon.

After Zeus left her, Europa married Asterius, King of Crete, who
raised her sons as his own, making Minos his heir. In due course
Minos became king and took the lovely Pasiphae for his wife. In his
pride and glory, Minos boasted that the gods themselves would grant
his requests. To prove it, he built an altar to Poseidon on the seashore
and prayed that a wonderful bull should come to him out of the sea.
Minos promised he would then sacrifice the bull to the gods.

Immediately, a white bull emerged from the waves. But it was such a
fine beast that Minos could not bear to sacrifice it; instead, he killed a
bull from his own herd, and kept the gift of the gods for himself. For
this insolence, the gods took a terrible revenge.

Aphrodite, goddess of love, made Minos's wife, Pasiphae, fall in love
with the bull. Horrified, but unable to
resist Aphrodite's power, Pasiphae
confided her secret to Daedalus, a
great craftsman who served King
Minos and his court at Knossos.

So Daedalus built a hollow, wooden
cow for Pasiphae to crouch inside.
From there, unseen, she was able to
spend time with the bull, her beloved.
But as further punishment, the gods
caused Pasiphae to give birth to a
monster, half-man, half-bull, that was
named the Minotaur.

*Pasiphae crouches inside the wooden cow that Daedalus
has made for her and waits for the white bull to approach*

Minos was filled with horror at what had happened to
Pasiphae, and sought advice from an oracle. "Conceal
your shame in cunning," he was told. So Minos asked
Daedalus to build the Labyrinth, a maze of
winding passages with sudden twists and
turns and dead ends, through which no
man could find his way. At the centre
of the maze he put the Minotaur.
To feed this monster,

*The Minotaur was
imprisoned in the middle
of Daedalus's Labyrinth*

Every nine years, seven young men and seven maidens are sacrificed to the Minotaur

King Minos demanded seven young men and seven maidens from the
city of Athens every nine years. They were sent by ship to Crete and
then into the maze, where the Minotaur glutted himself on their flesh.

   Twice Athens had paid this deadly tribute, owed by the king,
Aegeus, because some years before he had had an accidental hand in
the death of Minos's son. The third time was now due. But on this
occasion a young hero stepped forward, offering himself as one of the
youths, and promising to kill the Minotaur or be killed by it. His name
was Theseus, the adopted son of King Aegeus, whose real father was
the sea-god Poseidon. Theseus had already proved himself resourceful
and brave and Aegeus had to let him go. He told Theseus, "Before,
the ships I sent to Crete bore black sails, in mourning for the young
people who were to be killed by the Minotaur. This time, the ship will
also carry white sails, in token of our hope. If you slay the beast, be
sure to hoist the white sails on your return, so we will know that you
have been successful, and can rejoice." With that, the ship set sail.

MINOTAUR COIN
This 400-BC coin was
found at Knossos, in
Crete. The palace of
Knossos, with its many
winding corridors, may
have inspired the myth
of the Labyrinth.

When the ship landed at Crete, Theseus at once sprang to shore and, announcing himself as the son of Poseidon, challenged Minos.

"Son of Poseidon!" sneered Minos. "Great Zeus will bear witness that I am his son, but will Poseidon own up to you?"

Theseus dived headlong into the sea, where a school of dolphins, arching their backs above the foam, escorted him all the way down to the seabed. There he

A school of dolphins escorts Theseus to the depths of the ocean, where Amphitrite gives him a ring and a crown as a sign of favour

received from Amphitrite, goddess of the sea, a golden ring and a jewelled crown. When the dolphins brought him back to shore, he held up the precious gifts, so that all could see the favour he had found with the gods.

"Now, King Minos," he declared, "I have come to free the Minotaur from the misshapen body in which it has been trapped by the malice of the gods and the foolishness of mankind. If you are anything of a man, you will allow me to enter the Labyrinth and kill the creature, with my bare hands. If I succeed, Athens will owe you no more tribute. If I fail, let the Minotaur drink my blood."

"Very well," said King Minos. "You may try, son of Poseidon."

The next day, King Minos's daughter, Ariadne, who had fallen in love with the noble Theseus, approached him, saying, "If you will take me back to Athens and make me your bride, I will show you the key to the maze, given to me by Daedalus, its architect."

DOLPHIN OIL CONTAINER The ancient Greeks gave special power to dolphins, which often appear in their art. This dolphin pitcher would have held cooking oil.

Theseus readily agreed, and Ariadne handed him a ball of thread.

"Tie one end of this thread outside the entrance of the maze," she said. "Then let the ball roll where it will. Follow it, and it will lead you to the centre, where you will find the foul lair of my half-brother, the Minotaur. Go at night, when he is asleep, and you may throttle him where he lies. Afterwards, simply roll the ball back up again, and it will lead you safely out."

That night, Theseus did as Ariadne instructed. As he plunged into the dark warren of the maze, the thread seemed to glimmer and guide his footsteps towards his prey.

As Theseus laid hands on the sleeping beast, it awoke and, with a roar, seized him in its death embrace. But Theseus was the stronger, and as they wrestled, he broke the creature's back and killed it.

Ariadne waits anxiously at the door as Theseus wrestles with the Minotaur

When Theseus staggered out of the maze, his face a mask of white and his body spotted with blood, Ariadne was there to meet him. They boarded their ship, with the other Athenian youths, and fled before King Minos could learn what had happened.

But Theseus was not true to Ariadne. She had helped him out of love, and he had accepted her help knowing he did not truly want to marry her. When, a few days later, they landed on the island of Naxos, Theseus left Ariadne sleeping on the shore and set sail without her.

So taken up was Theseus with his desertion of Ariadne, that he forgot all about the promise that he had made to his father. And so, when his ship came within sight of Athens, it bore still the black sails of mourning, not the white sails of victory. King Aegeus, who loved Theseus more than life, cast himself into the sea, which ever since his death, has been called the Aegean.

Thus the heroism of Theseus was tainted by treachery, and his joyful homecoming darkened by grief.

✦

THESEUS

Aegeus's adopted son Theseus was one of the greatest Greek heroes. After killing the Minotaur and Aegeus's tragic death, he became King of Athens. He later lived the life of a wandering adventurer.

Theseus's ship returns with black sails

The Fall of Icarus, page 112 ➤

THE FALL OF ICARUS

O F ALL THE CRAFTSMEN and inventors of old, Daedalus was the best and most famous. Anyone who wanted any clever thing made came first to him, at his workshop in Athens.

Now Daedalus had a nephew, Talos, who was the son of his sister, Polycaste. He took on Talos as his apprentice, and the boy, although only twelve years old, rapidly showed signs of being even cleverer than his master! It was Talos who invented the first saw and the potter's wheel, and Talos who devised the first pair of compasses. Talos's reputation soon spread and people began to bring their most difficult problems to the boy, not the man.

GREEK POTTERY
Most towns in ancient Greece had an area where potters made and sold pots. The wine cup above, made c. 490 BC, shows a potter at his wheel, adding a handle to a cup. The cup painter was usually a different person from the potter. Painted scenes such as these tell us about the everyday life and mythology of ancient Greece.

❖

MASTER CRAFTSMAN
Daedalus, the father of Icarus, was well known in Athens for his skill as an artist and craftsman. When jealousy caused him to murder his nephew Talos, he took refuge with King Minos on the island of Crete. There he became the architect of the Labyrinth, the maze that housed the monstrous Minotaur.

A potter is delighted with the wheel young Talos has invented

Daedalus looks on, consumed by jealousy, as Talos perfects his latest invention – a pair of compasses

Overcome with jealousy, Daedalus lured the boy to the top of the temple of Athena and then pushed him to his death. Talos's mother, Polycaste, killed herself out of grief, and Daedalus, along with his own son, Icarus – a vain boy with none of Talos's quickness – was banished from the city of Athens.

Daedalus and Icarus took refuge on the island of Crete, where Daedalus placed his skill and cleverness at the disposal of King Minos. But he suddenly fell out of favour with the king when Theseus killed the Minotaur and managed to escape from the supposedly escape-proof Labyrinth Daedalus had built to house the creature. Furious, King Minos had Deadalus and his son thrown into prison.

◀ *Theseus and the Minotaur, page 108*

THE ISLAND OF SAMOS
It is said that when Icarus flew too close to the sun and melted his wings, he fell into the sea near the Greek island of Samos.

While Icarus spent his days preening himself and thinking idle thoughts, Daedalus sat in deep study, planning how to escape from Crete. It was too far to swim to the nearest land, and impossible to get away by boat, owing to the vigilance of King Minos's navy.

At last Daedalus conceived a daring plan. He made two pairs of wings, threading feathers together and sealing them with wax. When the wings were ready, he took Icarus aside. "Put these on and follow me," he said, "but take care not to fly too near the sun, or too near the sea. Keep a middle course. With these wings, we shall escape."

The pair took flight from a high ledge and swooped towards the horizon. For many miles young Icarus followed his father carefully, but at last, feeling young and carefree, and enjoying the buffeting of the wind, he began to soar upwards into the sky, free as a bird.

When Icarus flies too close to the sun, the wax binding his wings melts and he tumbles to his doom

When Daedalus looked around for him, he was nowhere to be seen.

"Icarus! Icarus!" called the anxious father. But no reply came. Only, in the water far below, a scatter of feathers bobbed on the waves, and a few faint ripples spread from the spot where Icarus had fallen to his doom. For the boy had flown too near the sun, and the wax binding his wings had melted like butter.

Aeneas in the Underworld, page 154 ➤

TALIESIN

SNOWDONIA, WALES
The tale of Taliesin unfolds against the wild, mountainous landscape of north Wales.

THE WITCH CERIDWEN had a daughter, Creiwry, who was the most beautiful girl in the world, and a son, Avagddu, who was the ugliest boy. Because Avagddu was so ugly, Ceridwen resolved to brew a cauldron of Inspiration and Knowledge for him. Once he had tasted it, he would know all the secrets of the future, and men would honour him for his wisdom, not spurn him for his ugliness.

She mixed the magic potion and set the cauldron boiling. It had to boil for a year and a day, and at the end of that time, it would yield just three precious drops of Inspiration and Knowledge.

She set a blind man named Morda to kindle the fire beneath the cauldron, and a boy named Gwion to stir it, and she herself gathered the special herbs that had to be added to the mixture each day.

But on the very last day, as Ceridwen was adding the final herbs, three drops splashed up from the cauldron on to Gwion's finger. The drops scalded him, and he put his finger in his mouth to ease the pain. At once he saw all that was, and is, and will be. Gwion fled.

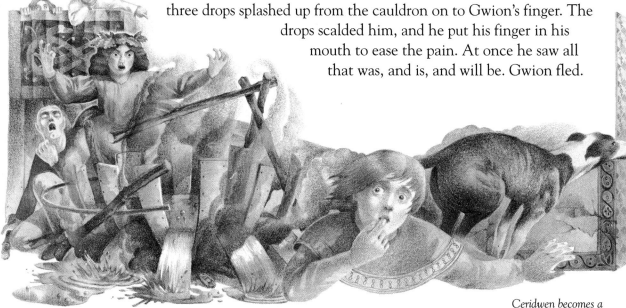

The witch Ceridwen brews a cauldron of Inspiration and Knowledge for her son, Avagddu

The boy Gwion licks three drops of the witch's brew from his finger

Ceridwen becomes a greyhound in order to pursue Gwion

Behind him, the cauldron cracked, and Ceridwen let out a curse. The witch set after Gwion. He saw her coming and changed into a hare, but she changed into a greyhound to chase him. He leapt into the river and became a fish, and she became an otter to catch him. He changed into a bird, and she became a hawk above him.

He dived into a pile of wheat and changed into a golden grain. Ceridwen turned into a black hen, and swallowed him whole.

Nine months she carried him, until at last he was born again. He was so beautiful that she could not bear to kill him, but cast him upon the sea, wrapped in a leather bag, to live or die.

Elphin

Ceridwen

Prince Elphin rescues the baby and calls him Taliesin

Each time Gwion changes into an animal to escape Ceridwen, she turns into a more cunning creature to catch him

The baby was found by a prince named Elphin, who rescued him from the water. Elphin called him Taliesin, which means "radiant brow", because of his beauty. Taliesin became Elphin's bard, or court poet and, because he had tasted the three drops of Inspiration and Knowledge, he soon became the greatest poet in all Wales.

At that time the quality of a prince's court was measured by the skill of its bard, and so Prince Elphin was a very proud man. But he went too far when he boasted that Taliesin was a greater bard than any who served the king, Maelgwyn. The king had Elphin cast into a dungeon until the time came when he could prove his boast.

EISTEDDFOD
The National Eisteddfod is an annual festival of Welsh poetry that celebrates the bardic arts of poetry, music, and literature. The word Eisteddfod means "sitting" or "gathering".

Now Taliesin, who was still only a child, went to King Maelgwyn's court, and stood at the door while all the king's bards and courtiers went in. As each one passed him, he cheekily stuck out his lips and played on them with his fingers, "Blerwm, blerwm!"

Then Taliesin entered the court, and when the king asked him who he was, he declared:

> "Primary chief bard am I to Elphin,
> And my original country is the region of the summer stars.
> Once men called me Merlin,
> Soon every king will call me Taliesin.

> "I have been in heaven, I have been in hell,
> I was with Noah when he made the ark.
> I know the names of every star;
> I am a wonder whose origin is not known.

> "I have been in every shape,
> I have been dead, I have been alive.
> I shall be on earth until the day of doom;
> It is not known if I am flesh or fish.

> "I was carried for nine months,
> In the womb of the hag Ceridwen.
> Then I was known as little Gwion,
> But at last I am Taliesin."

While Elphin languishes in the castle dungeon, King Maelgwyn decides on a contest between his own poet, grey-bearded Heinin, and Taliesin

❖

KING ARTHUR'S BARD
The real Taliesin lived in the 6th century AD. Legend tells that he became court poet to King Arthur.

Taliesin astonishes the court with his tales

Maelgwyn summoned his bards to listen. Then he ordered that Elphin, who had been bound with a silver chain, be brought up from the dungeon. While Elphin looked on, Maelgwyn told Heinin, his oldest and wisest bard, to challenge Taliesin to a contest of poetic skill. When Heinin tried to speak, all he could do was flap his fingers across his lips and make a "Blerwm, Blerwm!" sound, like a baby. The same was true for all of the king's bards. Taliesin replied with verses that revealed the world's mysteries and told of things to come.

There was no doubt in King Maelgwyn's mind that Taliesin was indeed the greatest poet in all Wales. He immediately ordered the silver chain to be struck off Elphin, and set the prince free.

GOING TO THE PALACE

One of the most powerful of all the many gods of Voodoo is Ghede, the Lord of Death, who is also known as Baron Samedi. He is the wisest of all the gods, for in his head he holds the knowledge of everyone that has ever lived. If he wishes, he can even bring the dead back to life.

When Ghede steps out of the dark into the light, he needs to wear dark glasses to protect his eyes. But he often takes out the right lens. As he explains, "With my left eye I watch over the whole world, but as for the right, I keep that eye on my food, to make sure that no thief steals it." For Ghede has an enormous appetite. He is a glutton for food, which he shovels into his mouth and swills down with his own special drink, a raw rum steeped in twenty-one hot spices. No one else can bear to swallow it, but Ghede doesn't mind. He will not blink even if the fiery liquid sprays into his eyes.

Sometimes Ghede comes as a ragtag beggarman, but more often he wears formal clothes: a top hat, a long black tailcoat, and a cane. Once, when President Borno ruled Haiti, a whole group of people dressed as Ghede – every one of them a Voodoo priest "ridden" by the spirit of the god himself – marched on the president's palace. They danced and sauntered down the street, singing, with a great crowd following them. They went right past the guards, who were powerless to stop them, through the gates, up the drive, and rapped on the palace door with their canes.

They demanded money, and the president gave plenty to them. For no matter how much power a man may have over other men when he is alive, even the president has no power over death, and in the end must pay his tribute.

Often Ghede sings a song to himself, recalling the day he and his followers danced their way to the palace and made the president pay them to go away:

"Papa Ghede is a handsome fellow,
In his coat and hat of black.
Papa Ghede is going to the palace!
He'll eat and drink when he gets back."

VOODOO DANCERS
In Voodoo ritual, the gods may possess worshippers – "ride" them in ecstatic dance. Voodoo has its roots in West Africa, from where many Haitians were once brought as slaves.

Papa Ghede and his followers set off for the president's palace

THOR IN THE LAND OF GIANTS

Flame-haired Thor, with his magic hammer, belt, and gloves, drives a chariot pulled by two goats

COOKING CAULDRON
The Vikings stewed meat in huge cooking pots, or cauldrons. This iron cauldron is from the Oseberg burial ship, in Norway. It hangs on a tripod, which would have been placed over the open fire to cook.

THOR IS THE MIGHTIEST of the Norse gods. Odin is his father; his mother is Earth. He drives a chariot pulled by two goats, and he has three great treasures: a belt that, when he wears it, doubles his strength; the terrible hammer Miollnir, with which he smites his enemies; and a pair of iron gloves, which he must wear to wield the hammer. Red-bearded god of the sky, Thor is the guardian of Asgard, home of the gods, and of the homes and farmsteads of his worshippers. But even Thor's great strength does not always prevail, as we learn from the story of his visit to the land of the giants, in the company of the trickster, Loki.

Thor's hammer, Miollnir

"I am tired of lazing around in Asgard," said Thor. "There is nothing here for me to test my strength against."

"There is certainly no point in testing it against my wits," said Loki, "for I would certainly win!"

"Brawn is better than brains," said Thor, "but it needs exercise. How do you think I'd fare in giant-land?"

"There's only one way to find out," said Loki.

So Thor and Loki set off together to look for adventure in the land of the giants. On the first evening of their journey, they stopped at a peasant's hut. The peasant had no food to offer his immortal guests, but Thor slaughtered the two goats who pulled his chariot, and put them in the pot. When the two gods sat down to eat, they invited the peasant and his family to join them.

When all had eaten their fill, Thor placed the goatskins on the floor by the fire and said, "Throw the bones on to the skins." He did not notice Thialfi, the peasant's son, split open a leg bone with his knife, to get at the sweet marrow.

Thor rose with the dawn, and, taking his hammer in his hand, raised it above the goatskins and blessed them, like newborn babies. The goats got up, but one of them was lame in one of its hind legs. Thor's fury knew no bounds. He gripped his hammer so tightly that his knuckles went white. "Someone will pay for this!" he shouted.

◄ *The Apples of Youth, page 72*

"My apologies, great Thor," mumbled the peasant. "My son acted in ignorance. Take all we have, but spare our lives, I beg you."

When he saw the man cowering in fear, Thor's anger cooled. He accepted, in compensation for the injury to his goat, the peasant's son, Thialfi, and daughter, Roskva, as his servants, and when he and Loki left they took Thialfi and Roskva with them. But they left the goats behind, while the injured goat's leg healed.

They journeyed east until they came to the sea, and crossed it to the land of the giants. When they got there, they found themselves in a deep forest. They walked until dark and at night took refuge in a huge cave with several long passages and one side-chamber. Thor kept guard, his mighty hammer at the ready.

At midnight there was a terrible earthquake, and all night there were rumblings and groanings. They were glad to see the dawn.

In the morning, when they stepped out of the cave, they found a giant, snoring away. The earthquake had been caused by the giant lying down. Thor put on his belt of strength and his iron gloves, and picked up his hammer, but at that moment the giant awoke.

"My name is Skrymir," said the giant, "and I can see that you must be Thor from Asgard. What have you been up to inside my glove?" And Thor saw that the cave in which they had sheltered was indeed Skrymir's glove, and the side-chamber was the thumb.

"We seem to be going in the same direction," said the giant, "and I'm fond of company, so why don't you come with me? If I carry your food in my knapsack, you can keep up with my long strides."

THOR
This small bronze statue of Thor holding his beard (which has turned into his hammer) was found in Iceland. It was made by Vikings in about AD 1000. Thor was the Norse god of thunder. Thursday (Thor's day) is named after him.

Thor and his companions find a safe place to sleep in the forest – little realizing it's a giant's glove

THOR'S HAMMER
Miollnir, Thor's magic
hammer, was his main
weapon. Charms made
in the shape of it
brought good luck.
This silver one was
found in Denmark.

That night, Skrymir came to a halt by a large oak tree. He tossed his knapsack to Thor and stretched out beneath the tree.

Thor busied himself with the knapsack, but whatever he did, he could not get a single knot undone. Hunger and fatigue made him furious, and he took his hammer Miollnir and struck the sleeping giant a fearful blow, right in the centre of his forehead.

Skrymir woke. "What was that?" he asked. "Did a leaf fall on me?" And then he turned over and went back to sleep. So Thor and Loki and Thialfi and Roskva had to go without their supper, and they couldn't sleep either, what with Skrymir snoring so loudly beside them.

At midnight, Thor took up his hammer again and struck another blow. This time he felt the head of the hammer sink

*"An acorn must have fallen on me," murmurs the sleeping giant
Skrymir when Thor strikes him on the head with his hammer*

into the giant's flesh. But Skrymir only murmured, "An acorn must have fallen on me," before going back to sleep.

Towards dawn, Thor decided that a third blow would surely settle this giant once and for all, so he swung with all his might and buried Miollnir up to the handle in Skrymir's head. But the giant just sat up, saying, "A bird must have dropped a twig on me from a tree. Ah well, it's time to get up, anyway. It's not far now to the giants' citadel at Utgard. There you'll meet some real giants, not little shrimps like me. But watch out: act respectful, or, better still, turn back now!"

Skrymir pointed them on the road to Utgard, and then went on his way, swinging the knapsack behind him. Thor and his companions

---
❖

SKRYMIR
The nickname given
to the giant Skrymir
was "Vasty", because
he was so enormous.
When Thor tried to
hammer in Skrymir's
skull, the giant merely
thought that first a
leaf, then an acorn,
and finally a twig, had
fallen on his head.

were not sorry to see him go, but they did not heed his warning. "We have come too far to turn back now," said Thor.

They soon arrived at Utgard, but found the gates locked. Thor tried with all his strength, but he couldn't open them. By wriggling and squeezing they could just get through the bars and into the courtyard.

They entered a great hall, full of giants who looked at them with sneers of contempt on their faces. The chief of them all, Utgard-Loki, bared his great teeth in a savage grin. "This puny fellow surely cannot be the famous Thor? But perhaps he's stronger than he looks. Whoever you are," he continued, "if you want to stay here, you must entertain us with some feat of strength or skill."

Loki, who was bringing up the rear, piped up, "I'm so hungry I'm sure I could out-eat any giant."

A giant named Logi was chosen to compete with Loki, and a huge dish was fetched and placed on the floor between them. It was piled high with meat. Loki started at one end, and Logi at the other.

Now Loki was famed among gods and men for his ferocious appetite, and he ate all the more hungrily now because he had had no supper

VIKING TRADER
Most Vikings were Christian by the early 11th century; however the Norse gods were not forgotten. This trader wears a Christian cross and a Norse hammer.

the night before, and no breakfast that day. He gobbled the meat down.

Loki and Logi met exactly in the centre of the dish: a dead heat. Except that where Loki had eaten only the meat, the giant had also consumed the bones and the dish, too. So Loki lost the contest.

Three giants

Logi

Loki

Logi and Loki start devouring the meat in the eating contest

The giant Hugi runs so fast that he comes back to meet Thialfi halfway

Next it was Thialfi's turn. Thialfi said he would run a race against anyone, for he was a wiry whippet of a man, and a very fast runner. So a track was cleared, and Thialfi was set to run against a giant named Hugi. Thialfi was so fast at the start that you could barely see him move, but Hugi was faster: so much faster that he turned around at the end of the course and ran back to meet Thialfi half way. So Thialfi, too, lost the contest.

Now it was Thor's turn. "What about a drinking match?" suggested Thor, for he was as thirsty as Loki had been hungry.

The giants brought out a great drinking horn and set it before him. "A good drinker can sink this in one draught," said Utgard-Loki, "though most take two. No one is so feeble as to need three."

No matter how much Thor drinks, he cannot empty the drinking horn

DRINKING HORN
At their feasts, the Vikings drank mead, an alcoholic drink made of fermented honey and water. They drank from horns, which were made from polished ox-horn or metal. The drinking horn could not be put down when full without overturning, so the drinker had to down the liquid in one gulp. The drinking horn above is a copy of one found in Jutland, Denmark, and later destroyed. The raised figures on the horn would have been added by craftsmen.

Thor did not think the horn looked as big as all that, so he set to, glugging the drink down in great gulps. But when he stopped, out of breath, the level in the horn was hardly lower than before. He tried again, but the level only fell a tiny bit. Thor tried a third time . He drank till he thought he would burst, but when he stopped, spluttering and out of breath, the horn was still not empty.

There was scorn in Utgard-Loki's voice. "Who would have thought that the great Thor was so feeble? It scarcely seems worth your while trying any other feat."

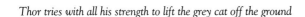

Thor tries with all his strength to lift the grey cat off the ground

"I'll try anything," said Thor.

"There is a simple game some of our youngsters play," said Utgard-Loki. "There's nothing to it, really. You just lift that grey cat off the ground. I wouldn't suggest it to a man of your reputation, except you really don't seem as strong as people say."

Thor went to the cat and put his arms around its belly and pulled. He pulled and pulled with all his strength, and the cat arched its back higher and higher until, as Thor's strength finally gave way, he did lift one of its paws from the ground. But that was all he could do.

"Never mind," said Utgard-Loki, in his silkiest voice. "After all, it is rather a big cat."

Thor was, by this time, in a raging fury. "If you think I am such a weakling, why doesn't one of you come and fight," he cried.

"You can't expect a self-respecting giant to fight someone who can't even lift up a cat," said Utgard-Loki. "But if you like, you can wrestle with my old nurse, Elli."

A withered old crone came into the hall and adopted a wrestler's stance. Thor seized her and tried to throw her to the floor, but however much he heaved and strained, he could not move her. Then, with unexpected strength, the old woman forced him on to one knee.

Utgard-Loki shouted, "Stop the fight! There's no point in continuing. Still, Thor and his companions have tried their best."

VIKING CONTESTS
The Vikings were fiercely competitive people who loved to play games and take part in contests. Norse myths such as this one reflect their fighting natures.

The old crone forces Thor on to one knee

123

The next morning, Utgard-Loki accompanied Thor and his companions on the road back towards Asgard.

"I have been made fun of," said Thor. "How can I hold my head up among the gods?"

"I will tell you how," said Utgard-Loki. "We giants had heard of your strength and prowess and, in truth, we were not eager to try ourselves against you. Therefore I myself met you in the forest, under the name of Skrymir, which means "Big Lad". If you look near my castle, you will see three great valleys. Those are the marks of your hammer blows. You thought you were hitting me, but you were deceived. So, too, in the contests. Loki's opponent was Flame, who devours everything in his path. Thialfi ran against Thought, which is the quickest thing of all. And as for you, Thor, when you were drinking from the horn, you did not realize that the other end was in the sea. No one could drink the ocean dry, but you have lowered it. And from now on, twice each day the sea will empty and then refill, in memory of your heroic draughts.

"As for the cat, to raise one of its paws was an even greater feat, for the cat was the Midgard serpent, which encircles the whole earth.

"But the wrestling match showed your true strength. For the crone Elli was Old Age, and there never has been anyone, and never will be, that old age cannot beat."

Thor was furious to hear how he had been tricked, and reached for his hammer to teach Utgard-Loki a lesson: but the giant was nowhere to be seen. Thor stormed back towards the castle, intending to smash it to the ground, but he found only green fields and grey sky.

So Thor and his companions returned to Asgard. "The cunning will always defeat the strong," said Loki.

"Tell that to my hammer," growled Thor.

The land around the castle of Utgard shows the marks of Thor's hammer.

DEEP CHASM
Cracks and crevasses are a feature of Iceland's landscape. However, they were probably not caused by blows from Thor's mighty hammer, but by volcanic activity deep under the ground.

The Death of Balder, page 162 ➤

CUCHULAIN

ONCHUBAR, KING OF ULSTER, had one hundred and fifty boys in his service. This is how he passed every day: one third of the day watching the boys at play; one third playing a board game called fidchell; and one third drinking until he fell asleep.

King Conchubar

Idle King Conchubar spends his days playing fidchell, watching his boys fighting and drinking

Young Cuchulain begs his mother to be allowed to go and fight with the older boys

Conchubar's nephew, Cuchulain, begged his mother to be allowed to join the boys. "You are too young," she answered, for he was only six. "Wait awhile." But Cuchulain would not wait. He set out with his stick and ball and his toy javelin and shield. He could throw the javelin ahead and run forward to catch it before it fell to the ground.

When he arrived at the playing fields, the boys laughed at him and told him to go away. They threw their javelins at him, but he warded them off with his toy shield.

The boys laugh and throw spears at him, but Cuchulain wards them off with his toy shield

THE ULSTER CYCLE
Cuchulain is the hero of the Ulster Cycle of myths, which dates from the 7th century AD.

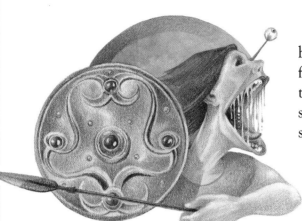

Enraged by the boys' teasing, Cuchulain's battle fury comes upon him for the first time in his life, transforming the handsome young lad into a fearsome sight

SIGN OF POWER
This tubular collar, called a torque, was worn around the neck by wealthy men and women. Gold torques, such as the one above, belonged only to the most powerful. As well as being a sign of rank, a warrior's torque brought him good luck in battle.

When they attacked Cuchulain, for the first time his battle fury came upon him. His hair seemed on fire. One eye closed, and shrank back into his head; the other eye glared, and stood out on a stalk. His snarl split his face from jaw to ear. His mouth stretched open so you could see right down his throat. Behind his head was a glare of red. He chased the boys all the way to where Conchubar was playing fidchell. And Conchubar took Cuchulain into his service, for the boy was the son of the king's sister. Some said his father was Lugh, the Master of Many Arts, a chieftain of the godlike Tuatha de Danaan, Ireland's first rulers.

Cuchulain achieved many great feats and became known as the Hound of Ulster. He grew into a handsome young man – except in his battle fury. His hair was brown at the base, blood-red in the middle, and golden yellow at the ends. King Conchubar, seeing what a fine young man his nephew had become, sent nine men out into the provinces of Ireland to find a suitable bride for him. But when they returned, none of them had found a girl fine enough for Cuchulain.

So Cuchulain himself set out, dressed in his best clothes – a white linen shirt, a crimson tunic, and a brooch of fine gold – to court Emer, the daughter of Forgall Manach the Wily. Emer was the loveliest girl in the whole of Ireland. She flirted with the young warrior and matched him wit for wit. And they pledged themselves to each other.

Cuchulain and Emer pledge their love – against the wishes of her father, Forgall the Wily

Now Forgall Manach was not pleased that his daughter should throw herself away on a mere warrior, especially one who, because of his horrifying battle fury, was known as the Warped One. And Forgall was not called the Wily for nothing. He went to King Conchubar and praised Cuchulain mightily for his great prowess in the arts of war. "But," he said, " he will never reach his full power unless he studies under Scathach, the Scottish warrior-woman." Forgall knew that no man had ever survived as Scathach's pupil, for she was the greatest warrior there had ever been.

As soon as Cuchulain heard this suggestion, he went in search of Scathach. She lived on an island, and the only way on to it was over a high bridge that, when a man stood on it, bucked like a frightened horse. Cuchulain made his hero's salmon-leap on to the middle of the bridge, and sprang off it again before he could be flung into the water.

Scathach accepted him as her pupil and taught him all the arts of war. She taught him the feats of the sword edge and the sloped shield, the cat's twist and the hero's scream, the blow that stuns and the

WARRIOR OF STONE
This stone bust of an Irish warrior, perhaps a chieftain or a god, comes from Tandaragee, County Armagh, Northern Ireland. It stands 60 cm (2 ft) high and dates from the 1st century AD. The bumps on the soldier's helmet could be the remains of a pair of horns.

Cuchulain springs across the magic bridge using his hero's salmon-leap and becomes the pupil of Scathach, the formidable warrior-woman

stroke that severs. Alone of all her pupils, she taught him the *gae bolga*, the lightning spear-thrust no enemy could withstand.

Then Cuchulain left Scathach and rode in his chariot to Forgall's fortress. Forgall barred the gate against him, but Cuchulain leapt the walls. Forgall fell to his death trying to escape the hero's fury, and Cuchulain took the lovely Emer for his wife.

RIDING HIGH
Irish warriors sallied forth into battle in beautifully decorated, horse-drawn chariots. These bronze mounts, inlaid with red enamel, would have adorned a horse's harness.

Now the men of Ireland in those days were great ones for fighting, and almost any excuse would do. And so it was that the armies of Ireland went to war when King Ailill and Queen Maeve of Connaught tried to steal away a fine prize, the great bull of Ulster.

Cuchulain

Alone, Cuchulain takes on the armies of Ireland

King Ailill and Queen Maeve steal the great bull of Ulster

Cuchulain's mother sees her son's wine turn to blood and realizes he is doomed

STANDING STONES
The Leganny dolmen (stone table) of County Down in Northern Ireland, may have been an ancient tomb. The dying Cuchulain must have strapped himself to similar stones.

At that time the men of Ulster were under a spell – struck down by weakness and pain so severe that they could not fight. Only Cuchulain was unaffected. Alone, he stood at a ford and held off the armies of Connaught and the other Irish provinces. First he challenged all the best warriors and killed them all. Then he took to his chariot and attacked the armies. He killed so many men that the battle that day is one of the three uncountable slaughters of Ireland.

The enmity between the men of Ulster and the other provinces of Ireland was not ended by Cuchulain's great deeds – it grew worse. And the day came when Cuchulain readied himself to fight them once again. He went to his mother to bid her goodbye, and she gave him a cup of wine in farewell. But when he came to drink it, there was only blood in the cup. Three times she rinsed the cup and filled it with wine; three times the wine turned into blood. "My luck has turned against me," said Cuchulain. "I will not come back alive."

Cuchulain's mother begged him to stay with her that day until his luck returned but he said, "I have never turned from a battle and I never will. A great name is better than a long life."

On his way to the battle, Cuchulain saw a young girl with white skin and red hair – one of the fairy folk, the Sidhe, – weeping at a ford. She was washing and washing a bundle of red-stained clothes. Cathbad the druid, who was with him, told him, "Those are your clothes she is washing. She is crying because she knows you are going to your death."

But Cuchulain did not turn back. He came upon the armies of Ireland in his chariot and slew them by the hundred. They fell like the leaves from the trees in autumn, and stained the plain red with their blood. But at last Lugaid, son of Curoi, drove a spear through Cuchulain's belly, and Cuchulain knew that he had received his death-wound.

He asked leave to go down to the lake and take a mouthful of water, and Lugaid granted his wish. Cuchulain went down to the water and drank and washed himself. Then he turned back to face his death.

In the middle of the battle plain there was a great standing stone, and Cuchulain tied himself to that stone with his breast-belt, so that he would die on his feet. He continued to fight until a crow landed on his shoulder, the bird of the war goddess Morrigan, or maybe even the goddess herself, and then Lugaid dealt the death-stroke.

And that was the passing of the mighty Cuchulain, the Hound of Ulster.

Riding to the battle with Cathbad the druid, Cuchulain glimpses a weeping fairy girl washing bloodstained clothes

Cathbad

Lugaid

Resolved to die on his feet like a hero, Cuchulain lashes himself to a standing stone. But as a crow flaps around his helpless body, his enemy, Lugaid, prepares to strike

THE LABOURS OF HERACLES

HERA
Zeus's wife, Hera, was the most powerful Greek goddess, and the patron of wedded love. Her jealous nature led her to take revenge on many of Zeus's lovers.

GREAT ZEUS, KING OF the gods, had many love affairs with mortal women, much to the distress of his wife, the goddess Hera. The children born of these love affairs were half gods themselves and, of them all, none was greater than Heracles, for he was conceived to be the protector of both men and gods.

Zeus lay with Alcmene, Heracles' mother, in the guise of her husband, Amphitryon, who was away at the wars. Zeus commanded time itself to slow down, so that one night was the length of three. When Amphitryon returned the following day, Alcmene was too tired to welcome him home; she was already carrying Zeus's child.

Nine months later, Zeus boasted in Olympus of the hero, his son, who was about to be born. "His name will be Heracles, and he will rule the noble House of Perseus."

Hera was furious, especially as the name Heracles means, "Glory of Hera". She went to Zeus and asked him, "Do you swear that the child to be born to the House of Perseus today will be king of Mycenae?"

"I swear," said Zeus.

Hera at once went to Mycenae, and there she hastened the birth of Eurystheus, Heracles's cousin. Then she went and sat outside the door of Alcmene's bedchamber and bewitched her so that she could not give birth until the next day. Zeus could not go back on his word, so Eurystheus, instead of Heracles, became king. However, Hera agreed that if Heracles could perform twelve Labours to be set by Eurystheus, he could become a god. Alcmene was so frightened at finding herself in the middle of a quarrel between Zeus and Hera that she abandoned her baby outside Thebes, Mycenae's main city.

Zeus, seeing what had happened, asked the goddess Athena to take Hera past the spot.

"Look at this strong child," Athena exclaimed. "His mother must be mad to leave him. You're nursing, Hera. Give him a drink."

And so, by letting the baby drink from her breast, Hera was tricked into saving Heracles's life. Athena later returned the baby to Alcmene. "Guard him well," she said.

Fearing Hera's anger, Alcmene abandons the baby Heracles outside the city walls

A year later, Hera tried again to foil the plans of Zeus. She sent two fearful serpents, with rippling blue scales and flame-filled eyes, to sink their poisoned fangs into the infant as he slept.

In the morning, Alcmene found Heracles sitting up, gurgling with pleasure, and dangling the dead serpents over the sides of his bed. He had strangled them with his bare hands.

This was just one of the amazing feats performed by Heracles in childhood. He grew straight and tall, with fiery eyes and strength beyond his years. He liked to roam under the stars, and learned to think as well as to fight. He was an expert with both bow and

Young Heracles strangles the deadly serpents with his bare hands

javelin, but his favoured weapon was a club cut from a wild olive tree.

At last the time came for Heracles to undertake the twelve Labours that would make him a god. The first task set by Eurystheus was intended to be the last, for he asked his cousin to kill the Nemean lion, a fearsome beast whose thick hide was proof against any weapon.

When Heracles arrived in Nemea, he could not find anyone to tell him where the lion was, for it had devoured everyone in its path. So he hunted it across the country and tracked it to its lair. There he waited, until the lion returned from hunting, its mane flecked with the blood of its victims.

Heracles shot at the lion with his bow, but his arrows just bounced off. He swung at it with his sword, but the weapon rebounded in his hands. So he followed the creature into its cave and there he seized it in his arms, and throttled it to death.

When Heracles returned to Thebes, wearing the lion's pelt as armour, King Eurystheus nearly fainted away. "Next time," he said, "just send me word that you have achieved your task. There is no need to come in person."

For Eurystheus was terrified that what his cousin could do to the Nemean lion, he might also do to a Theban king.

OLIVE TREE, CORFU
Heracles (known to the Romans as Hercules) cut his favourite wooden club from the olive tree. This evergreen, highly prized in ancient times, grows well in Mediterranean countries.

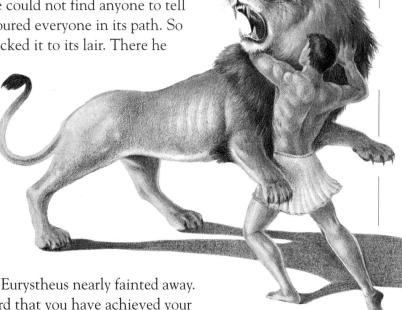

Heracles wrestles with the Nemean lion, slowly throttling it to death

Several of the Labours of Heracles were similar in nature – he was
sent to fight a monster and succeeded, by strength and guile, in
killing or capturing it. His second task was to kill the many-headed
Hydra, a creature so terrible that to smell its breath was fatal. Each
time he cut off one of its heads, it grew more. But at last he killed it.

In this way, Heracles was sent against the Cerynean hind, the
Erymanthian boar, the Stymphalian birds, the Cretan bull, the mares
of Diomedes, and the cattle of Geryon. He was also sent to steal the
golden girdle of the Amazon queen Hippolyta, which Eurystheus
wanted to give to his daughter, Admete.

Erymanthian boar
Stymphalian birds
Cretan bull
Cattle of Geryon
Hydra
Cerynean hind
Hippolyta, the Amazon queen
Mares of Diomedes

All these tasks Heracles achieved. But the three that remained were
of a different nature.

"It is clear that he can hunt and fight," said Eurystheus. "But let's
see how he likes hard work."

Heracles was sent to clean the stables of King Augeus, and
Eurystheus and his courtiers burst with laughter at the thought, for
the Augean stables had not been cleaned in living history. The dung
of the cattle and horses lay in such great mounds that the buildings
were pretty well covered in manure.

"He won't be able to look down his nose at me after a year or two of dung-carrying," joked Eurystheus, "even if he is the son of a god. He won't want to use his nose at all!"

But Heracles was not daunted. When he arrived at the stables, he told King Augeus, "I'll have it done by nightfall."

The first thing that Heracles did was to make two breaches in the stable walls. Then he diverted two nearby rivers so that they ran through the stables, and within a day they had swept the stables, and

The Garden of the Hesperides

Heracles wears the pelt of the Nemean lion as armour

Stables of King Augeus

the fields and valleys, clean again. And so Heracles removed the mountains of dung without soiling his hands at all.

The eleventh Labour was more tricky. Heracles was sent to fetch some golden apples from the Garden of the Hesperides, which can be found in the far west where the sun sets, on the slopes of Mount Atlas. The apples grew on a tree that was a wedding present to the goddess Hera from Gaia, mother of the earth. It was tended by three maidens, the Hesperides. In addition, a fierce serpent was coiled round the tree, to protect the precious fruit from thieves.

❖

ATLAS'S BURDEN
Atlas was one of the
defeated Titans, who
was sentenced by the
Olympian gods to carry
the sky on his shoulders
as a punishment. His
three daughters, the
Hesperides, looked after
the golden apples in
their garden.

---

*Atlas bears the weight
of the heavens on his
shoulders*

*In the garden of the
Hesperides, a serpent guards the golden apples*

Heracles was baffled as to how to steal this treasure and decided to take counsel from the gods. He was told that only Nereus, the Old Man of the Sea, knew how to find the Garden of the Hesperides. Heracles seized Nereus while he slept and held grimly on to him, even though Nereus changed his shape many times trying to escape. Eventually, Nereus told him everything he needed to know.

Instead of going straight to the Garden, Heracles approached Atlas, whose everlasting task it was to hold up the heavens on his shoulders. "You must be tired of bearing such a heavy weight," Heracles said. "If you'll do something for me, I'll take a turn for a while."

"What must I do?" asked Atlas eagerly.

"Only fetch for me the golden apples that your three daughters tend. Surely they will give them to you."

"My daughters may give me the apples, but the serpent that guards the tree will certainly kill me."

"I will shoot the serpent with my bow, from outside the garden."

"In that case, I shall do as you ask."

So Heracles killed the serpent, and took up the burden of Atlas. When Atlas returned with the apples, he was whistling a happy tune. "It is good to walk freely in the world again," he said. "I'll take these apples to Eurystheus myself. You're a big strong lad, quite capable of holding up the heavens in my stead."

Heracles had been warned by Nereus that this would happen. He said, "After all you've done for me, I'd be delighted. But I can already feel the heavens rubbing a sore spot on my head. If you'll just take them back for a moment, I'll make myself a pad out of grass."

Atlas set down the apples and took the heavens back from Heracles. But instead of making a pad, Heracles just picked up the apples and walked away.

"Thank you!" he called.

The twelfth Labour of Heracles was the most difficult of all. He had to descend to Hades, the Underworld, and bring back the watchdog of hell, Cerberus, who had three heads. It was Cerberus's job to keep the dead in Hades, and the living out.

When Heracles descended to the Underworld, he saw many friends and legendary heroes of long ago, who seemed to welcome, or to threaten him. But he knew they were mere shades, and ignored them in his quest for the dog.

He was greeted by Hades himself, and his wife, Persephone. Hades laughed and said, "The dog is yours, if you can take him." And Heracles, gathering all his courage, threw his powerful arms around the dog, throttling it as he had done the Nemean lion at the start of his adventures, and dragged it up into the world of day.

Cerberus whined and snarled all the way into the light, and where the flecks of slaver that flew from its mouth fell to the ground, poisonous aconites grew.

When Heracles arrived at Tiryns with the dog, his cousin Eurystheus was so terrified he begged him to take it back where it had come from. And that was the end of Heracles's Labours.

In the end, death came to the mortal part of Heracles when he put on a shirt accidentally soaked in poison by his wife. However, his immortal part, which lives for ever, could not be conquered. While his mortal shade wanders in Hades, his immortal self guards the door of Heaven.

It is said that when Heracles ascended to join the gods, Atlas staggered under the extra weight.

Heracles descends into the Underworld to find the three-headed dog, Cerberus

135

The Winged Horse, page 148 ➤

GODS AND ANIMALS

Humans have always shared the world with animals and, as prehistoric cave paintings attest, animals have always exerted an endless fascination over people's minds. We have hunted animals, worked with them, and even worshipped them. The ancient Egyptians so revered cats, that when one died it was mourned, mummified, and entombed with mummified mice to eat in the hereafter.

The myths of the world reflect every facet of our relationship with real animals, as well as telling tales of fabulous beasts, such as Pegasus, the winged horse, and the Phoenix, the immortal bird of harmony.

Quetzalcoatl, the serpent god, recoils in horror when he sees he has been given a human face in The Plumed Serpent, *a story that places the innocence of animals above the lusts of humans*

ROMULUS AND REMUS

THE ETERNAL CITY
According to legend, Romulus and Remus founded Rome, "The Eternal City", in 753 BC. They built the city on seven hills near the River Tiber in what is now Italy.

N UMITOR, KING OF ALBA, had been ousted by his brutal brother, Amulius. Amulius made sure Numitor would have no heirs by forcing Numitor's only child, his daughter, Rhea Silvia, to spend her days as a vestal virgin, serving in the temple of Vesta, goddess of the hearth. Nevertheless Rhea subsequently gave birth to twin boys, Romulus and Remus. Their father was not a man, but Mars, god of war. When Amulius found out what had happened, he slew Rhea Silvia and had the two boys thrown into the River Tiber.

The river bore the twins safely ashore, where they were found by a she-wolf who suckled them with her milk.

Faustulus the shepherd comes upon the twins, Romulus and Remus, being suckled by a she-wolf

ROMAN GAMES
Athleticism, skill, and bravery were tested in organized games, which were hugely popular with the Romans. This mosaic from the 3rd century AD shows two women athletes.

The wolf looked after them until they were found by Faustulus, one of the old king's shepherds, who adopted them as his own.

When the boys were grown, Faustulus told them who their father was and described their mother's fate. Romulus and Remus avenged her by killing Amulius, and they restored Numitor to the throne.

They then decided to build a city on the River Tiber. Realizing that only one of them could be its ruler, they sought guidance from the gods. Each climbed a high mountain, to see what he could see. Remus saw a flight of six vultures, but Romulus saw twelve. Therefore Romulus, judging that the gods had favoured him, began to lay the foundations of the city of Rome. He ploughed a furrow to mark where the walls would be. But Remus mocked him, leaping over the thin furrow and saying that Rome's enemies would be able to get over its walls just as easily. Romulus was so furious he struck his brother dead.

The city was built. It had a ruler, but no citizens. So Romulus declared Rome's sacred grove to be sanctuary, and it soon filled with

Remus mocks the thin furrow that Romulus is digging

outlaws and fugitives, whom Romulus welcomed as his subjects.

But there were still no women. So Romulus organized some games and invited his neighbours, the Sabines. While the Sabine men were enjoying themselves, he and his men carried off many of the Sabine women to Rome. Bloody war followed, but eventually the women themselves stopped the fighting, begging their new husbands and their fathers not to slaughter themselves needlessly.

Romulus, the founder of Rome, was not to be its earthly ruler for long. For his father, Mars, begged almighty Jupiter to make Romulus a god. When Jupiter agreed, Mars descended in his chariot and swept Romulus away. The body of the living man melted into thin air, and he became a god. From heaven, Romulus oversaw the rise, and fall, of the great nation he had founded.

Having distracted the Sabine menfolk, Romulus and his men seize the Sabine women and carry them off to Rome

THE PLUMED SERPENT

QUETZALCOATL'S MASK
This 15th-century turquoise mosaic mask represents Quetzalcoatl, the Aztec god of creation, learning, and the wind. The Aztecs believed that they lived beneath the sun of Quetzalcoatl, the plumed serpent god. The sun moved only when carried by his breath. When warriors died, their souls became rare feathered birds after four years, and flew to meet this sun.

❖

TEZCATLIPOCA
According to Aztec myth, Tezcatlipoca was the god of warriors, the night sky, and the thunderbolt. His name, "smoking mirror", comes from his magic mirror, in which he could see everything, as well as read people's thoughts.

QUETZALCOATL, THE SERPENT GOD, was the king of the City of the Gods. He was totally pure, innocent, and good. No task was too humble for him. He even swept the paths for the rain gods, so that they might come and rain.

Quetzalcoatl's cunning brother, Tezcatlipoca, was infuriated by his perfect goodness. With some friends, Tezcatlipoca decided to play a dirty trick on Quetzalcoatl and turn him into a pleasure-seeking rascal. "We will give him a human face and body," he grinned.

They showed Quetzalcoatl his new features in a smoking mirror. As soon as Quetzalcoatl looked into the mirror and saw his face, he felt himself possessed by all the worldly desires that afflict mankind.

Tezcatlipoca shows Quetzalcoatl his new, human face and body in a smoking mirror

Tezcatlipoca pours wine into a bowl to give to Quetzalcoatl

Quetzalcoatl drinks the wine and makes love to his sister, Quetzalpetatl

Xolotl, the coyote, makes Quetzalcoatl a coat of green, red, and white feathers

He cried out in horror. "I am no longer fit to be king. I cannot appear like this before my people." He called the coyote Xolotl to him. Xolotl, who was as close to Quetzalcoatl as his own shadow, made him a coat of green, red, and white feathers from the Quetzal bird. He also made him a turquoise mask, and a wig and beard of blue and red feathers. He reddened the king's lips, painted his forehead with yellow dye, and drew on his teeth to make them look like serpent's teeth. And so Quetzalcoatl was disguised as a plumed serpent.

However, Tezcatlipoca had thought of a new trick to play on his brother. He gave Quetzalcoatl wine, telling him it was a potion to cure his malady. Quetzalcoatl, who had never drunk alcohol before, soon became drunk. While he was in a stupor, Tezcatlipoca persuaded him to make love to his own sister, the beautiful Quetzalpetatl.

When Quetzalcoatl awoke, he was bitterly ashamed of what he had done. "This is an evil day," he said, and he resolved to die.

COYOTE
This Toltec ornament, which is covered with mother-of-pearl mosaic, represents a warrior from the Toltec city of Tula. It shows a man's head held in the jaws of a coyote. Xolotl, the coyote, was the Aztec god of the evening star. The name Xolotl means "twin", and so the god is often referred to as Quetzalcoatl's double, or twin brother.

QUETZAL BIRD
This colourful bird from Central America is associated with the plumed serpent god, Quetzalcoatl. The Aztec people used the bird's long tail feathers in their ceremonies.

Quetzalcoatl ordered his servants to make a stone box, and he lay in it for four days. Then he arose and told the servants to fill the box with all his rarest treasures and seal it up.

Quetzalcoatl went to the sea and there he put on his coat of quetzal feathers and his turquoise mask. And then he set fire to himself until there was nothing left but ashes on the shore. From these ashes, rare birds rose into the sky.

When Quetzalcoatl died, the dawn did not rise for four days, because Quetzalcoatl had descended to the land of the dead with his double, Xolotl, to see his father, Mictlantecuhtli. He told his father, the Lord of the Dead, "I have come to take the precious bones that you have here to people the Earth."

And the Lord of the Dead replied, "It is well."

*Quetzalcoatl's servants
fill the stone box with
his treasures*

*Rare birds rise from the
ashes of Quetzalcoatl's
funeral pyre*

❖

KING QUETZALCOATL
A king named Quetzalcoatl ruled the Toltecs, who were conquered by the Aztecs. He was a man of exceptional gifts, similar to the King Arthur of Celtic myth. The Aztecs believed they were his successors and many legends grew up about him.

Quetzalcoatl and Xolotl took the precious bones, and made their way back to the land of the living. As dawn rose once more, Quetzalcoatl sprinkled his blood over the bones and gave them life. The bones became the first people.

Quetzalcoatl taught humankind many important things. He found maize, which the ants had hidden, and stole a grain of it to give to the people he had created so that they could grow food for themselves. He taught them how to polish jade, how to weave fabrics, and make mosaics. Best of all he taught them how to measure time and understand the stars, and he laid down the course of the year and the seasons.

FEATHER HEADDRESS
This headdress, made from Quetzal birds' feathers, belonged to Montezuma, the last Aztec ruler. In 1519 he gave the headdress to the Spanish adventurer Cortes, thinking he was Quetzalcoatl returned. Two years later, the Spanish had conquered his whole empire.

Quetzalcoatl

Quetzalcoatl teaches people how to weave, polish jade, and make mosaics

Quetzalcoatl and Xolotl make each person out of bones from the land of the dead

Xolotl

At last it was time for Quetzalcoatl to leave humans to fend for themselves. When that day dawned, there appeared in the sky the star Quetzalcoatl, which we know as Venus. For this reason Quetzalcoatl is called Lord of the Dawn. Some say Quetzalcoatl sailed to the east on a raft of serpents, and one day he will return.

Quetzalcoatl sails away

THE ELEPHANT GOD

❖
SYMBOL OF STRENGTH
The elephant is a symbol of power, wisdom, fidelity, peace, and happiness. In Indian mythology, an elephant is described as holding up the heavens. For this reason the pillars of old buildings are often supported by stone elephants.

ART MASTER
Shiva is often portrayed as destructive, but he also has peaceful forms. This bronze statuette shows Shiva as Vinadhara, "Master of the Arts".

ALL MEN HAVE THE GOD SHIVA in their soul, just as all women have the goddess Devi, who is sometimes called Parvati. The ebb and flow of the universe, which moves and is still, is the union of Shiva and Parvati.

Now Parvati, as Shiva's wife, wanted to have children. But Shiva, who was free from all passions, did not feel the same way. "I can never die," he said, "so I have no need for a son to make offerings to my soul. It is enough for me that we can enjoy helping men and women to make children. We don't need our own." But Parvati longed for a child, and she fell into a terrible sadness.

Shiva is jealous of the new arrival

The bundle of cloth Parvati cradles in her arms turns into a baby, Ganesha

When Shiva saw how much she wanted a child, he told her, "There is no need to pine. If you want a son to kiss, I will give you one." And he made a bundle out of material from her dress, and gave it to her. "There is a son for you," he said.

◀ *Mother of Life and Death, page 98*

The goddess clutched the bundle of cloth to her breast. Suddenly it quivered with life. She caressed it with lotus flowers. It began to breathe. It was a real baby, calling out for the milk from her breast.

As the baby drank, he smiled up at his mother.

But Shiva was not pleased that his cloth-baby had come to life. Jealous of all the attention the new arrival was getting from his wife, he scowled at the child – and the burning rays of Shiva's middle eye scorched away the baby's head!

❖

THE SENSIBLE RAT
Although the rat is generally associated with death, decay, disease, and cowardice in the Western world, in the East it is often highly respected. For a Hindu, for example, the rat stands for good sense and foresight – a fitting mount for Ganesha.

Given a new head by Shiva, Ganesha thrives as the elephant god of good fortune

Parvati was beside herself with grief, so Shiva guiltily looked around for another head. The nearest creature was a one-tusked elephant. Shiva quickly cut off its head and gave it to the child.

And that is how the little pot-bellied god, Ganesha, who rides around this world on a rat, and is the patron of learning and the giver of good fortune, comes to have the head of an elephant.

Ganesha's mount is a rat, an animal renowned for its good sense

GANESHA
Indian schoolchildren often have the god's picture on the covers of their exercise books, to bring them good luck. Ganesha is often pictured carrying a weapon, a warning for those that fail to pay him respect.

THE CAT GODDESS

BASTET
This figurine of Bastet the cat goddess shows her with kittens at her feet, emphasizing her link with fertility. In one hand she carries a sistrum, a percussion instrument, in the other she has an image of the lion goddess Sekhmet, her dangerous aspect.

THE NILE
The sacred cats of old Egypt got their fish from the Nile. The river's regular floods created a highly fertile valley that enabled a civilization to flourish.

IN ANCIENT EGYPT, all cats were sacred. If a house was on fire, the owners would save the household cat before anything else. It was death to kill a cat.

The cat deity, who each night saved Re, the sun god, from Apep, serpent of chaos, came to be called Bastet. She was a love goddess, full of the sun's warmth.

The centre of her worship was the city of Bubastis, which boasted a fine temple in her honour. Each spring, the citizens would go out of the city and sail back in ships, playing drums and pipes, singing and clapping. The merrymaking would go on all night. Cats going about their business would add their voices in praise of Bastet.

The people of Bubastis celebrate the springtime festival dedicated to the cat goddess Bastet

◄ *First Things, page 16*

KING OF THE BIRDS

ONCE UPON A TIME, in the first cycle of the world's history, the four-legged creatures chose the lion as their king, the fishes chose the monster-fish Ananda, and the birds chose the golden mallard duck. This golden mallard was one of the early forms of the Buddha, who was born many times, in many shapes, both human and animal, before he at last achieved release from the wheel of life. Always he showed wisdom, leadership, and humility, and there are many lessons to be learned from the stories of his lives, which are known as the Jataka tales. Even when he was born as an outcast pariah dog, living on scraps he found among the rubbish, the Buddha became leader of all the stray dogs, and earned the king's favour.

Now the king golden mallard had a lovely daughter, who was the apple of his eye. She asked him to allow her to choose her own husband, and he agreed. He summoned all the birds to a plateau of bare rock high in the mountains of the Himalayas so that she could make her choice. Every single bird came.

As the king's daughter inspected the vast flock of birds, her eye was caught by the shimmering, many-hued beauty of the peacock. "This one shall be my husband," she said.

When the peacock heard this, he was overcome with pride and vanity. He danced and he pranced; he spread his wings and fanned out his beautiful tail, displaying himself for all to see.

The king mallard declared, "This bird has no modesty in his heart or decency in his bearing. My daughter shall never marry such a vain wretch."

So instead the king gave his daughter to a young mallard, his nephew, and the peacock flew away in shame.

Human vanity often causes people to lose a treasure that is nearly within their grasp.

DUCK TILES
The golden ducks on these tiles from the Man Singh palace in Gwalior, northern India, symbolize the Buddha, founder of the Buddhist religion.

The vain peacock is dismissed by the king mallard and flaps away in shame

The king mallard decides that his daughter shall marry his modest nephew

THE WINGED HORSE

BIRTH OF PEGASUS
This story tells how the Greek hero Perseus killed the fearsome Medusa, releasing Pegasus, the winged horse (shown in the relief above). It also tells how Pegasus later became the mount of Bellerophon in his quest to kill the terrible Chimaera.

When Perseus cuts off Medusa's head, Pegasus springs from her body

ACRISIUS, KING OF ARGOS, had only one child, a daughter called Danae. He wanted a son, and asked the oracle what the future held. The oracle replied: "You will have no son and your grandson will kill you." The terrified king locked his daughter away in a high tower behind doors of brass. However, the god Zeus came to her in a shower of gold, and, in time, she bore a son, Perseus.

Fearing Zeus's wrath if he killed his daughter and grandson, Acrisius cast Danae and Perseus adrift on the sea in a wooden chest. Danae prayed to Zeus for help and, instead of being swamped by the waves, their chest was washed up on the island of Seriphos.

At length, the island's king, Polydectes, met Danae. He desired to marry her, but she refused him. With Perseus, who was by now fully grown, to protect her, the king knew he would never bend her to his will. He decided to get rid of Perseus. He held a banquet for the island's young men. All the guests brought gifts, except Perseus, who was too poor. Ashamed, he promised the king a present. "Bring me the head of the Gorgon Medusa," Polydectes sniggered.

Medusa was a terrible monster, with snakes for hair and a glance that turned people to stone. The task was impossible.

Zeus took pity on Perseus and sent two Immortals, Athena and Hermes, to him. Athena lent Perseus her polished shield, saying: "Look only on Medusa's reflection in the shield and you will not be turned to stone." Hermes lent Perseus a sickle to cut off the Gorgon's head. He also told Perseus how to find the Nymphs of the North Wind, who would lend him winged sandals, a wallet to hold Medusa's head, and fetch for him the Cap of Invisibility from Hades, god of the Underworld.

Wearing sandals and cap, Perseus flew unseen to the far west. He found Medusa and her two sisters asleep among the weatherworn statues of other heroes, all turned to stone by her glare. Looking only at Medusa's reflection in his shield, Perseus swung the sickle, cut off her head and thrust it into the wallet. From her body sprang the marvellous winged horse, Pegasus.

On his way home, Perseus saw a girl chained to a rock. Her name was Andromeda and she was about to be sacrificed to a sea monster, to prevent it laying waste her father's kingdom. As the creature rose from the deep, Perseus pulled out Medusa's head and turned the monster to stone. Perseus and Andromeda, who had fallen in love at first sight, were married soon after.

By the time Perseus returned to Seriphos, Polydectes had made Danae a slave. The king was amazed to see Perseus alive and did not believe he could have killed Medusa. Perseus promptly showed him the Gorgon's head – and he was turned to stone where he stood.

The oracle's prophecy came true, for Perseus did eventually kill his grandfather. He was throwing a discus one day when, by the will of the gods, it hit Acrisius.

The winged horse Pegasus became the steed of another hero, Bellerophon. He rode the horse in his fight against the fire-breathing Chimaera, a monster with a lion's head, a goat's body, and a serpent's tail. Bellerophon killed the creature by thrusting his spear into its throat. The spear had a lump of lead on the end, which the Chimaera's hot breath melted, searing its insides.

Bellerophon was such a great man that he came to think himself the equal of the gods. He rode Pegasus right up to Olympus. But Zeus sent a gadfly to sting the horse, which shied. Bellerophon was flung to earth and ended his days a beggar. As for Pegasus, Zeus used her to carry his thunderbolts.

PEGASUS
The winged horse is shown on this coin from Athens. Bellerophon is supposed to have tamed Pegasus using a bridle given to him by Athena, goddess of wisdom.

Mounted on Pegasus, Bellerophon attacks the fearsome, fire-breathing Chimaera

Atlantis, page 170 ➤

BENTEN AND THE SERPENT KING

LUCKY RIDE
This detail from a
Japanese painting shows
Benten riding an ox, an
animal linked with
good fortune.

BENEATH THE SEAS live the serpent peoples. There the dragon king Ryu-wo reigns in a wonderful palace built of coral and crystal. He has a human body, but a serpent adorns his crown, and his followers are serpents, fishes, and monsters of the deep. He is wise and noble, a guardian of the Shinto faith. Many of those who have fallen by chance into the sea, have lived on, transformed, in the court of the dragon king.

At Kamakura on the Pacific coast of Japan, there is a great temple, something like the dragon king's palace, built to commemorate the marriage of the goddess of love, Benten, and a serpent king, who lived in a pond above the beach on Picture Island.

This serpent was terrorizing the villages, and devouring the children for miles around. Benten could not bear to witness such destruction. Therefore she stirred up an earthquake, and hovered above the serpent's lair in the dust clouds. Descending, she called it forth.

Unlike Ryu-wo, this king was ugly and repulsive, with a serpent's scales and a serpent's flicking tongue. At first Benten was filled with loathing. But the serpent king wooed her with soft and tender words until her heart was melted, and – making him promise to mend his savage ways – she married him.

Words alone won Benten, for she is the goddess of eloquent speech, and also of music. She always carries with her a little stringed instrument called a biwa, and sometimes she will appear in person to great musicians, when they play with all their soul.

Benten wears long, many-coloured robes, and a jewel in her crown, and she is worshipped at beautiful spots all along the sea coast. It is to her that

Benten agrees to marry the serpent god if he will end his reign of terror

people pray when they are in need of money, for she will give wealth to those who win her favour with well-argued pleas.

THE PHOENIX

THE PHOENIX IS BORN in the sun. Its plumage blends all colours and its call is a sweet harmony of five notes. It bathes only in the purest water that flows from the K'un-lun mountains and it passes the night in the cave of Tan. It can raise its beautiful tail higher than a tall man's head, and wherever it goes the three hundred and sixty varieties of bird gather to pay homage.

Like the other spiritual animals, the dragon, the unicorn, and the turtle, the phoenix contains all things, both male and female, Yin and Yang. Its head is the rooster of the sun, and its back the curve of the crescent moon. Its wings are of the wind, its tailfeathers are the trees and flowers, and its feet are the earth. Whenever a phoenix appears, it is an omen of prosperity. But when it leaves, bad luck will surely follow.

The body of the phoenix contains all things

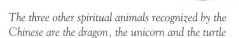

The three other spiritual animals recognized by the Chinese are the dragon, the unicorn and the turtle

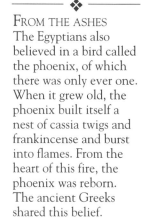

❖

FROM THE ASHES
The Egyptians also believed in a bird called the phoenix, of which there was only ever one. When it grew old, the phoenix built itself a nest of cassia twigs and frankincense and burst into flames. From the heart of this fire, the phoenix was reborn. The ancient Greeks shared this belief.

BIRD OF HARMONY
In Chinese myth, the fabulous phoenix (shown here with a fairy in a 15th-century painting on silk), represented beauty and harmony. For this reason, the phoenix was especially associated with weddings.

◄ *The Cosmic Egg, page 22*

VISIONS OF THE END

Every human being foresees an end to his or her life, and all mythologies foresee an end to the world as we know it. Often, as in Norse or Iranian myth, we are told that a new world will arise, purged and purified, from the destruction of this one. Some traditions even look forward to this day of judgement, seeing it not as an end but as a new beginning.

But at the same time, we value our life in the here and now. The mythologies of the world are full of brave men and women who descend into the depths of the dread underworld in search of immortality, advice or – in heartbreaking stories such as *Orpheus and Eurydice* – of loved ones they have lost. Many stories are told, too, of heroes for whom death is not a final end, but merely an interval before they return once more to champion humankind.

Two old men, close to death, meet up after wasting their lives journeying around the world in How Big the World Is!

AENEAS IN THE UNDERWORLD

VENUS
As set down in the *Aeneid* by Virgil, Aeneas's mother was Venus, Roman goddess of love and beauty. The head above is of the famous statue called the Venus de Milo.

TO THE UNDERWORLD
This fresco (wall painting) shows a soul being escorted to the Underworld between two attendants. The Romans believed that a soul was taken by spirits at the moment of death.

AENEAS, SON OF THE goddess Venus and the humble Trojan shepherd Anchises, is famed as the father of the Romans. He became one of the greatest warriors of the city of Troy, which was besieged by the Greeks for many years. When at last the Greeks captured the city, he escaped, carrying his father on his back. After long wanderings, he finally reached Italy.

On the way, Aeneas had many adventures. His father, Anchises, died; he loved and lost Queen Dido of Carthage. But always the will of the gods, and his own great destiny, drove him on.

It happened that, on his journey, Aeneas and his ships arrived at Cumae where the Sibyl lived in her cave, speaking the prophecies of the god Apollo in a voice that echoed and boomed through a hundred mouths in the rock. The temple of Apollo at Cumae had been founded by Daedalus, at the spot where he had landed after his flight from Crete. It was Daedalus himself who had wrought the golden doors of the temple, which captured every scene of the story of King Minos, Queen Pasiphae, and the Minotaur. Every scene that is, except one. Twice Daedalus tried to show the fall of his son Icarus, but his hands trembled too much for the task.

Aeneas approached the Sibyl, and she answered his questions about his future. Then he asked, "Is it true that the gate to the Underworld is here? For I wish to look once more upon the face of my father."

The Sibyl replied, "The door to the Underworld is always open and it is easy to pass through it. But to return: that is hard. If you must go, pluck a golden bough from the sacred grove to take as an offering to Proserpina, Queen of the Underworld. I will guide you."

Aeneas plucked the bough, and it gave a glimmering light as they plunged down into the black hole from which the poisonous breath of the Underworld escaped to heaven. Charon, the grim ferryman, took them across the River Styx, which encircled the Underworld.

In the dark realms, Aeneas saw many that he knew – even Dido, his love, but she would not speak to him. He passed the damned enduring punishments in Tartarus and at last came to the blessed meadows of Elysium. There, he found his father's shade.

"Father," cried Aeneas, "let me embrace you." But when he put his arms around Anchises, it was like trying to hold mist.

◀ *The Fall of Icarus, page 112*

Near them, Aeneas saw many souls eagerly drinking the waters of forgetfulness from the River Lethe. "Why do souls wish to forget this beautiful place and return to the strife of the world?" he asked.

Anchises replied, "In the beginning, all was pure spirit. Some of that spirit burns in the body of each person. But we are bound to life, compelled by love and fear. Only a few souls desire to remain in these fields until the circle of time is completed, when we will all become pure spirit once more. Most souls hunger, sooner or later, for the open sky, and come to drink forgetfulness, and be born again."

Anchises then showed Aeneas a glorious sight: the noble race that would be his descendants. Anchises said that they would be called the Romans and that they would create a great empire that would last for hundreds of years.

At last father and son had to part. Aeneas and the Sibyl made their way back to the land of the living, Aeneas pondering the magnificent destiny the gods had decreed for him.

As Troy burns, Aeneas flees with his father on his back

The Sibyl tells Aeneas to take a golden bough to Proserpina, Queen of the Underworld

The Sibyl looks on as Aeneas tries to embrace the ghost of his father, Anchises

Souls longing to be reborn drink from the River Lethe

THE DEATH OF KING ARTHUR

Guinevere is rescued by her lover, Sir Lancelot

Arthur's knights ride out to fight Mordred's army

King Arthur

AFTER THE QUEST OF THE HOLY GRAIL, King Arthur and the Knights of the Round Table, who had touched the heart of this world's mystery, were left to live once again in the world of everyday. They continued to uphold right and justice, and to go on quests and take part in jousts and feasts, but somehow the savour was gone from life. Petty squabbles arose and a faction grew up at court that sneered at the lofty aims of the Round Table. Its leader was King Arthur's own son, Mordred. Worst of all, the love between Sir Lancelot and Arthur's wife, Queen Guinevere, became obvious to all. Because of it, the fellowship of the Round Table was broken for ever.

❖
THE LAST BATTLE

The site of the battle of Camlann is a mystery. Sources place it in Wales, in Scotland, and on Salisbury Plain in England. One of the most likely sites, however, is Slaughter Bridge, near Camelford in Cornwall, southwest England. Legend has it that the fighting was so fierce the River Camel ran red with blood.

For loving Sir Lancelot, the queen was condemned to be burned at the stake. Lancelot rescued her, but in doing so he killed Sir Gareth and Sir Gaheris, two of the kindest and bravest of all the knights. King Arthur and Sir Gawain, brother of Gareth and Gaheris, declared war on Sir Lancelot to avenge the deaths. The Knights of the Round Table were forced to take sides, friend against friend, in a bitter, futile struggle. And while they were fighting each other, the evil Mordred seized the throne of England and declared himself king.

King Arthur's army faced Mordred's at Camlann. The two sides had just agreed peace when a knight saw an adder in the grass, and struck at the snake with his sword. The sun flashed on the drawn blade, and both armies, suspecting treachery, fell upon each other.

That was the grimmest, bloodiest battle ever fought, a nightmare of shrieking steel and dying men.

Near the end, King Arthur looked around him, and saw that of all his host of knights, only two, Sir Lucan and Sir Bedivere, were still alive, and they were sorely wounded.

"Alas," said King Arthur, "that ever I should see this doleful day. For now I have come to my end."

Then Arthur saw Sir Mordred, leaning on his sword by a heap of dead men. "Give me my spear," said the king to Sir Lucan. "There is the traitor who has brought us to this."

"Let him be," said Sir Lucan. "He is in anguish."

But Arthur challenged Mordred and ran him through with his spear. And when Mordred felt his death blow, he hauled himself bodily up the spear to strike his father down with his sword. Sir Mordred fell dead, and Arthur swooned away.

LOVERS' MEETING
This illustration from a 15th-century French manuscript shows Lancelot and Guinevere's first kiss. Their meeting has been arranged by a courtier called Galleot, who looks on.

The wounded king commands Sir Bedivere to throw his sword into the lake

Mordred

Sir Bedivere

Arthur

Sir Lucan

THE ISLE OF AVALON
Glastonbury Tor in Somerset, southwest England, is believed to be the Isle of Avalon where Arthur was buried after the battle of Camlann. It was once surrounded by marshes and deep pools.

Sir Lucan and Sir Bedivere carried the wounded king from the field of battle. They took him to the lakeside where, when he was young, Arthur had received his magic sword, Excalibur, from the Lady of the Lake. The effort was too much for Sir Lucan, and he too died.

Then the king told Sir Bedivere, "Take my sword, and throw it in the lake. Then come back and tell me what you saw."

Sir Bedivere took the sword. But, thinking that no good could possibly come from throwing away such a valuable blade, he did not cast the sword into the lake as the king had ordered.

*Sir Bedivere, the last of Arthur's knights, waves
a sad farewell as the dying king is borne away*

"What did you see?" asked King Arthur on his return.

"Sire," Sir Bedivere answered uncertainly, "I saw nothing but waves and winds."

"Go back," said the king sadly, "and do as I asked."

Sir Bedivere returned to the lakeside, and this time threw the sword as far as he could into the lake. To his amazement, an arm appeared from under the water, caught the blade, and brandished it three times, before sinking beneath the water.

Sir Bedivere told the king what he had seen.

"Then my end is truly come," whispered King Arthur. "Now take me to the shore."

Sir Bedivere took the king upon his back and staggered to the water's edge. A barge appeared, with three ladies sitting in it, one of whom was King Arthur's half-sister, the witch Queen Morgan le Fay. She said, "Ah, dear brother, why have you tarried so long?" And she helped the king into the barge.

Then Sir Bedivere cried, "Lord Arthur, what shall become of me?"

King Arthur replied, "You must look after yourself, for in me there is no trust to trust in. I am going to the isle of Avalon, to heal me of my grievous wounds. If you never hear of me again, pray for my soul."

And the barge moved slowly out across the still water, into the grey mist, and disappeared.

Some say King Arthur died of his terrible wounds. But others say that he recovered, and lives still in the magical isle of Avalon, waiting to return at the moment of England's direst need. For on the monument that was raised to his memory by Sir Bedivere, the wording reads, "Here lies Arthur, the Once and Future King."

MORT D'ARTHUR
Faithful Sir Bedivere returns Arthur's sword to the Lady of the Lake in this illustration from a 14th-century French manuscript. In the foreground, the wounded king waits for death.

THE VOYAGE OF BRAN

O NE DAY, AS BRAN, SON OF FEBAL, walked near his fort, he heard sweet, tinkling music in the air. Listening to it, he fell asleep. When he awoke, he found lying beside him a silver apple branch with white blossom on it.

He took the branch and returned home, where his warriors awaited him. There he found a woman who greeted him and sang to him of the joys of the sea and the world beyond, with its many islands, each with its own delights.

"Leave this lazy life," she said, "and take to the sea."

"I will," he replied. With that, the silver apple branch leapt from his hand to hers.

So Bran set to sea, with three companies of nine men, each led by one of his foster brothers. After two days and two nights, they met Manannan, god of the sea, riding over the waves in his chariot – for to him the ocean was as easy to cross as solid earth. Manannan, too, sang to Bran, telling him of the wonders of the deep, and the numberless islands of the sea.

CELTIC BROOCH
Known as the Hunterston brooch, this beautiful piece was made in Ireland around AD 700. Following the destruction of the Roman Empire, Ireland had become an important centre of Christianity, art, and learning. The Celtic myths were first written down by Irish monks.

Bran hearkens to the woman's thrilling songs of voyaging and adventure

Manannan, god of the sea, tells Bran of the wonders of the deep

❖

BRAN THE BLESSED
Welsh legend tells of
another hero called
Bran – Bran the Blessed.
He was killed by a
poisoned arrow while
battling the Irish king
Matholwch. His head was
buried on the White Hill
in London (where the
Tower of London now
stands) as a protection
against invasion. King
Arthur dug it up,
preferring to rely on his
people's valour.

The first island they came to was called the Isle of Joy. All the people on it were smiling and laughing – not at anything in particular, just for the sake of happiness. Bran sent a man ashore to find out what was happening. As soon as the man set foot on the island, he too began to gape and grin, and would not respond to questions from the ship, or return to it. So they left him there, and sailed on.

The next island they came to was the Isle of Women. The chief woman called out, "Welcome, strangers. Come ashore."

For what seemed only a year, Bran and his men stayed in revelry and delight on the Isle of Women. Then, one man began to speak of the green hills of home, and one by one they all began to feel homesick.

*Bran's voyage takes him to the Isle of Joy
and to the Isle of Women*

❖

THE OTHERWORLD
The magical isles Bran
sails to were known as
the Otherworld. They
were believed to lie
somewhere in the west,
across what we now
know as the Atlantic.

Happy as they were, there was nothing for it but to leave.

The women begged them not to go, but their minds were made up. "Whatever you do," said the chief woman, "first pick up your friend from the Isle of Joy. After that, I advise you to carry on your journey. Don't go back."

Bran picked up the man from the Isle of Joy; but the man could not remember what it was he had been smiling at all this time. Then,

disregarding the chief woman's advice, they set a homeward course for Ireland.

As they neared the coast, they saw a large gathering of people on the beach. Bran hailed them, declaring that he was Bran, son of Febal, home from his sea-wanderings. The people answered, "We know of no such man."

Then an old man said, "But there is a legend of a man of that name, who set out on a voyage and was lost for ever."

The man who had first grown homesick, impatient with this prattle, leapt from the ship on to the beach. But as soon as his feet touched the ground, his body turned to ashes, like one long dead. For time runs differently in

THE RETURN OF BRAN
This dramatic seascape, looking westwards from the southwest coast of Ireland, may be near the spot where Bran and his men attempted to land after their voyage to the magical isles.

Bran and his crew at last return home, but find that the people have forgotten them

the magical isles, and one year on the Isle of Women was the same as many, many years back home.

Bran related his adventures to the people on the beach, so that the record of his voyage should not be lost, then turned the prow of his ship away from land and sailed away. From that day, no one has set eyes on Bran, son of Febal. But surely he is sailing still, from island to island in the seas beyond the sea.

VOYAGER HEROES
The tale of Bran, the voyager hero, is echoed by other countries' myths and epics, especially the wanderings of the Greek hero Odysseus.

THE DEATH OF BALDER

Odin rides Sleipnir to the hall of Hel in the land of the dead to find out why his beloved son Balder is tormented by nightmares

SLEIPNIR
This picture stone from Gotland, Sweden, shows Odin's eight-legged stallion, Sleipnir, who was faster than any other horse. The rider may be Odin, or a dead warrior entering Valhalla, Odin's hall.

B ALDER THE BEAUTIFUL, Odin's son, suffered from nightmares. Though by day he knew he was loved by all, night after night he dreamed he was about to be killed.

So Odin mounted his eight-legged steed Sleipnir and rode over the rainbow bridge to Hel in Niflheim, land of the dead. Past the hound of Hel he rode, to the grave of a prophetess, long dead. With his magic he raised her from her sleep, asking, "Why are the halls of Hel prepared as if for a feast, with jewels and gold everywhere?"

She replied, "The mead is brewing for Balder in Hel."

"Who shall slay him, the best of the gods?" asked Odin.

"The blind god Hoder shall strike the blow."

"And who shall grieve for him?"

"You shall, Odin. Ask me no more." And with that, the prophetess sank back into her sleep of death.

The news that Odin brought back from Hel was of no comfort to the gods. Still Balder tossed and turned, dreaming of his own death.

So Balder's mother, Frigg, set out through the world, asking every thing she came across to swear never to hurt Balder. Fire swore. Water swore. The animals and birds swore. The snakes swore. The diseases swore. The earth and the trees swore. The metals swore. The very stones swore never to harm him.

At last, Balder was safe. Soon the gods had a new game to play. Balder would stand still, and each of the gods would hurl some deadly thing at him. They pelted him with rocks, cut at him with swords, and stabbed at him with spears,

◀ *Thor in the Land of Giants, page 118*

but nothing hurt him at all. He came away without a scratch, and all the gods roared with laughter.

That is, all the gods but one. Sly Loki had no taste for such innocent fun. He took on the guise of an old woman and went to see Frigg. He asked her what all the laughter was about, and Frigg explained how everything in the world had sworn not to hurt Balder. "What, everything in the whole world?" exclaimed Loki. "Everything except that young sprig of mistletoe," said Frigg.

Loki went straight away and plucked the mistletoe, and took it to the assembly of the gods. He approached the blind god, Hoder, and asked, "Why are you not throwing things at Balder?"

"I can't see where he is," said Hoder, "and I have no weapon."

"Why don't you throw this little stick?" said Loki. "I will guide your hand."

So Hoder threw the mistletoe at Balder, and it pierced him, and killed him. And that was the unluckiest deed ever done among gods or men.

The gods' laughter died in their throats. They could not speak or move. They just stared at the golden god, as he lay dead.

No one lifted a hand against Loki, for this was hallowed ground. They let him go. And then their tears burst out of them, in terrible sobs.

As Loki guides Hoder's hand to throw the deadly mistletoe, the other gods pelt Balder with sticks and stones, knowing they cannot harm him

MISTLETOE
This evergreen plant with soft, sticky, white berries grows high up in broad-leaved trees, particularly old apple trees. For centuries it has been associated with superstitions and customs. In ancient Scandinavia, mistletoe hanging outside a house meant a welcome within – it was the plant of peace.

They built Balder's funeral pyre on his great ship, and launched it with the help of the giantess Hyrrokkin. All the gods were there when Odin bent to whisper his last farewell into Balder's ear. Odin slid his gold ring, Draupnir, on to Balder's arm. Then he lit the pyre, and sent Balder on his long journey.

FRIGG

The fertility goddess Frigg was the wife of Odin and mother of all the gods. She had an unfortunate gift: she could see into the future, but could do nothing to change it. Frigg was also the goddess of marriage and so her day, Friday, was a lucky day for weddings.

SILVER ARM RING

This solid silver Viking bracelet, found in Fyn in Denmark, would have been worn on the upper arm. Armlets such as this were prized possesssions, often given by a king to a brave warrior. Odin's gold arm ring, Draupnir, was one of the three treasures of the gods.

Frigg asked, "Is there any one among the gods who will ride to Hel, and bargain with Hel to let Balder come back to us?" And Hermod, another of Odin's sons, leaped on Sleipnir and set off for Hel. He rode through dark valleys, until he came to the gates of Hel. He begged to be let in, and there he found his brother Balder.

Hermod pleaded with the goddess Hel to let his brother return with him to the land of the living. "Everyone loves Balder. Everyone weeps for him," he said.

"If it is as you say," said Hel, "Balder may return to life. But everything in the world must weep for him. If one refuses, he must stay with me." Hermod took leave of his brother, who gave him back the arm ring Draupnir as a token for his father, Odin. Forever afterwards, on every ninth night, Draupnir has wept, and its tears always form eight more arm rings of the same size.

Frigg went once again through the world, and everything that had sworn not to harm Balder wept for him. Even the mistletoe that killed him wept for him. But at last she came to a cave with a giantess sitting in it. And the giantess told her, "I will weep no tears for Balder. I had no use for him, alive or dead. Let Hel keep what she has." For the giantess was Loki in disguise, and Loki would not weep.

The gods had tolerated Loki's mischief-making, but this time he had gone too far. Loki fled from their fury to a house on a mountain. The house had doors facing in every direction so he could see anyone coming. By day he hid under a waterfall, in the form of a salmon.

Hermod begs Hel to let Balder return to the land of the living

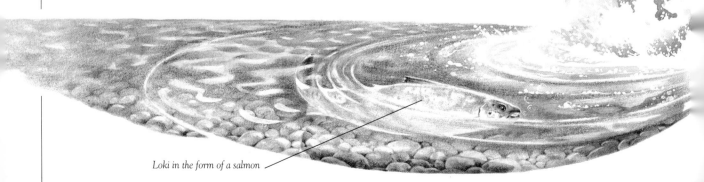

Loki in the form of a salmon

Sitting in his house one night, Loki began to wonder if the gods might catch him, even in his salmon form. Idly he wove a net and tossed it into the fire. Suddenly he saw the gods approaching, and fled to the safety of his waterfall.

Loki's mountaintop hideout

Odin

The gods entered the house, looked into the fire, and saw the net. Realizing that Loki must be disguised as a fish, they made a new net to the pattern Loki himself had devised.

They caught Loki, carried him to a cave, and bound him across three stones, tied down with the entrails of one of his own sons.

LOKI THE TRICKSTER
Loki was a mischievous spirit of air and fire, who could be malicious. His nickname, "the shape-changer", referred to his ability to change his shape when he wanted to trick or deceive the other gods . On the stone bellows-shield above, Loki is depicted with his lips sewn together. This refers to another story about Loki, in which a dwarf sews up his lips to stop him from talking.

The gods realize that Loki is hiding under the waterfall, disguised as a fish, and so they make a new net to catch him

Loki's wife tries to catch the serpent's venom in a cup before it drips on to his face

There they left him, with a serpent hanging above him, dripping venom on to his face.

His faithful wife, Sigyn, still sits beside him, catching the venom in a cup. But every so often, the cup becomes full, she turns away to empty it, and the poison drops on to Loki's face. As he writhes in agony, the earth shakes.

Thus was the death of Balder, Odin and Frigg's favourite son, avenged. But it is said that, one day, after Ragnarok, twilight of the gods, he will return to life again.

Ragnarok, page 174 ➤

ORPHEUS AND EURYDICE

O RPHEUS, THE SON OF the muse Calliope, was the most
gifted musician who ever lived. When he played his lyre,
birds stopped in their flight to listen and wild animals lost their
fear. The trees would bend to catch his tunes on the wind. He
was given his lyre by Apollo; some say Apollo was his father.

Orpheus was married to Eurydice. Now Eurydice was so lovely
that she attracted a man named Aristaeus. When she refused his
advances, he chased her. Fleeing him, she trod on a serpent,
which bit her, and she died.

Orpheus was beside himself with sorrow. Taking up his lyre he
travelled to the Underworld to try to win her back. The
plaintive, weeping song of his lyre charmed the ferryman,
Charon, into carrying him alive over the dread River Styx. The
lyre's lullaby sent Cerberus, the three-headed watchdog of the gates,
to sleep; its caressing call relieved the torments of the damned.

Finally Orpheus came before the throne of Hades himself. The king
of the dead was annoyed that a living man had entered his realm, but
the agony in Orpheus's music moved him, and he wept iron tears. His
wife, Persephone, begged him to listen to Orpheus's plea.

Orpheus *Persephone* *Hades* *Eurydice* *Cerberus*

Persephone begs her husband to help Orpheus, whose
mournful playing and singing has moved Hades to tears

So Hades granted his wish. Eurydice could follow Orpheus to the upper world. But only on one condition: that he did not look at her until she once more walked under the sun.

So Orpheus set off on his journey up the steep track that led out of death's dark kingdom, playing tunes of joy and celebration as he walked, to guide the shade of Eurydice back to life. He never once looked back, until he reached the sunlight. But then he turned, to make sure Eurydice was still there.

For a moment he saw her, nearly at the entrance to the dark tunnel, nearly alive again. But as he looked, she frayed once more into a thin ghost, her final cry of love and grief no more than a whisper on the breeze from hell. He had lost her for ever.

In black despair, Orpheus became bitter. He refused to look at any woman, hating to be reminded of the loss of his beloved Eurydice. Furious at being scorned by him, a group of wild women called the Maenads set upon him in a frenzy and tore him limb from limb. They cast his severed head into the River Hebrus, and it floated away, still singing, "Eurydice! Eurydice!"

Weeping, the Nine Muses gathered up his limbs and buried them by Mount Olympus. It is said that from that day onwards, the nightingales that live nearby always sing more sweetly than any others. For Orpheus, in death, was reunited with his beloved Eurydice.

NIGHTINGALE
This small, rather ordinary-looking bird has a rich melodious song, hence the compliment "she sings like a nightingale".

The gods turn Orpheus's murderers, the Maenads, into oak trees

As for the Maenads who had so cruelly murdered Orpheus, the gods did not grant them the mercy of death. Even as they stamped their feet on the earth in triumph, they felt their toes lengthen and curl into the ground. The more they struggled, the more deeply rooted they became. Their legs became wooden and heavy, and so on up their bodies, until they were changed completely into mute oak trees. And there they stood through the years, battered by the angry winds that once had thrilled to the sound of Orpheus's lyre, until at last their dead, hollow trunks toppled to the ground.

❖

THE MAENADS
These female followers of Dionysus, god of wine and pleasure, roamed mountainsides, playing flutes, banging tambourines, and dancing themselves into a frenzy. In this wild state the Maenads were capable of killing with their bare hands.

SEDNA

SPIRIT MASK
In Inuit myth, several spirits influence the forces of nature. This wooden mask contains references to a number of spirits. It moves in a different way as the wearer moves – showing how interlinked the nature spirits are.

S EDNA IS KNOWN as the Mother of Sea Beasts. Once she was a human girl, but now she is a goddess who lives at the bottom of the sea. This is how it happened.

Sedna did not want to get married. She rejected all the young men of her village. But then she fell in love with a dog, and married him.

"This will bring bad luck," said the rejected young men, who had all wanted Sedna for themselves. So they took her out to sea in a boat, and pushed her overboard. Sedna clung to the side of the boat, but they chopped off her fingers. As the fingers fell into the sea, they turned into the first seals, and other sea creatures. Sedna sank to the bottom of the sea, where she became ruler of the Underworld, mistress of all living things.

Because of the cruel fate she suffered, Sedna is quick to anger. When anyone offends her, she shuts away all the beasts, so that men cannot fish or hunt.

Then some daring man with the special powers of a shaman, a priest who can communicate with the spirits, must make a perilous descent under the sea, to soothe her. He must venture past the terrible guardians of Sedna's house, which include a big fierce black dog, until he reaches Sedna herself.

Now, the sins of mankind fall down through the water and collect in Sedna's hair as grease and grime. But because she has no fingers, she cannot do anything about it. So the shaman must dress Sedna's filthy hair into two thick braids, untangling its knots and picking out the dirt. In gratitude, Sedna frees the beasts, and mankind can eat again.

As Sedna sinks to the bottom of the sea, her severed fingers turn into the first sea creatures

Sedna's fingers become seals and walruses, whales and dolphins

168

HOW BIG THE WORLD IS!

The two couples set off in opposite directions with their dog sledges

SEALSKIN PAINTING
In the Arctic lands, the Inuit people are dependent on hunting and fishing for food. The pictures on this painting show people riding in sledges drawn by reindeer, paddling in canoes, and harpooning seals, a valuable source of meat and skins.

TWO COUPLES lived together. One day, the two men fell to talking. "The world is big," said the first.

"How big?" wondered the second.

"Let's find out," answered the first.

So they took their sledges and set off in opposite directions. Their wives cried at parting from each other, but each accompanied her husband, running beside his sledge.

Year after year they travelled. The wives had babies, and the babies grew up. Then they had children, and so on, until there were two whole tribes travelling across the ice.

The original couples grew old and frail. The men could no longer drive their sledges; the women could no longer keep up the pace beside them. But still they travelled.

At last, each of them saw movement in the far distance. They kept on going, and, finally, they met, back where they had started.

"The world is big," said the first man.

"Even bigger than we thought," answered the second. And then they died.

The two old men meet after their long journey

ATLANTIS

GOD OF THE SEA
This bronze head of
Poseidon is part of a
statue dating from 450
BC. Zeus's brother, the
god of the sea, the lake,
and of the earthquake,
Poseidon was one of the
most powerful of the
immortals. He was often
shown wielding a trident,
a three-pronged weapon
used by tuna fishermen.

THE GREEKS HAD many legends of the distant past: of Phoroneus, the first man, and of Deucalion and Pyrrha, who survived a flood sent by Zeus to rid the world of evil men. But when the Greek statesman Solon related these tales to the priests of ancient Egypt, they laughed. "You Greeks know nothing of your own history. You talk of one flood, but there have been many. It was in such a flood that your ancestors perished!" And the priests told Solon the story of the island of Atlantis, from where, nine thousand years before, the noblest race of men that ever lived ruled most of the known world.

A poor couple named Evenor and Leucippe once lived on a rocky island with their daughter, Clito. Poseidon, god of the sea, was smitten by Clito's beauty and married her. He then reshaped the island to make it a dwelling fit for his new bride.

He fashioned it into a series of circular belts of sea and land, with an island at the centre that basked in sun and beauty. The rich plains brought forth wheat, fruit, and vegetables in abundance, the forested hills sustained all kinds of animals – even herds of elephants – and beneath the soil were many precious ores.

Clito bore Poseidon five sets of twin boys. They were all kings, and the oldest, Atlas, was the high king, and his sons after him. The beautiful kingdom came to be called Atlantis.

SHADES OF ATLANTIS
Ancient ruins lying
beneath the waters of
a mountain pool in
Pamukkale, Turkey,
bear witness to quick-
tempered Poseidon's
destructive power.

*The beautiful kingdom of Atlantis is a series
of belts of land connected by bridges*

The people of Atlantis were wise in the arts of peace and war and soon ruled all the peoples of the Mediterranean. All of the island's kings added to the country's store of riches. The outer wall of the city of Atlantis was coated with brass, and its inner one with tin. The palace at the centre, with Poseidon's temple, was covered in gold. The buildings were built of white, black, and red stones: sometimes all one colour, sometimes in intricate patterns. A great harbour was opened up to the sea, and bridges were built between the belts of land.

Thus was Atlantis, in the days of its greatness.

For many years, the ten kings ruled wisely and well, each passing on his wisdom to his heir. But as generation succeeded generation, the kings' divine blood grew thinner and they fell more and more under the sway of mortal passions and worldly desires. Where once they had valued precious things simply for their beauty, they now fell prey to greed. Where once the people had lived

Poseidon stirs up a tidal wave to engulf the city of Atlantis

together in friendship and harmony, they now squabbled over power and glory. Great Zeus, seeing this favoured race descend day by day into the pit of human ambitions and vices, rebuked Poseidon for allowing such a thing to happen. And Poseidon, in sorrow and anger, stirred up the sea. A huge tidal wave engulfed Atlantis and the island sank for ever beneath the waters.

Where it lies, no one knows for certain – nor whether, under the ocean, Poseidon's children once more walk the streets of Atlantis in peace and wisdom, or if only the fishes play among the sea-worn bones of this fabled city.

The great city of Atlantis lies beneath the waves

❖

THE REAL ATLANTIS? Archaeologists believe Atlantis may have been the island of Stronghyle (Santorini) in the eastern Mediterranean. Around 1500 BC, a volcanic eruption submerged the island.

THE DEATH OF PAN

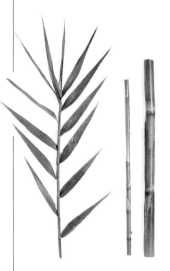

PAN'S PIPE
Pan was famous for playing reed pipes. This is the reed he might have used: *Arundo donax*, or Spanish reed. It has been used as a pipe instrument for 5,000 years.

P AN, GOD OF HUNTERS, shepherds, and all wild things, was one of the strangest of all Greek gods. He had two little horns like a goat, a goat's hairy legs, and delicate goat's hooves. He haunted lonely, wild places, playing tunes on a set of pipes made from reeds. He played reed pipes because the nymph Syrinx, with whom he had fallen in love, had escaped him by begging the gods to turn her into a reed.

Pan was worshipped by the Egyptians as well as the Greeks. Those who felt his presence were often seized with a terrible fear, and fled, in what we now call a panic. Some people say his presence can still be felt in lonely spots. However, a strange story is told that, during the reign of the Roman Emperor Tiberius, between AD 14 and 37 , a ship sailing to Italy past the Greek island of Paxoi was hailed by a godlike voice saying, "The great god Pan is dead!"

Pan haunts lonely country places. Panic grips those that sense his presence

Sailors on a ship spread the news of Pan's death

The sailors on board ship repeated the cry whenever they saw land, shouting out to anyone with ears to hear: "The great god Pan is dead!" And a terrible weeping rose up from the empty countryside.

◄ *King Midas's Ears, page 104*

THE RAINBOW SERPENT

T HE WORLD WAS CREATED by Nana-Buluku, the one god, who is neither male nor female. In time, Nana-Buluku gave birth to twins, Mawu and Lisa, and it is they who shaped the world and control it still, with their fourteen children, the Vodu, the lesser gods.

Mawu is the moon. She lives in the west and the night-time is her time. Lisa is the sun; he lives in the east and the daytime is his time.

In the beginning, before Mawu had any children, the rainbow serpent Aido-Hwedo already existed – created to serve Nana-Buluku. The creator was carried everywhere in Aido-Hwedo's mouth. Rivers, mountains, and valleys twine and curve because that is how the rainbow serpent Aido-Hwedo moves.

Wherever they stopped for the night, mountains arose, formed from the serpent's dung. That is why if you dig down deep into a mountain, you find riches.

Now when Nana-Buluku had finished his work, he realized that the earth just couldn't carry everything that he had created – all the mountains, trees, people, and animals. So, to keep the earth from capsizing, the creator asked Aido-Hwedo to coil beneath it, to cushion the earth – like the pad people wear on their heads when carrying a heavy burden.

Because Aido-Hwedo cannot stand heat, the creator made the ocean for the serpent to live in. And there Aido-Hwedo has remained since the beginning of time, with his tail in his mouth. Even though the water keeps Aido-Hwedo cool, he sometimes shifts about trying to get comfortable, and that's what causes earthquakes.

Nana-Buluku charged the red monkeys that live beneath the sea to keep Aido-Hwedo fed, and they spend their time forging the iron bars that are the serpent's food. But sooner or later the monkeys' supply of iron is bound to run out and then Aido-Hwedo will have nothing to eat. Famished with hunger he will start to chew his own tail and then his writhings and convulsions will be so terrible that the whole earth will tilt, overburdened as it is with people and things.

The earth will slip into the sea, and that will be that!

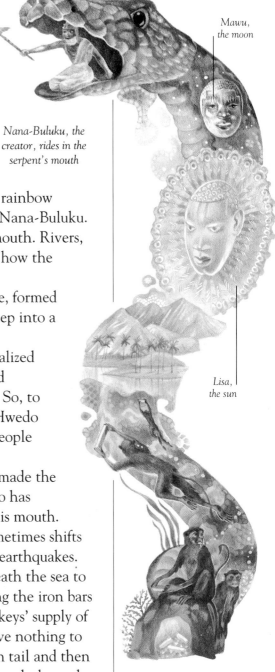

Mawu, the moon

Nana-Buluku, the creator, rides in the serpent's mouth

Lisa, the sun

Red monkeys living under the sea forge iron bars for the rainbow serpent to eat

RAGNAROK

THE GOLDEN ROOSTER crows to wake the gods to each bright morning. But there will come a last twilight of the gods. It will be an axe-age, a sword-age, a wind-age, a wolf-age. This is Ragnarok, when all will be brought to wreck.

Brother will fight brother; all barriers will fall.

The Fenris-wolf will break free from his fetters; Loki the trickster will sail to the world's ruin with an army of the dead, in a ship made of dead men's nails. A bitter winter it will be.

Surt, who has waited at the entrance to Muspell with a blazing sword since the beginning of time, will go to war against the gods, and all nine worlds will be seared with his flames. At his side will come the Fenris-wolf, its jaws agape. The Midgard serpent will spew poison over land and sea.

Then Heimdall the watcher will blow his horn, and the gods will ride to battle, in glorious array. Thor will destroy the Midgard serpent, but when he steps back nine paces from it, he will fall down dead from its poison. The wolf will swallow Odin, the All-Father; Odin's son Vidar will rend the wolf apart in vengeance. Heimdall and Loki will destroy each other.

VIKING SWORD
The Viking, or Norse, warrior's favourite weapon was his sword. Odin, the Norse god of victory in battle, had a magic sword, which was sometimes called "Odin's flame".

The rooster crows as Ragnarok, the last battle of the gods, begins

Surt

Thor

The Midgard serpent

Loki and the army of the dead

The Fenris-wolf

Odin on Sleipnir

Vidar

◀ *The Death of Balder, page 162*

The earth will sink into the sea. The sun will turn black. The bright stars will fall from the heavens. The very sky will burn.

Death will come to the gods, to the giants, to the elves and dwarfs, to men and women, the sons and daughters of Ask and Embla.

But two will be saved, hidden by Yggdrasil, the world tree. Lif and Lifthrasir are their names. The morning dew will be their meat and drink, and from them mankind will be reborn.

Earth will rise a second time, fair and green.

Odin's sons Balder and Hoder will return to life. The rivers will fill with fish, and the fields with corn.

Heimdall

THE DEATH OF ODIN
This detail from the Ragnarok Stone shows Odin, with a raven on his shoulder – either Huginn or Munnin – being swallowed by the Fenris-wolf. Carved by a Viking sculptor, the stone is at Kirk Andreas on the Isle of Man.

Lifthrasir

Lif

Death and destruction come to all on earth, except for Lif and Lifthrasir

Balder

And walking the meadows of the risen earth, talking in wonder of what was and will be, the children of Lif and Lifthrasir shall find in the grass the gold chessboards on which the gods played out their games, and remember Odin, the High One, the All-Father, and his children in their glory, in the golden halls of Asgard.

Balder and Hoder come back to life

Hoder

175

THE PURIFYING STREAM

AS TIME NEARS its end, Saoshyant, the saviour, will come to prepare the world to be made anew and help Ahura Mazda, the one who knows, destroy the evil Ahriman. Mashya and Mashyoi, the first humans, first drank water, then ate plants, then milk, then meat. In the time of Saoshyant, people will cease to need food, giving up first meat, then milk, then plants, then water, until finally they need nothing.

Gayomart leads the faithful over the Cinvat Bridge

Mashya and Mashyoi

Gayomart

The Cinvat Bridge

Mashya and Mashyoi

Gayomart

Wise Ahura Mazda listens patiently as the evil Ahriman begs for mercy

Ahura Mazda

Ahriman

Saoshyant

JUDGES OF SOULS
In Iranian myth, three judges, Rashnu, Mithra and Saosha, judge the dead. The good go to heaven, but the bad are sent down into hell, called Druj.

There will be no more sin and self-indulgence, so Az, the demon of lust, created by Ahriman, will be starved of the sensations on which she has glutted. She will turn to her creator, and seek to swallow him up. Ahriman will beg Ahura Mazda, the wise, the all-knowing, to save him, and Ahura Mazda will cast him from creation through the very hole Ahriman made when he broke in.

◀ *An Earthly Paradise, page 30*

Then time will come to an end, and there will be a new start for the world. Saoshyant will raise the dead, and Ahura Mazda will marry body to soul. First to rise will be Gayomart, the first fire-priest; then Mashya and Mashyoi, our mother and father; then the rest of humanity. They will come back across the Cinvat Bridge from the joys of heaven or the horrors of hell, wherever their acts and their consciences have sent them. Even those who have killed a dog will come, although – because dogs go out at night to battle the creatures of the evil spirit – anyone who kills a dog kills his own soul for nine generations, and cannot cross the Cinvat Bridge until he atones for his sin. That bridge is wide for the faithful, but it is narrow as a needle for the sinner.

All the metal in the mountains of the world will melt, and each man and woman will pass though the stream of molten metal and emerge purified.

Those who were faithful to Ahura Mazda and lived a holy, creative, generous, productive life will feel that they are walking through warm milk. However those who were seduced by Ahriman will suffer terrible agony as all their sins are burned away.

The new world will be immortal and everlasting. Those who lived to adulthood will be brought back to life at the age of forty; those who died as children will be brought back at fifteen; all will live happily with their family and friends.

CULT OF FIRE
This Persian coin from the 4th century AD shows a sacrifice being made by fire-worshippers. Fire is the symbol of Ahura Mazda, the supreme god. In Ahura Mazda's temples, fire-priests always keep a flame burning as a sign of the god's presence.

Those that have lived good lives bathe happily in the stream of molten metal, but those that have lived bad lives suffer agony

RUGGED ROCKS
The landscape of Iran provides a suitable setting for this story, in which molten metal pours down mountains to cleanse the world.

GODS AND PANTHEONS

The mythologies of the world contain gods and goddesses of every description: supreme beings who create the world, minor deities only associated with a particular place or thing, gods of the underworld, sun gods and sea gods, gods of war, gods of music, gods of farming, trickster gods and gods of love.

These wonderful beings may be worshipped by a great empire or just a single village.

Gods and Pantheons contains a brief who's who of all the major mythological figures – the gods, the goddesses, the heroes, and the monsters – that appear in this book. This section also provides a simplified guide to the pantheons of Greek and Norse mythology.

This stone from the island of Gotland, Sweden shows Odin arriving in Valhalla, riding on his horse, Sleipnir. A Valkyrie holds out a drinking horn in welcome

Who's who in mythology

Athena, goddess of wisdom

AENEAS (in-ee-us)
❖ *Roman*

Aeneas, the son of Anchises and the goddess Venus, was a prince of Troy. When the Greek army captured the city of Troy at the end of the long Trojan War, they allowed Aeneas to take with him whatever he valued most: he chose his aged father, Anchises. After a long voyage, during which Aeneas fell in love with, then abandoned, Dido, Queen of Carthage, Aeneas landed in Italy; the Roman emperors claimed descent from him. His story is told in the *Aeneid*, an epic poem written between 29 and 19 BC by the Roman poet Virgil.

AHRIMAN (ah-ri-mun)
❖ *Iranian*

In the Zoroastrian religion, Ahriman is the god of darkness and evil and the bitter foe of the lord of light, Ahura Mazda. Ahriman sent down death and disease to bring misery to human beings and to spoil the earthly paradise that Ahura Mazda created.

AHURA MAZDA (ah-hoor-a maz-da)
❖ *Iranian*

Ahura Mazda became the focus of a one-god religion founded by the prophet Zoroaster around 600 BC. The god represents light and truth; his enemy is Ahriman. A flame, symbolizing Ahura Mazda's presence, is always kept burning in the god's temples.

AIOINA (eye-oy-na)
❖ *Japan, Ainu*

Aioina is the divine man sent down to this, the floating world, by the supreme god Kamui to teach the Ainu, the first inhabitants of Japan, how to hunt and cook. Some say that Aioina actually made the Ainu; the word Ainu means "men".

AMATERASU (ah-ma-tay-rah-soo)
❖ *Japanese*

Amaterasu is the Shinto goddess of the sun. The chief story about her centres on the sun's crucial role in the earth's fertility. When Amaterasu hid her face in a cave, the crops withered. Only when she was lured out by the other gods did the world revive.

ANU (ah-noo)
❖ *Sumerian*

Anu, or An, is the supreme god of Sumerian mythology and the father of Enlil, the god of earth and air. He is associated with the heavens and his sign is a star.

ANUBIS (a-nyoo-bis)
❖ *Egyptian*

The son of Osiris and a goddess of the dead, Nepthys, Anubis is the jackal-headed god of the dead. He guides the souls of those who have recently died to Osiris, ruler of the Underworld, for judgement. Anubis is the lord of embalming and guardian of tombs.

APHRODITE (aff-ro-die-tee)
❖ *Greek*
VENUS (vee-nus)
❖ *Roman*

The daughter of the Titan Uranus, Aphrodite is the Greek goddess of love (she was known as Venus to the Romans). Although married to Hephaestus, the lame god of fire and metalwork, she had many love affairs, notably with the god of war, Ares. Her other loves included the beautiful boy Adonis, and the humble herdsman Anchises, father of the Roman hero Aeneas.

APOLLO (a-poll-oh)
❖ *Greek*

The god of healing, poetry, music, and light, Apollo is also identified with the movement of the sun. The god's shrine at Delphi was the home of the oracle, through whose prophecies Apollo revealed the future to mortals. Apollo is the son of Zeus and the Titaness Leto and the twin brother of Artemis. The brilliant musician Orpheus was one of his sons.

ANUBIS (a-nyoo-bis)
ARES (air-eez)
❖ *Greek*
MARS (marz)
❖ *Roman*

The son of Zeus and Hera, Ares is the god of war, a bloodthirsty fighter highly disliked by the other gods on Olympus – except for Aphrodite. Mars, the Roman god of war, was a more important and noble figure, and was regarded as the father of Romulus, founder of Rome.

ARTEMIS (ar-tem-iss)
❖ *Greek*
DIANA (die-an-a)
❖ *Roman*

Artemis, the goddess of hunting, is the beautiful twin sister of Apollo. She is the protector of all young girls. If offended, she has a fierce temper. When a hunter, Actaeon, accidentally caught sight of her bathing naked in a river, she turned him into a stag and he was caught and torn to pieces by his own dogs.

ARTHUR (ar-thur)
❖ *Celtic*

Presiding over his court at Camelot with his queen, Guinevere, King Arthur is the central figure in a mass of medieval literature, much of it French. These tales tell of the deeds of his Knights of the Round Table, who included Lancelot, Gawain, and Galahad. In real life, Arthur may have been a Celtic chieftain who resisted the invading Saxons in southwest England around AD 500 .

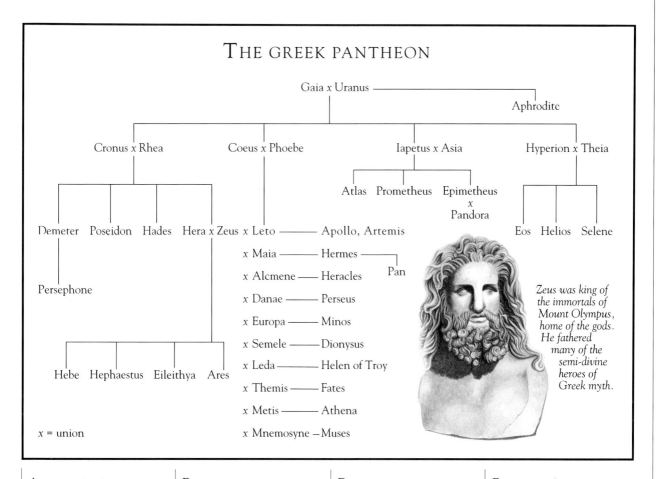

THE GREEK PANTHEON

Gaia *x* Uranus

Aphrodite

Cronus *x* Rhea — Coeus *x* Phoebe — Iapetus *x* Asia — Hyperion *x* Theia

Atlas   Prometheus   Epimetheus
x
Pandora

Eos   Helios   Selene

Demeter   Poseidon   Hades   Hera *x* Zeus *x* Leto ———— Apollo, Artemis

x Maia ———— Hermes

x Alcmene ——— Heracles

Pan

Persephone

x Danae ——— Perseus

x Europa ——— Minos

x Semele ——— Dionysus

Hebe   Hephaestus   Eileithya   Ares

x Leda ———— Helen of Troy

x Themis ——— Fates

x Metis ——— Athena

x = union

x Mnemosyne — Muses

Zeus was king of the immortals of Mount Olympus, home of the gods. He fathered many of the semi-divine heroes of Greek myth.

ATHENA (a-**thee**-na)
❖ *Greek*
MINERVA (min-**urv**-a)
❖ *Roman*
The goddess of wisdom and the daughter of Zeus and the wise Titaness Metis (whom Zeus turned into a fly and swallowed), Athena helped many heroes, including Heracles, Perseus, and Bellerophon. On her shield she had the head of Medusa, which turned her enemies to stone. Athens was named after her.

ARURU (ah-**roor**-roo)
❖ *Sumerian*
Aruru is the goddess of creation. She created Enkidu out of clay to be the friend and rival of the hero Gilgamesh.

BALDER (**bol**-dur)
❖ *Norse*
Son of Odin and Frigg, the wise and beautiful Balder was the most beloved of the gods. All things, save a sprig of mistletoe, swore not to hurt him. Through Loki's malice, Balder was slain with this mistletoe by his blind brother, Hoder. After the final battle of Ragnarok, Balder will return to lead mankind.

BAMAPAMA
(**ba**-ma-**pa**-ma)
❖ *Australian Aboriginal*
Bamapama is a "crazy man", a trickster who breaks taboos and delights in stirring up arguments. Another name for him is Ure.

BASTET (ba-**stet**)
❖ *Egyptian*
Also known as Bast, the Egyptian cat goddess Bastet is a daughter of Re, the sun god. In her fiercer aspect she is depicted as a lioness named Sekhmet, however she is also the goddess of love and fertility. The centre of her worship was the city of Bubastis.

BENTEN (**ben**-tun)
❖ *Japanese*
The Shinto goddess of beauty, wealth, and fertility, Benten is also associated with the arts and with educational success. She married a serpent king and is often represented riding upon a serpent or a dragon.

BEOWULF (**bay**-o-woolf)
❖ *Anglo-Saxon*
Beowulf, legendary prince of the Geats (a tribe that lived in what is now southern Sweden), is the hero of an 8th-century epic poem. Beowulf travels to Heorot, the hall of King Hrothgar, and slays first the monster Grendel, and then Grendel's even fiercer mother.

BRAN (**bran**)
❖ *Celtic*
Bran, son of Febal, is the hero of an Irish epic in which he and his men travel from one magic island to another. When they return home, so much time has passed that they are only remembered as a legend.

CADMUS (**cad**-mus)
❖ *Greek*

Cadmus was the brother of Europa, who was carried off by Zeus. While searching for his sister, Cadmus was sent by the god Apollo to found the city of Thebes. When Cadmus asked for followers to people the city, Athena gave him some serpent's teeth to sow in the ground. A tough warrior race sprang up from the earth and became the first citizens of Thebes.

CHARON (**ka**-ron)
❖ *Greek*

One of the gods in Hades, the Underworld, grey-bearded Charon ferries the souls of the dead across the River Styx in return for a small coin.

Demeter, goddess of corn

CHIMAERA (kim-**ear**-a)
❖ *Greek*

A fire-breathing monster with the head of a lion, body of a goat, and tail of a serpent, the Chimaera ravaged the realm of King Iobates until the hero Bellerophon slew it.

CHUKU (**choo**-koo)
❖ *West African, Ashanti*

Chuku is the supreme god of the Ibo of southeastern Nigeria and the father of the earth goddess Ale.

COYOTE (ky-**oh**-tee)
❖ *Native American*

Mischievous, cunning, and endlessly resourceful, the trickster Coyote (sometimes called Hare) is both a comic and shocking figure in Native American mythology. Whether behaving well or badly, he seems to represent a kind of essential appetite for life.

CUCHULAIN (koo-**kul**-in)
❖ *Irish*

Cuchulain is the hero of the Ulster Cycle of Irish stories, which are full of fighting and bloodshed. He was known as the Hound of Ulster because he accidentally killed the watchdog belonging to Culann, a blacksmith, and as penance had to take the dog's place for a time. When fighting, Cuchulain was terrifying: one eye bulged and the other shrank into his head; his mouth gaped, his hair bristled and a column of dark blood rose up from his head.

DAEDALUS (**deed**-a-lus)
❖ *Greek*

Daedalus was a famous craftsman and inventor from Athens. After murdering his nephew, Talos, he served King Minos of Crete and devised the maze in which the Minotaur was kept. With his son, Icarus, he tried to escape from Crete using wings made of feathers and wax. But Icarus flew too near the sun, the wax binding his wings melted, and he fell to his death.

DEMETER (de-**mee**-ter)
❖ *Greek*
CERES (**seer**-eez)
❖ *Roman*

Demeter is the corn goddess and the mother of Persephone. When Persephone was snatched away by Hades, god of the Underworld, Demeter's grief made the world barren. So Zeus arranged for Persephone to return to Demeter for six months of every year.

DEVI (**deh**-vee)
❖ *Indian*

Devi, the Hindu great mother goddess, also appears under many other names, including Parvati (wife of Shiva and mother of Ganesha, the elephant-headed god), Durga, and the bloodthirsty Kali.

DIONYSUS (die-on-**eye**-sus)
❖ *Greek*
BACCHUS (**back**-us)
❖ *Roman*

The god of wine and ecstasy, Dionysus is the son of Zeus and a mortal woman, Semele. She insisted that Zeus appear to her undisguised and was immediately struck dead by the lightning that flashed from his glorious presence. Zeus rescued her unborn child. Dionysus loved wild parties with his women followers, the Maenads, and his male followers, the Satyrs.

EA (**ay**-ah)
❖ *Sumerian*

The god of earth, water, and wisdom, Ea sent the Seven Sages to teach skills to mankind. He is the father of Adapa, the earth's first man.

EARTH-MAKER
❖ *Native American*

Earth-maker is the benevolent supreme god of the Maidu of California; his rival is the trickster Coyote.

ENKIDU (**en**-kee-doo)
❖ *Sumerian*

The friend and rival of Gilgamesh, Enkidu was a Sumerian/Akkadian hero.

ENLIL (en-**lil**)
❖ *Sumerian*

Enlil, the air god, separated the heavens from the earth.

ERLIK (**airr**-leek)
❖ *Siberian*

This evil spirit was made from mud by Ulgan, the creator, to be his helper. Erlik became the lord of the dead.

EROS (**ear**-oss)
❖ *Greek*
CUPID (**kew**-pid)
❖ *Roman*

The god of love and son of Aphrodite, Eros is a beautiful boy. He has a quiver full of arrows, which he shoots at people to make them fall in love.

ESTSANATLEHI (**est**-sa-**nat**-le-hee)
❖ *Native American*

Estsánatlehi means "the changing woman", for she grows old during the winter, but becomes young again in spring.

FENRIS-WOLF (**fen**-ris wolf)
❖ *Norse*

The ferocious Fenris-wolf was tied up with a magic chain, Gleipnir, by Tyr, the god of war. It will break free at Ragnorok.

FIRST CREATOR
❖ *Native American*
First Creator, together with Lone Man, creates the world in the creation myth of the Mandan Sioux. First Creator is said to have turned into a coyote when his work was finished.

FREYJA (**fray**-ya)
❖ *Norse*
Freyja, the goddess of love, fertility, and of seeresses is the most beautiful of the gods. Her most precious possession is the necklace Brisingamen, which she won from the dwarfs. She can turn herself into a falcon and often travels in a carriage drawn by two cats.

Freyja, goddess of love

GEB (**gebb**)
❖ *Egyptian*
The earth god Geb married the sky goddess Nut, and is the father of Isis and Osiris.

GHEDE (ga-**hed**-a)
❖ *Haitian*
The top-hatted god of death in Voodoo mythology, Ghede is also known as Baron Samedi. He bestrides life and death and possesses all the knowledge of everyone who has died.

GIANTS, THE
❖ *Norse*
The frost giants are all descended from Ymir, the first frost giant, whom Odin slew. They are the brutal, devious, and envious enemies of the gods, and will fight against them at Ragnarok.

GILGAMESH (**gil**-ga-mesh)
❖ *Sumerian*
The epic of Gilgamesh was developed by the Akkadian peoples of Babylon and Assyria from the myths of the Sumerians. Gilgamesh was a semi-divine hero-king of the city of Uruk, who searched for the secret of immortality.

FREYR (**frayr**)
❖ *Norse*
God of fertility and plenty and the brother of Freyja, Freyr owned a magic ship, Skidbladnir, that could hold all the gods, yet could be folded up small when not in use. He fell in love with Gerd, a giant's daughter. Wooing her cost him his sword, which will leave him weaponless at the battle of Ragnarok.

FRIGG (**frig**)
❖ *Norse*
Frigg is the goddess of childbirth and the wife of Odin. Like him, she can see into the future.

GANESHA (ga-**nay**-sha)
❖ *Indian*
Ganesha is the elephant-headed son of Shiva and Parvati and the Hindu god of good fortune. Those beginning any new enterprise pray to him.

GLOOSKAP (**gloo**-skap)
❖ *Native American*
The major hero of the Algonquin tribes, Glooskap brought many gifts to men and defeated various enemies before sailing away in his canoe.

GORGONS, THE (**gore**-gonz)
❖ *Greek*
The Gorgons lived in the far west and had snakes for hair, bodies covered in scales, tusks, and stares so horrifying that they turned people to stone. They were sisters, and their names were Stheno, Euryale, and Medusa. When the hero Perseus killed Medusa, the winged horse Pegasus sprang from her headless body.

HADES (**hay**-deez)
❖ *Greek*
DIS (**deess**)
❖ *Roman*
Hades is the god of the Underworld and the brother of Zeus. His wife is Persephone. His realm, which is also named Hades, lies on the other side of the River Styx. Hades contains Tartarus, where the wicked are punished, and the beautiful Elysian Fields, where the virtuous enjoy their reward.

HEIMDALL (**haym**-dahl)
❖ *Norse*
Heimdall is the watchman of Asgard and the guardian of the rainbow bridge Bifrost. His eyesight and hearing are very acute. Heimdall will blow the horn Gjall to signal Ragnarok, the last battle between gods and giants.

HEPHAESTUS (heff-**eest**-uss)
❖ *Greek*
VULCAN (**vul**-can)
❖ *Roman*
The god of the forge, Hephaestus is the husband of Aphrodite. His parents, Zeus and Hera, quarrelled, and Zeus flung him from Olympus, leaving him lame in one leg.

HERA (**hair**-a)
❖ *Greek*
JUNO (**joo**-noh)
❖ *Roman*
The haughty wife of Zeus, Hera is a goddess of marriage and childbirth. There are many stories of her anger at Zeus's amorous escapades.

Heimdall, the watchman

HERACLES (**hair**-a-kleez)
❖ *Greek*
HERCULES (**her**-kyoo-leez)
❖ *Roman*
Heracles was the greatest of all the Greek heroes, and is especially famous for the twelve Labours he undertook. Zeus was his father, and a mortal, Alcmene, his mother. Hera, Zeus's jealous wife, was thus his deadly enemy and placed many obstacles in his path.

HERMES (**her**-meez)
❖ *Greek*
MERCURY (**mer**-kyoo-ree)
❖ *Roman*
The son of Zeus and the nymph Maia, Hermes is the messenger of the gods. He wears winged sandals and sometimes a *petarsus*, a hat worn by Greek travellers. Hermes is also the patron god of merchants and thieves. He escorts the souls of the dead to Hades.

HORUS (**hore**-us)
❖ *Egyptian*
Horus, the falcon-headed sky god, is the dutiful son of Isis and Osiris. Horus is the sworn enemy of Set, who murdered Osiris. Horus and Set are locked in eternal struggle.

ILMARINEN (**eel**-ma-ren-en)
❖ *Finnish*
The smith of the heavens, Ilmarinen forged the magical mill of plenty called the Sampo.

Hermes, messenger of the gods

ISHTAR (**ish**-tar)
❖ *Sumerian*
Also called Inanna, Ishtar is the goddess of love and war. She became furious when Gilgamesh rejected her love and asked the god Anu to create the Bull of Heaven to ravage Gilgamesh's kingdom.

Horus, the sky god

ISIS (**eye**-sis)
❖ *Egyptian*
The Egyptian mother goddess, Isis is the daughter of Nut and Geb. She is the sister and wife of Osiris and the mother of Horus, the falcon-headed sky god.

IZANAGI (iz-an-**nah**-gee)
❖ *Japanese*
In Shinto mythology, Izanagi created the Japanese islands, together with his wife, Izanami. After she became goddess of the Underworld, Izanagi created several other gods. These included Amaterasu, the goddess of the sun, Tsuki-Yomi, the god of the moon, and Susanowo, the god of the tempest.

IZANAMI (iz-an-**nah**-mee)
❖ *Japanese*
The female spouse and opposite of Izanagi, Izanami died giving birth to Fire, and then became the goddess of the Underworld.

KAMRUSEPAS (kam-**roos**-pas)
❖ *Hittite*
The Hittite goddess of spells and healing.

KAMUI (**ka**-moo-wee)
❖ *Japan, Ainu*
Kamui is the sky god of the Ainu, an aboriginal people living on the northern Japanese island of Hokkaido. He is also called Tuntu, support, or pillar, of the world.

KUMUSH (kum-**ush**)
❖ *Native American*
Kumush, "the Old Man of the Ancients", is the central figure in the creation myth of the Modoc of northern California. He created the Native American people by fetching bones from the underworld land of the spirits before leaving this world for ever for a home in the sky.

KUNITOKOTATCHI (**kun**-i-tok-**oh**-ta-chee)
❖ *Japanese*
The remote supreme deity of Shinto belief, who grew as a reed in the primeval swamp. His name means "eternal land ruler", and he is believed to live on the slopes of sacred Mount Fuji, whose spirit, Fujiyama, is the guardian of the nation.

KURENT (kur-**rent**)
❖ *Serbian*
The stories about the sly trickster god Kurent, who makes a fool out of mankind's representative, the giant Kranyatz, by getting him drunk with wine, were collected in Carniola in Serbia. The tales record a native, pagan, Slavonic mythology, to which Christian elements – in particular a single, all-knowing god – have been added.

KWAKU-ANANSE (**kwa**-koo-a-**nan**-say)
❖ *West African, Ashanti*
The spider-man trickster of West Africa. Kwaku-Ananse's exploits lie behind many of the Brer Rabbit fables of African Americans, made famous in the Uncle Remus stories of J. C. Harris.

LEMMINKAINEN (lem-**mink**-eye-non)
❖ *Finnish*
Lemminkainen helps Vainamoinen and Ilmarinen steal the magic mill of plenty, the Sampo, from Louhi, the witch of the Northlands.

Ishtar, goddess of love and war

LOKI (**lo**-kee)
❖ *Norse*
The trickster Loki is the son of two giants, Farbauti and Laufey, and is Odin's foster brother. Loki's playfulness often caused harm to the gods and, in the end, his tricks led to the death of Balder. Imprisoned by the gods for this crime, Loki will break free to lead the giants against the gods at the battle of Ragnarok. Loki's children include the Fenris-wolf, the Midgard serpent, Hel, and Sleipnir, Odin's eight-legged steed.

LOUHI (**loo**-hee)
❖ *Finnish*
Louhi the witch is the mistress of the North and the enemy of the heroes of the *Kalevala*.

Maui-of-a-Thousand-Tricks

MAUI (**mah**-oo-ee)
❖ *Polynesian*
Maui fished up the islands of the South Pacific from the ocean bed, stole fire for human beings, and had many other adventures. He is known as "Maui-of-a-Thousand-Tricks".

MERLIN (**mer**-lin)
❖ *Celtic*
Merlin was the wizard and seer who helped to bring up and advise King Arthur. He later fell in love with a scheming fairy named Nimue. He taught Nimue magic, and she cruelly repaid him by imprisoning him for ever in an enchanted wood.

MINOTAUR, THE (**my**-no-tore)
❖ *Greek*
The monstrous offspring of Pasiphae, the wife of King Minos of Crete, the flesh-eating Minotaur was half man, half bull. It lived in a labyrinth devised by the craftsman Daedalus and was fed on human flesh – until the hero Theseus killed it.

MICTLANTECUHTLI (mek-**tlahn**-ha-coot-lee)
❖ *Aztec*
This god of the dead rules the silent, peaceful kingdom of Mictlan.

MIDGARD SERPENT, THE (**mid**-gard **ser**-pent)
❖ *Norse*
One of Loki's and the giantess Angrboda's monstrous children, this menacing sea serpent (also known as Jormungand) encircles the world of human beings. At Ragnarok, it will be killed by Thor, who will die from its poisonous bite.

MORRIGAN (**morr**-i-gun)
❖ *Irish*
This goddess of war appears on battlefields in the shape of a crow. She fell in love with the hero Cuchulain. When he rejected her, she became his bitter enemy.

NANA-BULUKU (**na**-na-ba-**loo**-koo)
❖ *West African, Fon*
The creator god of the Fon of Bénin, Nana-Buluku is the father and mother of Mawu and Lisa, who shaped the world that Nana-Buluku had created. Mawu is associated with the moon and with fertility; Lisa with the sun and with war. Mawu and Lisa's children are the Vodu, the lesser gods.

NORNS, THE (**nornz**)
❖ *Norse*
The Norns – Fate, Being, and Necessity – are the three maidens who guard the spring of fate at one of the roots of Yggdrasil, the world tree.

NUT (**noot**)
❖ *Egyptian*
Nut, the sky goddess is the wife of Geb and the mother of Isis and Osiris.

NYANKONPON (ny-**ang**-cong-pon)
❖ *West African, Ashanti*
Nyankonpon is the sky god whose tales are won by Kwaku-Ananse.

ODIN (**oh**-din)
❖ *Norse*
The oldest and the highest of the gods, Odin is the god of battle. He gave one of his eyes to drink from the spring of Mimir, which brought wisdom. He won the mead of poetry from the giants, and it is his gift to men.

Odin, god of battle

ORPHEUS (**or**-fee-uss)
❖ *Greek*
Son of Apollo and the muse Calliope, Orpheus was the greatest musician ever. He pursued his wife, Eurydice, into the Underworld to persuade Hades to let her return to life. But Orpheus lost her when he looked back to see if she was following.

OSIRIS (o-**sire**-is)
❖ *Egyptian*
Osiris, husband of Isis, was a fertility god who taught people farming. He was murdered by his brother, Set, and became judge of the dead.

PAN (**pan**)
❖ *Greek*
FAUNUS (**fawn**-us)
❖ *Roman*
The son of Hermes, Pan is the god of wild places and of shepherds and their flocks. He has the horns and legs of a goat. Pan plays haunting music on a set of reed pipes called a Syrinx. He can inspire fear – "panic" – in people and animals.

P'AN-KU (pahn-**koo**)
❖ *Chinese*
The gigantic being who burst out of the cosmic egg, P'an-ku created the world and everything in it.

PERSEPHONE (per-**seff**-on-nee)
❖ *Greek*
PROSERPINA (pro-**sir**-pi-na)
❖ *Roman*
The beautiful daughter of Demeter, Persephone was snatched away by Hades, who made her his queen in the Underworld.

PERSEUS (per-**see**-us)
❖ *Greek*
Perseus, one of the best known Greek heroes, was the son of Zeus and a mortal woman, Danae. With the help of the goddess Athena and the god Hermes, he slew the Gorgon Medusa and saved Andromeda, his future wife, from a sea monster.

POSEIDON (poss-**eye**-don)
❖ *Greek*
NEPTUNE (**nep**-tyoon)
❖ *Roman*
Poseidon is the god of the sea and the brother of Zeus and Hades.

PROMETHEUS (prom-**ee**-thee-us)
❖ *Greek*
The only Titan to fight with Zeus against Cronus, Prometheus angered Zeus by giving fire to humans. He was cruelly punished until Heracles freed him.

QUETZALCOATL (**ket**-sal-koh-**atl**)
❖ *Aztec*
Quetzalcoatl is the divine priest who struggles with his warrior brother, Tezcatlipoca. With his twin, Xolotl, he made people by grinding up the bones of the ancient dead and sprinkling them with his own blood.

Poseidon, god of the sea

RE (**ray**)
❖ *Egyptian*
Re, or Ra, the sun god, is, as Atum, the creator god of ancient Egypt. Every night Re does battle with the gigantic serpent of chaos named Apep. One story about Re relates how, in his old age, he was tricked into revealing his secret name by Isis. The knowledge made her immortal.

Re, the sun god

SAOSHYANT (**sow**-shyunt)
❖ *Iranian*
The saviour in the Zoroastrian religion, Saoshyant will come at the end of the world to scour away all traces of the evil Ahriman and bring into being a new, perfect world. The dead will rise and a mighty stream of molten metal will pour from the earth. This will be like warm milk to the good, but the bad will suffer agonies as their sins are burned away.

SEDNA (**sed**-na)
❖ *Inuit*
Sedna is the mother of the sea beasts and queen of the underworld, Adlivun. She is the most important figure in Inuit mythology, for by releasing or withholding the fish and animals that the Inuit hunt, she grants life or death.

SET (**set**)
❖ *Egyptian*
Set, also known as Seth, is lord of the desert and god of storms, confusion, and destruction. Set murdered his own brother, Osiris, by sealing him in a coffin. His eternal enemy is the sky god Horus, the son of Isis and Osiris.

SHIVA (**shee**-va)
❖ *Indian*
Shiva is the great destroyer, but in this way he creates the conditions for new life to flourish. He forms part of the "trimurti", a trinity of Hindu gods that includes Vishnu, the helper of mankind, and Brahma, the creator. Shiva's wife is called Parvati, one of the forms of the goddess Devi. Shiva rides on Nandi, a white bull who is the guardian of animals.

Quetzalcoatl, the divine priest

SUSANOWO (soo-sa-**noh**-woh)
❖ *Japan*
The spiteful storm god of Shinto belief, Susanowo's destructive actions brought his sensitive sister Amaterasu, the sun goddess, near to despair.

TALIESIN (**tal**-i-ay-sin)
❖ *Welsh*
The legendary Welsh bard Taliesin was originally a humble boy named Gwion. By accident, a magic potion brewed by the witch Ceridwen gave him amazing knowledge of the past, the present, and the future.

Shiva, the great destroyer

TELEPINU (tell-a-**pee**-noo)
❖ *Hittite*
The god of agriculture and the son of the weather and fertility god, Telepinu nearly laid waste to the earth in his anger. The goddess Kamrusepas finally succeeded in calming him down with her magic, and fertility returned to the earth once more.

TEZCATLIPOCA (tes-**kat**-lee-**poh**-ka)
❖ *Aztec*
Tezcatlipoca, "the smoking mirror", is the Aztec warrior god and the god of vengeance. It is he whose cruel tricks and bitter jealousy prove the undoing of the pure and innocent Quetzalcoatl, the plumed serpent god.

THESEUS (**thee**-see-us)
❖ *Greek*
Theseus was the son of King Aegeus of Athens, or, in some versions, Poseidon, god of the sea. One of the best known of all the Greek heroes, the Athenian prince's most famous exploit was the slaying of the flesh-eating Minotaur. This he achieved with the help of Ariadne, the king of Crete's daughter.

THOR (thor)
❖ *Norse*

Son of Odin and the Earth, Thor is the sky and thunder god. He carries a hammer, Miollnir, which is his most precious possession; when he throws it, it always returns to his hand. Many Vikings wore hammer amulets in his honour. Thor had many battles with the giants, and once tried to fish up the Midgard serpent. His wife is golden-haired Sif, a fertility goddess.

TUATHA DE DANANN
(**thyoo**-a-ha day **dai-**nan)
❖ *Celtic*

The Irish gods, including Lugh, the sun god and the father of Cuchulain. Their chief was Dagda, god of life and death.

TYR (**ti-**uh)
❖ *Norse*

Tyr is the god of war. He sacrificed his left hand when binding of the Fenris-wolf with the magic fetter Gleipnir.

Miollnir, the hammer of Thor

ULGAN (**ool**-gun)
❖ *Siberian*

The high god of the Tartars, Ulgan created the world out of mud, which his helper, Erlik, fetched from the bottom of the ocean.

THE NORSE PANTHEON

THE VIKINGS BELIEVED that a great ash tree named Yggdrasil towered above the world. One root reached down into Asgard, the realm of the gods. The second reached down into Midgard, the land of men, and Jotunheim, land of the giants. The third reached down into Niflheim, land of the dead.

Ymir
(Frost giant)

Audhumla
(Giant cow who discovers Buri in ice)

Giants

Buri

Loki
x
Angrboda

Sigyn
x

Bestla *x* Bor

Hel — Fenris-wolf — Midgard Serpent

Vali — Narvi

Vili — Ve — Odin
x
Frigg

Earth
x

Grid
x

Balder
x
Nanna

Njord
x
Skadi

Bragi
x
Idun

Tyr — Heimdall — Hermod — Hoder

Thor
x
Sif

Vidor

Forseti — Frejya — Freyr

THE NAMES OF the Norse gods survive in four of the English names for the days of the week: Tyr in Tuesday; Thor in Thursday; Frigg in Friday; and Odin in Wednesday – the Germanic tribes and Anglo-Saxons called Odin "Woden".

Modi

x = union

URANUS (you-**rain**-us)
❖ *Greek*

Uranus was the god of the heavens. His children by Gaia, the earth goddess, were the race of Titans, including Cronus ("Time"), who killed him. Aphrodite, the goddess of love, sprang from the foam of the sea when Cronus cut him into pieces.

UTNAPISHTIM
(oot-na-**pish**-tim)
❖ *Sumerian*

Utnapishtim and his wife were the only survivors of the flood caused by the god Ea. Utnapishtim was Gilgamesh's ancestor.

UZUME (oo-**zoo**-mee)
❖ *Japanese*

Ama-no-uzume is the Japanese goddess associated with the dawn whose rude and uproarious dance enticed Amaterasu, the sun goddess, from the cave where she hid.

VALKYRIES, THE
(val-**ky**-reez)
❖ *Norse*

Daughters of Odin, the Valkyries are female warrior spirits who ride into battle, giving victory or defeat as Odin wills. They wait on the dead warriors in the halls of Valhalla.

ZEUS (**zyoos**)
❖ *Greek*
JUPITER (**jyoo**-pi-ter)
❖ *Roman*

The greatest of the gods, Zeus waged war against his father, Cronus, and the other Titans. He is married to Hera, but has had many love affairs.

Valhalla, Odin's hall for heroes

PART TWO
FAIRY TALES

❧ for Cortina and Rosie ❧

*Beauty's father is caught stealing a rose
by the furious, roaring Beast*

CONTENTS OF PART TWO

Introduction   192

The Story of Fairy Tale   194

The Storytellers   198

Under a Spell

The Sleeping Beauty
French   202

The Shape-Changer
Kenyan   206

Little One-Inch
Japanese   207

The Frog Prince
German   208

The Lame Fox
Czech   210

A princess hurls a frog across her room – and is pleasantly surprised – in "The Frog Prince"

A Whale's Soul & Its
Burning Heart *Inuit*   218

Beauty & the Beast
French   220

Three Magic Oranges
Costa Rican   226

Urashima & the Turtle
Japanese   228

Why the Sea Moans
Brazilian   230

The witch cuts off Rapunzel's golden hair in "Rapunzel"

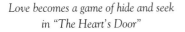

Love becomes a game of hide and seek in "The Heart's Door"

Jamie Freel & the Young
Lady *Irish*   213

The Unknown Sister
Surinamese   216

Riches & Rags

Rumpelstiltskin
German   236

Cricket, the Fortune-Teller
Trinidadian   239

Mushkil Gusha
Iranian   240

I Ate the Loaf
Spanish   243

There is something very strange about grandma in "Little Red Riding Hood"

A cook hears cries coming from a dead whale, cuts it open, and out crawls a girl in "The Girl Who Combed Pearls"

The Girl Who Combed Pearls • *Portuguese*   244

That's a Lie! • *Norwegian*   246

The Boat That Sailed on Land • *North American*   248

Lazy Jack • *English*   250

Prince Nettles • *Hungarian*   252

The Fly • *Vietnamese*   254

The Endless Tale • *English*   255

Shoes That Were Danced to Pieces • *Cape Verdean*   256

The Wonderful Brocade • *Chinese*   258

Easy Come, Easy Go • *Dutch*   262

The Fisherman & His Wife • *German*   264

A business deal has an unusual witness in "The Fly"

The Poor Girl Who Became Queen • *Irish*   267

Heroes & Heroines

Little Red Riding Hood • *French*   272

The Dancing Water • *Italian*   274

The Girl Who Pretended to Be a Boy • *Romanian*   278

Man-Crow • *Jamaican*   282

Kahukura & the Net-Makers • *Maori*   284

The Demon in the Jug • *Jewish*   286

Baba Yaga • *Russian*   288

The Flying Head
☙ *Native American*   290

Jack & the Beanstalk
☙ *English*   291

A Magic Whistle
☙ *Australian*   296

Bluebeard
☙ *French*   298

The Twin Brothers
☙ *Congolese/Zaïrian*   302

An Eating Match With
a Troll ☙ *Norwegian*   304

Snow White
☙ *German*   306

A girl escapes from a fiendish witch who relentlessly pursues her in "Baba Yaga"

A little man helps a poor girl spin straw into gold for the king in "Rumpelstiltskin"

True Love Conquers All

Cinderella
☙ *French*   312

Rapunzel
☙ *German*   316

The Heart's Door
☙ *Finnish*   319

The Goodman of
Wastness ☙ *Scottish*   322

The Snake Prince
☙ *Indian*   324

Falling Star
☙ *Native American*   328

The Snow Wife
☙ *Japanese*   331

The Sleeping Prince
☙ *Greek*   332

Ivan & the Firebird
☙ *Russian*   334

The Black Bull of
Norroway ☙ *Scottish*   338

Index   347

A king finds that a fisherman and a cottager's daughter can make a fool of him in "The Poor Girl Who Became Queen"

Introduction

THE CLASSIC fairy tales – "Cinderella", "Snow White", "Little Red Riding Hood" – are among the first stories we encounter as children. These stories, with their magic and wonder, cast an unforgettable spell – a spell that can last a lifetime.

When, at the end of a fairy tale, we are told that the characters "lived happily ever after", we readily believe it. The optimism of fairy tales, in which the good overcome the wicked and the humble outwit the proud, gives hope to everyone who reads them.

Cinderella's stepmother and stepsisters treat her like a servant

However fairy tales are much more than just wish-fulfilment fantasies. Fairy-tale heroes and heroines achieve perfect happiness only after many trials and tribulations have been overcome, and fairy tales find room for grief as well as joy. As *Lord of the Rings* author J. R. R. Tolkien wrote: "The realm of fairy-story is ... filled with many

things: all manner of beasts and birds are found there; shoreless seas and stars uncounted; beauty that is an enchantment, and an ever-present peril; both joy and sorrow sharp as swords."

THE COLLECTION

The fairy tales chosen for this book are *all* traditional stories (tales that have been created by writers, such as Hans Christian Andersen, are not included). The selection combines classic tales made famous by Europeans such as Charles Perrault and the Brothers Grimm alongside others from many different cultures.

The Frog Prince agrees to fetch the princess' ball

Before our tales were first collected in books, they, and thousands of others, had been told around the world's firesides and hearths for centuries. In bygone times, many people could not read, so storytelling was a vital part of their entertainment and also education. For example, telling a fairy tale such as "Little Red Riding Hood" was a thoroughly memorable way for a parent to warn children not to talk to strangers. When the children grew up, they might tell the same story to their own children. And so tales were handed down from generation to generation.

The wolf licks its lips when it sees Little Red Riding Hood

The fairy tales in this book have been grouped together to show how similar themes recur all over the world. Care has also been taken to place each one in a suitable visual setting. Details of landscape, costume, and design have been

Soliday shoots the monstrous Man-Crow

considered to make the illustration that accompanies each tale magical and authentic.

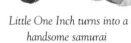 Tales for the Telling

Fairy tales are meant to be shared. An old Korean tale tells of a boy who loved to be told stories, but never told them to others. The boy hoarded stories like a miser hoards coins. Every time he heard a new one, he put its spirit into an old purse, which was soon full to bursting.

At last the boy was old enough to marry. On the morning of his wedding, his servant heard whispers coming from the old purse. The imprisoned story spirits were muttering angrily among themselves. "We're suffocating in here. But what does he care? Today is our chance to get our own back!"

One spirit suggested that a bush of poisonous strawberries would tempt the boy on the way to his wedding. Another spirit hoped that he might burn himself on a red-hot poker. Finally, a third spirit said that, if all else failed, a snake in the bridal chamber would surely bite him to death!

The servant, hearing all this, was able to prevent each of these disasters. After he had cut off the snake's head, he told his master that he had heard the imprisoned story spirits plotting against him.

"It's not natural, keeping them confined like that," he said. "You must set them free."

The young man realized his mistake,

Little One Inch turns into a handsome samurai

untied the old purse, and let the story spirits out. And from that day on, he told his stories to anyone who would listen.

Writing fairy stories down in a book is a bit like tying them up in an old purse. There is a danger they might suffocate. Open up the book, and set the story spirits free!

❧ *The Story of Fairy Tale* ❧

FOR AS LONG AS HISTORY, people have told each other fairy tales. A papyrus dating from around 1700 BC reveals that the pharaoh Cheops, builder of Egypt's Great Pyramid, was fond of fairy tales, and the surviving fairy tales of ancient Egypt show many striking similarities to modern stories. One, "Anpu and Bata", has much in common with the Congolese story "The Twin Brothers" in this book; the plot of "The Twin Brothers" is, in turn, similar to the German tale "The Gold Children", retold by the Brothers Grimm, and to stories from Russia, Greece, Italy, Ireland, Chile, and elsewhere.

Fairy tales are found all over the world – among the English and the Inuit, the Americans and the Ainu. Many of them are clearly very old, because the same plots and plot details recur in different cultures and on different continents. But if fairy tales are old, they are also always being made new. Whenever someone says – or, nowadays, writes – "Once upon a time...", a fairy tale comes to life, as fresh as the first time it was ever told.

The timeless, dreamlike imagery of fairy tale, portrayed by John Anster in The Stuff That Dreams Are Made Of

Magical transformations are a key fairy-tale ingredient. This study of a man turning into a frog is by Jean Grandville

"The Girl Who Pretended To Be a Boy", the heroine even changes from female to male – and marries the princess.

Added to this topsy-turvy world is one of fairy tale's most vital, timeless ingredients, magic – capable of turning a pumpkin into a coach, sending a princess to sleep for a hundred years, or, in the hands of the wicked, turning a prince into a beast. Magic in fairy tales mirrors the human imagination, where just to *think* something is to make it real. In "The Frog Prince", a slimy frog suddenly becomes a handsome prince; in "The Lame Fox", a fox turns herself, in turn, into a golden girl, a golden horse, and a golden apple tree. In

In some ways, fairy tales resemble dreams, flowing from image to image or scene to scene with the same magical speed and transporting the reader in a flash to places where literally anything can happen.

Once we step beyond the threshold of "Once upon a time..." – we enter a

In a fairy tale, the landscape can take on a life of its own. This unusual painting is by an anonymous 16th-century Dutch artist

world where, as in dreams, reality appears topsy-turvy. Suddenly, animals can not only talk, but, like the cat in "Puss in Boots", are far cleverer than human beings. The poorest, simplest, laziest, most good-for-nothing rascal, such as the Ash Lad of "An Eating Match With a Troll" or Jack of "Jack & the Beanstalk" becomes a daring, irresistible hero, capable of the most wonderful feats. At the end of a Romanian story,

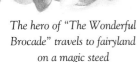

The hero of "The Wonderful Brocade" travels to fairyland on a magic steed

"Baba Yaga", a girl fleeing from a witch drops a towel – it becomes a broad river. When that does not stop the witch she flings a comb behind her – it becomes a forest so dense the witch cannot chew her way through it, and the girl escapes to her father's hut.

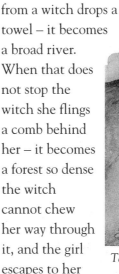

Talking animals are not at all unusual in fairy tales. This illustration from "Puss in Boots" is by Warwick Goble

It is because fairy tales speak so clearly to our imaginations as well as to our hearts that they have remained so popular. The influence of classic stories such as "Cinderella", "The Sleeping Beauty", "Bluebeard", and "The Frog Prince" echoes and reechoes through modern films, novels, poems – even advertising.

FAIRY-TALE JUSTICE

The real world is rarely fair, but in fairy tales the good are nearly always well rewarded and the wicked severely punished. Even death itself cannot stand in the way of a just and happy ending. Although the wicked queen in "Snow White" appears to have killed the heroine with a poisoned apple, when the piece of apple luckily falls out of Snow White's mouth, she comes alive again. She marries the prince and the wicked queen meets a fittingly gruesome fate.

Brave St George rescues a princess from an evil dragon. This classic image of fairy-tale heroism is attributed to the 14th-century artist Altichieri

This sense that at the root of life there is such a thing as natural justice is a powerful part of fairy tales' appeal. But they are enjoyed, too, for their sheer excitement. Their monsters and villains make us shiver; and we suffer with their heroes

A fairy godmother such as Mother Goose (painted by Arthur Rackham) embodies goodness

Evil may be represented by a hideous witch mixing up magic potions to harm the innocent, as depicted by Hans Thoma

Fairy-tale heroes can be princes or paupers – such as the Norwegian Ash Lad, here shown teasing a troll in an illustration by Theodor Kittlesen

On the 14th of October, 1892, the Irish poet W. B. Yeats visited a place that was widely believed to be a fairy haunt and invoked the fairies. The very next day he wrote, "Once there was a great sound as of little people cheering & stamping with their feet in the heart of the rock. The queen of the troop came then – I could see her – & held a long conversation with us & finally wrote in the sand 'be careful & do not seek to know too much about us'."

Scary creatures, like this jinn illustrated by René Bull, are a major part of fairy tales' appeal

and heroines and rejoice when everything comes right. Most enticing of all, fairy tales are full of wonders – even if fairies do not always appear!

Such a warning may serve for all those who try to explain away or pour scorn on fairies or fairy tales. After all the scholarly theories of fairy tales' hidden meanings, the tales are still there – pure, untouched, and full of mystery. And perhaps the fairies are, too.

THE "GOOD PEOPLE"

Fairies are part of many countries' folklore, and belief in them was once widespread, particularly in rural areas. It was said that the fairies were spirits, or fallen angels, or the descendants of the children that Eve hid in the shadows from God, or the remnants of an earlier race of beings. They were thought to have little sympathy for humankind and to exact terrible revenge on anyone who offended them. Country folk called them "the good people" as a mark of respect.

The fairies are always with us – a typical image of fairyland from Shakespeare's A Midsummer Night's Dream, painted by William Blake

The Storytellers

FAIRY TALES ARE living things. They have been handed down through generations for centuries. At first they were passed on by word of mouth at a time when many people could not read or write and lived in isolated farms and villages. Later, when schools opened and more families moved to towns, the old storytelling ways were in danger of coming to an end. Then, it was the turn of the collectors to preserve the stories by listening to storytellers and writing down their words. Although time

A handsome frontispiece to an early 20th-century French edition of Charles Perrault's tales

may have changed some of the tales in the telling, they continue to delight, entertain, and even frighten young listeners the world over. Today, the magic of fairy tales is rekindled when parents read to their children, or when the family is captivated by a film such as Walt Disney's *Snow White and the Seven Dwarfs*. In much the same way, generations ago, children listened open-mouthed as grandparents spun tales by the warmth of the fire, while shadows flickered on the walls.

Tale-spinning the traditional way: a family gathers around the fire to listen to grandma's story in A Winter Night's Tale *by Daniel Maclise.*

CHARLES PERRAULT

The modern writing down of tales dates from 1697 when *Stories, or Tales of Past Times* by Frenchman Charles Perrault (1628–1703) was published. A man of letters and civil servant – he helped oversee the building of Louis XIV's palace at Versailles and the Louvre – he concealed his authorship, and the book was attributed to his teenage son, Pierre. Its eight traditional fairy tales, which included "Cinderella", "Sleeping Beauty", "Little Red Riding Hood", "Puss in Boots", and "Bluebeard", started a craze for fanciful, made-up stories.

Left: The Brothers Grimm: Wilhelm (left) and Jacob. The brothers were orphans who were well educated thanks to a generous aunt

Right: the cover of this late-19th-century German collection of Grimms' fairy tales features Snow White and the seven dwarfs

THE BROTHERS GRIMM

In the early 19th century, German brothers Wilhelm (1786–1859) and Jacob (1785–1863) Grimm followed Perrault's lead and began to collect traditional fairy tales from their family and friends. Wilhelm's future wife, Dortchen Wild, contributed more than a dozen stories, including "Rumpelstiltskin", and family friends Jeannette and Amalie Hassenpflug, gave them "Snow White". The brothers also discovered a remarkable storyteller in her fifties named Dorothea Viehmann, who told them many stories, including "The Twelve Brothers" (similar to "The Unknown Sister" in this book). Grimms' fairy tales soon found their way into the homes and hearts of children all over Europe.

The Grimms' success encouraged others to try to preserve for posterity the riches of world folklore. Intrepid collectors tracked down gifted storytellers in every continent in order to record their tales in their exact words.

HANS CHRISTIAN ANDERSEN

The Grimms inspired writers to create new tales in traditional fairy-tale form. The most famous of these writers is Hans Christian Andersen (1805–75). The son of a poor shoemaker, he was brought up in a hospital in Odense, Denmark, where he often listened, enthralled, to the old women's stories as they worked in the spinning room. Andersen's tales, which include "The Ugly Duckling" and "The Snow Queen", are made-up, literary works, and so are not included in this traditional story collection.

Hans Christian Andersen, painted by Albert Küchler

Today, although fewer people tell stories by word of mouth, a gifted storyteller can still

Since the 1930s, Walt Disney's animated films have introduced children to many traditional fairy tales, such as Sleeping Beauty

hold an audience spellbound, and we can also listen to stories on radio or tape, read them ourselves, or watch them on film and video. The magical spell cast by fairy tales shows no sign of losing its power.

Under a Spell

Many characters in fairy tales, such as Beast in "Beauty and the Beast", are under a spell. They have been transformed by magic, often into the shape of an animal. It is the task of the hero or heroine to recognize the essential person behind the spell; in the end Beauty's courage and willingness to love Beast for his inner goodness breaks the spell. Most fairy tales about people under a spell end with the cruel enchantment being broken, but not all, as the story "Why the Sea Moans" shows. Usually a spell must work itself out, for good or ill, like the workings of fate. When Urashima in "Urashima & the Turtle" falls under a spell of eternal youth, his happiness is fated to end when he opens the fairy casket and ages hundreds of years in seconds.

In the beautiful Inuit story "A Whale's Soul & Its Burning Heart", the spell that is broken by the raven's meddling is nothing less than life itself, the most precious and most fragile magic spell of all.

The fairy princess gives Urashima a box and warns him not to open it if he wishes to return to her

The Sleeping Beauty

ONCE UPON A TIME a king and queen longed for a child. Year after year they waited and at last they had a daughter. Overcome with joy, the royal parents asked seven fairies to be godmothers to the little princess. They knew that if the fairies each gave the child a gift, as was the custom, she would grow to be the most perfect princess in the whole world.

The youngest fairy

The royal couple and the fairies cower in fear, but the youngest fairy hides behind a curtain

TIMELESS TALE
The tale of "The Sleeping Beauty" dates back at least to the 14th century. However the best-known version was set down by Frenchman Charles Perrault in 1697 under the title *"La Belle au Bois Dormant"*. This version formed the basis for later retellings (by the Brothers Grimm and others), including this one.

FAIRY-TALE CASTLE
Built in 1462 as a fortress and later ornamented with turrets, towers, and windows, the Chateau of Ussé inspired Perrault to write "The Sleeping Beauty". It overlooks the River Indre in western France.

At the christening feast, each fairy godmother was given a plate, knife, and fork of solid gold. But just as the guests sat down, an eighth fairy, ugly and shrivelled with age, entered the hall. No one had seen her for fifty years and so she had not been invited. The king could not give her a gold plate, a gold knife, and a gold fork because only seven sets had been made and the old fairy grumbled and muttered, believing herself insulted. To undo any evil the old fairy might be planning, the youngest fairy decided to save her gift until last and hid.

The feast over, the fairies presented their gifts to the princess. The first gave her the gift of beauty; the next of wisdom. The other fairies declared that she would be exquisitely graceful, a superb dancer, a wonderful singer, and a skilled musician. Then the old fairy croaked spitefully: "The princess will prick her finger on a spindle and die!"

At this the youngest fairy stepped forward and said: "The princess will not die! When she pricks her finger, she will fall into a deep sleep. She shall slumber a hundred years, when a prince shall come to wake her." This was not enough for the king. He ordered that every spindle should be burned, and the princess grew up safe from harm.

The king orders that every spindle be burned

The royal family leaves to spend summer at a castle in the country

In a lonely tower room an old lady sits spinning thread

distaff

spindle

The spiteful old fairy puts a curse on the baby princess

The princess climbs a winding staircase

One summer, the king and queen took her to a castle in the country. At the top of a tower she found a little room. There an old lady sat, spinning thread, using a spinning wheel and spindle. She knew nothing of the king's order. Eager to try, the princess reached out her hand. But when she took hold of the spindle, she pricked her finger and fell down in a faint…

Her eyes were shut, but her cheeks were rosy and she was breathing softly. In vain they tried to wake her. Finally the king ordered the servants to take her to the finest room in the castle.

There, on a bed embroidered with gold and silver, the princess lay like a sleeping angel.

THE FATEFUL SPINDLE
The spindle with which the princess pricks her finger might have been horizontally attached to a spinning wheel, or a hand-held type, such as the one above.

BRIAR ROSE
Grimm's version of the tale is called "Little Briar-Rose". In this title, the name of the princess combines thorns – associated with suffering and also with fairy power – with a flower that symbolizes beauty, perfection, and love.

CLASSIC BALLET
Princess Aurora (Ravenna Tucker) faints after pricking her finger in a scene from the great classical ballet *The Sleeping Beauty*, first performed in Russia in 1890 with choreography by Marius Petipa. The thrilling music by Tchaikovsky also featured in the 1959 Walt Disney cartoon.

When the youngest fairy heard what had happened, she came straight to the castle. "It is well that the princess sleeps in peace," she said, "but I am worried that, when she wakes, she will find herself among strangers."

The fairy took her wand and touched every living thing in the castle, except for the king and queen – all the servants and soldiers, the horses and watchdogs, and even the princess's own pet spaniel, Mopsie, lying next to her on the bed. They all fell asleep, too.

The king and queen sadly kissed their daughter goodbye and left the castle, forbidding anyone to approach it. To keep the princess safe from harm, the fairy encircled the castle with a forest of brambles and thorns so thick that no one could get through, and so high that only the very tops of the castle's turrets could be seen above the bushes.

A hundred years went by. The king and queen died, and another royal family came to rule the kingdom. One day the king's son was riding out in search of adventure when he glimpsed what looked like the towers of

An old farmer tells the prince that a princess sleeps in the castle in the forest

a castle rising above a gloomy forest. He questioned some passers-by, who agreed that the towers were indeed those of a castle. But some said it was full of ghosts, some that it was the haunt of witches, and others that a foul ogre lived there who ate children. Then an old farmer spoke up: "As a boy, I heard that a beautiful princess sleeps in that castle, waiting for the prince who will wake her!"

His heart pounding with excitement, the prince at once set out for the castle. When he reached the forest surrounding it, the thickets of brambles and thorns mysteriously parted to let him through. Then, just as mysteriously, they closed again behind him.

The thorns part, allowing the prince to pass.
All the people and animals in the courtyard are asleep

He reached the courtyard and
marvelled at all the bodies of people and
animals that lay, as if dead, all around him. He went into the
guardroom and saw the guards standing in line, pikes at their
shoulders, snoring away. Then he went into each room in turn until
at last he found the chamber where the princess lay sleeping.

Amazed by her beauty, which seemed to surround her with radiance,
he fell to his knees, and woke her with a kiss.

"Is it you, my prince?" she smiled. "I have waited for such a long
time." And he took her in his arms.

Meanwhile, all over the castle, men, women, and animals were
waking up. The roast was once more crackling on the spit, and even
the flies were buzzing again.

The prince and princess dined in a mirrored room to music played
on instruments that, though silent for a hundred years, still sounded
sweet and true. And the priest married them that very night, for, as
the princess said, a hundred years' wait was quite long enough!

The prince at last finds
the room where the
princess lies sleeping

———— ✿ ————

A STICKY END
In Perrault's version,
the story continues after
Sleeping Beauty's
marriage. The prince's
mother, an ogress with a
taste for human flesh, is
determined to eat the
princess and her two
children. When the
prince discovers the
plot, the ogress kills
herself by jumping into
a tub of snakes.

The Shape-Changer

LION TRACKS
In this tale, collected from the Akamba people of Kenya, the tracks of a lion (above) fool a buyer into thinking that his bull has been eaten.

THERE ONCE WAS A MAN called Mbokothe, who lived with his brother. Their parents had died, and left them two cows. Mbokothe said, "If I take the cows to a medicine man, he'll give me magical powers."

He drove the cows across the country to a famous medicine man, who took the cows and gave Mbokothe the power to take on the shape of any animal he chose. Mbokothe went home and told his brother, telling him to keep it a secret.

One day Mbokothe changed himself into a huge, handsome bull, and his brother drove him to market to sell him. A man paid Mbokothe's brother two cows and five goats.

On the way home, Mbokothe the bull escaped from his buyer. The man chased him, but Mbokothe changed his back legs into those of a lion. When the man saw the tracks, he said sadly, "It is no use. The bull has been caught and eaten by a lion."

And Mbokothe turned back into a man and strolled home.

The next market day, Mbokothe turned himself into a bull again and his brother sold him for ten goats. But Mbokothe didn't know that the man who bought him had visited the same medicine man and won magical powers of his own.

Mbokothe drives his cows to a medicine man, who gives him magical powers

When Mbokothe the bull ran off, the man turned into a lion and caught up with him. Mbokothe turned himself into a bird and flew away, but the man quickly became a powerful kite and flew after him. Mbokothe landed and changed into an antelope, but the man turned into a wolf. Every time Mbokothe changed shape, the man did, too, until Mbokothe was worn out.

"You've won," he said.

"Let's go back to my house, and I'll give you back all your goats."

Even a man of power will meet his match one day.

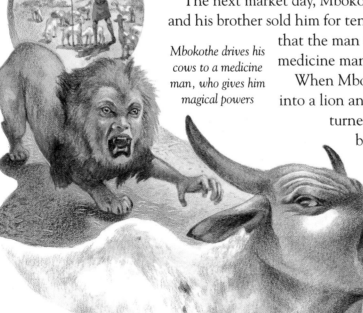

Later, Mbokothe tries to trick a man by turning into a bull, but the man – a shape-changer, too – becomes a raging lion

✥ Little One Inch ✥

ONCE THERE WAS a man and a woman who longed to have a child. They prayed and prayed, and eventually the gods sent them a baby boy. He was a fine, healthy baby, but he never grew, and so they called him Little One Inch.

When he was old enough, his parents sent Little One Inch out into the world, armed with a needle instead of a sword.

He sailed down the river to the capital, Kyoto, using a rice bowl as a boat and chopsticks as oars. There he was taken in by a family that lived in a big house. The family thought he was cute.

One day, Little One Inch went on a journey with the daughter of the house, who was fond of him.

Little One Inch sails to Kyoto in a rice bowl

They were attacked by an ogre, who wanted to steal the girl away.

"You'll have to deal with me first!" Little One Inch shouted, waving his needle in the air.

The ogre laughed, seized Little One Inch, and swallowed him whole.

The ogre picks Little One Inch up and swallows him

Inside the ogre's stomach, Little One Inch stabbed with his needle until the ogre coughed him up. Then he jabbed the needle in the ogre's eye. The ogre howled with pain and ran away, dropping a small metal object as he did so.

"It's a magic hammer that grants wishes," cried the girl, snatching it up.

"Then hit me with it, and see if it'll make me grow," said Little One Inch.

The girl gave him a terrific smack on the head and he began to grow… Soon Little One Inch was a tall, handsome young samurai whom any girl would be pleased to marry.

PINT-SIZED HERO
Little One Inch is the Japanese equivalent of the European fairy-tale hero Tom Thumb, seen above in a 19th-century picture book being chased by Old Grumbo the giant. The Japanese ogre in this tale is an *oni*. These tusked, malevolent ogres are usually bright red or blue in colour.

Little One Inch turns into a samurai

The Frog Prince

THE FAIRY-TALE FROG
In many parts of the world, frogs symbolize new life, and so usually appear in stories as kind and helpful. But for Christians, the frog, like the toad, also has links with witchcraft. For a prince to be changed into a slimy frog, as in this story, is therefore to fall from being the noblest of God's creatures to one of the most despised.

WISHING WELL
It is a traditional belief that good spirits live in wells. People toss coins into wishing wells in the hope that the spirits will grant their wishes. The frog in this story lives near a well – a sign he may bring the princess good luck.

LONG AGO THERE lived a king who had a beautiful daughter. Near his castle was a forest and in the forest was a well and that was where the princess liked to play with her golden ball. One day – splash! – the ball fell into the well. The princess began to cry.

"What's wrong, princess?" croaked a voice. But there wasn't anybody there, just a frog.

"Is it you, old puddle-squelcher?" the princess sniffled. "My golden ball has fallen into the well."

"What will you give me if I fetch it?"

"Whatever you want, you dear frog," said the princess. "My clothes, my jewels – even my crown!"

The frog answered, "I don't want your clothes, your jewels, or your crown. But if you will love me and be my friend, if I can eat off your plate and sleep in your bed, then I will get your golden ball."

The frog offers to dive in the well and fetch the princess's golden ball

"I promise," said the princess. "Anything you like." The frog dived into the well. What an ugly frog, the princess thought. Only fit to sit in a pond and croak!

Soon the frog returned and in his mouth was the golden ball. Delighted, the princess snatched it up and ran home. "Wait! I can't run as fast as you!" croaked the frog.

The next day, when the princess was dining with the king, there came a knock. When she saw who it was, she slammed the door.

"Who was that, dear?" asked the king.

"A slimy frog," shuddered the princess.

"And what did the frog want?"

"Yesterday my golden ball fell down a well and this frog fetched it. In return I promised he could be my friend. I never thought he would follow me home."

"You must keep your promise," the king said. So the princess opened the door and the frog hopped in. The frog said, "Lift me up." The king told the princess to lift the frog onto the table. Then the frog said to her, "Push your plate nearer, so I can share your food." The frog slurped up his share; the princess barely touched hers.

Afterwards the frog said, "I'm tired. Let's go to sleep in your bed." The princess began to cry, but the king told her, "You accepted his help. You cannot turn him away."

She picked the frog up in two fingers, carried him to her room, and dropped him in a corner. But when she got into bed, the frog jumped onto her pillow and said, "I'll sleep here!"

"Let me be!" cried the princess and she threw him against the wall. To her amazement, the frog changed into a handsome prince!

"I was turned into a frog by a witch," he explained. "But your promise of love has broken the spell! Now let us sleep, and in the morning we will go to my kingdom."

Next morning, a coach arrived. The coachman was the prince's old servant Henry, who had been so unhappy when his master was turned into a frog that a blacksmith had fixed three iron bands around his heart to stop it from breaking. As they drove along, the prince and princess heard a loud crack. The prince cried, "Henry, the carriage is breaking!"

"It's not the carriage, master," answered Henry. "It's an iron band from around my heart!" Twice more they heard a crack, and each time they thought the carriage was breaking, but it was only an iron band springing from around the heart of old Henry, in joy and happiness.

The princess keeps her promise and lets the frog eat from her plate

HOW EMBARRASSING! This story was first written down by the Brothers Grimm in the early 19th century, but its classic tale of a pretty princess highly embarrassed by a promise to a repulsive creature is probably far older, and many countries have their own versions.

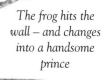

The frog hits the wall – and changes into a handsome prince

The princess hurls the frog out of her bed

Henry joyfully drives them to the prince's kingdom

The Lame Fox

The man's right eye was always laughing and his left eye was always weeping

T HERE ONCE WAS a man who had three sons. Two were bright boys, but the youngest was a foolish lad. Now this man's right eye was always laughing, but his left eye was always weeping. The man's sons decided to ask him why this was so.

The eldest son asked, but the man threw a knife at him. The second son asked and the same thing happened. Both sons fled. Then the third son asked. The man seized his knife, but the boy did not run.

The man put down the knife and said, "My other two sons are cowards, but you are brave, so my right eye laughs. But my left eye weeps because my magic vine, which gives twenty-four buckets of wine a day, has been stolen."

The three brothers agreed to set out in search of the magic vine. The road forked three ways, and each took a path.

The man's three sons set off in search of his magic vine. The road forks three ways

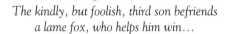

The kindly, but foolish, third son befriends a lame fox, who helps him win…

HELPFUL FOX
The fox is celebrated as the most cunning of animals. The fox in this story, unlike foxes in most tales, is not sly or greedy, but a patient helper for the hero.

The two older boys soon met up once more. "Praise God, we've managed to shake off that ninny!" they laughed and sat down to eat the food they had brought. Along came a lame she-fox, looking very hungry. But the brothers didn't spare her a crumb; they just said, "There's a fox! Let's kill it!" The fox limped away.

When the foolish lad sat down to eat, the same fox came up to him. "These are hard times," he said. "Share my meal."

After they had eaten, the fox said, "Where are you going?" The simpleton, amazed the fox could speak, told her everything.

"Follow me," said the fox.

They came to a garden. "The vine is in there," the fox said. "You must pass twelve guards. Their eyes are open, but they are asleep. You'll find a gold shovel and a wooden shovel. Dig up the vine with the wooden shovel and come back to me."

But when the lad reached the vine, he forgot what the fox had said, and took up the gold shovel. As soon as he pushed it into the ground, it woke the guards, and they took him to their master.

"But the vine is my father's," the foolish lad exclaimed.

"That's as may be," said the lord, "but I will not give it back unless you bring me the golden apple tree that bears golden fruit every day."

The lad went back to the fox and the fox said, "Follow me." She took him to another garden and said: "To reach the golden apple tree, you must pass another twelve guards. By the tree are two poles: a golden one and a wooden one. Take the wooden pole, beat the tree, and come back to me."

But the silly lad beat the tree with the golden pole and woke the guards. The lord said, "I'll give you the tree, if you bring me the golden horse with the golden wings."

The lad went back to the fox and the fox said, "Follow me." She led him through a dark forest to a farmyard

… a golden apple tree…   *… a golden horse…*   *… and a golden girl*

and said, "First you must pass twelve guards. The golden horse is in a stable and hanging near it are two bridles, one of gold and one of straw. Bridle the horse with the straw one, and ride him back to me."

But the silly lad bridled the horse with the golden bridle and woke the guards. The lord said, "I'll give you the golden horse, if you bring me the golden girl in the golden cradle."

The lad went back to the fox and the fox said, "Follow me." She took him to a cave and said, "Inside the cave, past twelve guards, is the golden girl, rocking herself in her golden cradle. Nearby is a huge spectre, screaming, 'No! No!' Pay it no mind. Pick up the golden cradle, and bring it to me."

This time, the lad did as the fox said. They went back to the farmyard and the lad said, "The golden girl is so beautiful, it seems a pity to give her up." So the fox turned herself into a golden girl,

except her eyes were a fox's eyes. The lad gave the fox-girl to the lord, and took away the golden horse.

That night, the lord was gazing at the golden girl when he cried out, "You have a fox's eyes!" The girl changed back into the fox, which ran to where the lad was waiting with the real golden girl and the golden horse.

The fox next changed herself into a golden horse, except she still had a fox's tail. The lad swapped her for the golden tree. Later, when the lord was admiring the horse, he said, "You are so beautiful, except for that scruffy fox's tail!" The horse changed back into the fox, which ran to where the lad was waiting.

Lastly, the fox changed herself into a golden apple tree and the lad swapped her for his father's vine. But as the lord was admiring the tree, he suddenly said, "How strange! The apples look like fox's heads!" And the tree turned back into the fox, which ran off to join the lad, the girl, the horse, the tree, and the vine.

On the way home the lad encountered his brothers. They threw him down a well and stole his treasures. But when they took them back to their father, the vine wouldn't make wine, the apple tree wouldn't bloom, the golden horse wouldn't neigh, and the golden girl wouldn't smile. And still their father's left eye wept.

Meanwhile the lame fox rescued the lad from the well. While he lay gasping for air on the grass, she changed into a princess. She had been cursed to walk the world as a fox until she saved the life of a friend. "Now I am free," she said, "and so are you. Farewell, my friend."

The princess went her way, and the lad went home. There he told his father the whole story, and, as he did so, the vine began to make wine, the apple tree bloomed, the horse neighed, and the golden girl sang. Best of all, his father's left eye stopped weeping and began to laugh.

The lord suddenly realizes that his golden girl has fox's eyes

TRUE TO NATURE
A human changing into an animal, and vice versa, is a common fairy-tale event, but in this story the fox does not completely change into the golden girl. The fox's true nature shines through – just like that of the main character in the La Fontaine fable "The Cat Who Changed into a Woman" (above). Although a good wife to her husband, the cat-woman just cannot help chasing mice.

As the lovers embrace, the father drives out his two wicked sons

The father drove his two bad sons out, the foolish lad married the golden girl, and they lived happily ever after.

✿ *Jamie Freel & the Young Lady* ✿

EVERY HALLOWEEN lights were seen burning in the ruined castle and sounds of dancing and music could be heard. But no one ever went near; it was known to be a favourite haunt of the "wee folk", the fairies.

But one Halloween, Jamie Freel, a poor widow's son from Fannet, said, "I am going to the castle to seek my fortune."

His mother begged him not to go, but he was a brave lad and he strode out into the moonlit night. Wild music carried on the breeze and, as Jamie drew nearer to the old castle, he could also hear laughter and singing. The sounds were coming from the castle hall, where windows were ablaze with light. Jamie nervously peered in.

The whole fairy host, none of them taller than a child of five years, were feasting and drinking, stamping their feet and dancing, while flutes and fiddles played.

As soon as they spotted Jamie the fairies shouted, "Welcome, Jamie Freel! Welcome! We're going to Dublin tonight to steal a young lady. Will you ride with us, Jamie Freel?"

"Yes, I will," Jamie boldly replied.

FAIRY LAND
This tranquil landscape is part of the real-life setting of this fairy tale. It shows Fannad (Fannet) Head in County Donegal, Northern Ireland, with the waters of Lough Swilly on the right.

———— ✿ ————

BELIEF IN FAIRIES
At the beginning of this century it was estimated that more than ten per cent of the Irish rural population genuinely believed in fairies. Fairies were often blamed for minor mishaps, such as milk turning sour. Anyone who offended the fairy folk risked serious illness, even death. It was believed to be unlucky to tell stories about fairies in the daytime.

As Jamie approaches the castle, he hears music and sees lights in the windows

The fairies invite Jamie on a wild night-time ride

So Jamie mounted a fairy horse and rode through the air with the fairy host whooping around him, over the roof of his mother's cottage, over hills, fields, and villages, over deep Lough Swilly, and past the spire of Derry Cathedral, until at last they reached Dublin. The fairies chose the finest house in Stephen's Green for their visit. The shimmering host halted by a window where a beautiful girl lay sleeping. Jamie looked on in amazement as the fairies swept into the room and stole her from her own bed.

The host reaches Dublin and steals a beautiful girl from her bed

In her place they leave a stick

The girl in Jamie's arms turns into a snarling dog, but he will not let go

ST STEPHEN'S GREEN
The wealthy young lady of the story would most probably have grown up in a house like this one – a beautiful Georgian terrace in St Stephen's Green, Dublin.

In her place, they left a stick that took on her shape, but was lifeless.

The fairies took turns carrying the girl as they galloped homeward across the starlit sky.

"Don't I get a go?" shouted Jamie as they whirled over the village of Tamney, not far from his mother's cottage. So they gave her to him – and he jumped from his fairy mount with the girl in his arms.

The fairies pursued them, crying with rage in their high-pitched voices. Before Jamie could bundle the girl inside the cottage, they turned her into a black dog, barking and snapping; into a glowing bar of iron; into a sack of wool. But Jamie would not let go of her.

At last one fairy, a tiny woman, said, "Jamie can have her, but he shall have no good of her, for I'll make her deaf and dumb!" She sprinkled something over the girl and the fairies rushed away into the night sky. Jamie lifted the latch and entered the cottage.

"How will we look after a lady like her?" cried his mother, when he had told her of all the night's wonders.

"I'll work for you both," said Jamie, turning to the girl. But tears were rolling down her cheeks; she could neither hear nor speak.

A year passed by and Halloween came again. Jamie decided to pay another visit to the ruined castle. As he entered the hall, he overheard the tiny woman fairy say, "What a poor trick Jamie Freel played on us last year, stealing the girl from us; but at least we struck her deaf and dumb. But he does not know that just three drops from this glass in my hand would give her back her hearing and speech."

Then the fairies caught sight of Jamie and made him welcome. "Drink our health out of this glass!" cried the tiny woman. Jamie took the glass from the fairy and darted out of the hall before the fairies knew what was happening.

Jamie ran till he thought his heart would burst and at last reached home. There were just three drops left in the glass. He gave them to the girl and straightaway she was herself again. She couldn't thank Jamie enough, but naturally she wanted to go back home to see her mother and father. The very next day, she and Jamie set off on the long walk to Dublin.

It took far longer than the fairy journey but at last they found the grand house in Stephen's Green and knocked on the door.

"The daughter of the house died a year ago!" said the servants, and refused to let them in. Jamie and the girl insisted, and finally her father came to the door. But he just said, "My daughter is dead. Go away."

"Please, leave us alone," added her mother.

Then Jamie Freel spoke up and told them all about the fairies and the piece of wood they had left in the girl's bed, and at last the mother and father began to believe that their daughter really had come back to them. Jamie's mother was fetched from Fannet in a coach and Jamie and the beautiful girl he had saved from the fairies were married in a splendid wedding.

RUINED CASTLE
Burt Castle, Inishowen, County Donegal, is typical of the many picturesque castles scattered over the Irish countryside. At night, of course, they can look distinctly forbidding, and with moonlight shining through the windows, a castle might well appear to be mysteriously lit up from within by a fairy host.

The girl's parents cannot believe that their daughter has returned

The Unknown Sister

SAVED BY SWANS
This story is of European origin, and formed the basis of Hans Christian Andersen's "The Wild Swans". In this illustration, by Anne Anderson, the heroine is being rescued by her swan-brothers.

BIRD CHANGES
Story details change to suit a particular audience. Macaws are common in Surinam, so the brothers become macaws. In German versions, however, they turn into ravens.

ONCE THERE WAS a king who had twelve sons. He longed for a daughter, and he told his wife, "If we could have a daughter, I would kill all our sons."

When the queen was with child once more, the king had to go to war, but he left instructions that if she had a daughter, his sons were to be put to death. "Fly!" said the frightened queen to her sons. "If I give birth to a son, I will raise a white flag and you can come back. But if I bear a daughter, I will raise a red flag and you must stay away!" And her sons ran away.

One morning they saw a red flag flying, so they sadly built themselves a hut in the jungle.

As their sister grew, she often asked about the twelve chests of clothes in her mother's house, but her mother would not tell her who they belonged to.

At last the girl could bear it no longer. She picked up a revolver and told her mother, "The first bullet is for you, and the second is for me, if you won't explain the mystery of these chests." So her mother told her about her twelve brothers, and her father's terrible oath.

The girl comes upon her brothers' hut

At gunpoint, a mother tells her daughter about her missing brothers

The girl took her father's ring and went to look for her brothers. She walked a long way, until she happened upon her brothers' hut.

Now the brothers had sworn to kill any woman who came to their hut, because it was for the sake of a woman that they had been exiled. For that reason, one of them always stayed behind when the others went hunting. When he saw a girl approaching, he menacingly asked her who she was and what she wanted. She showed him her father's ring, and he knew she must be his sister.

"Hide," he said, "or my brothers will kill you!"

When he cooked supper that night, he accidentally laid plates for thirteen, not twelve, so his brothers guessed someone else was there.

The girl had to show herself; but when they saw her ring, they forgave everything and begged her to stay with them.

The next day, the sister cooked for her brothers. They had a rose tree with twelve buds on it, and she picked the buds and laid one on each plate. But when the brothers came home and sat down to eat, they changed into twelve macaws and flew away. The girl resolved to search for them and vowed that, until she found them, she would not speak a single word to anyone.

A prince falls in love with the silent girl and takes her home

She cooks a meal for her brothers, but they turn into macaws and fly away

The girl

She vows not to speak until she finds them

Her silence angers the prince's sisters who condemn her to death as an evil spirit

She wandered until her clothes were in tatters. A prince found her, fell in love, and took her home to be his bride, but she would not speak. The prince's sisters said, "She does not speak because she is an evil spirit." The girl would not speak to deny the charge and was condemned to death.

Just as she was about to die and the prince was begging her to speak to save herself, twelve macaws flew out of the jungle. The girl heard them calling "raf-raf!" and spoke at last. "Here are my brothers, come to save me!" she cried. The macaws turned back into her twelve brothers and the girl and the prince were married.

Her brothers arrive to save her from death

A Whale's Soul & Its Burning Heart

THERE WAS ONCE a stupid and self-important raven who flew far, far out to sea. It flew and flew, until at last it grew tired. It looked for somewhere to rest, but there was no land. The raven grew so tired it barely had the strength to flap its wings. Just as it was about to sink into the ocean, a great whale came up to the surface, and the raven flew straight into its mouth.

The raven flies straight into the whale's mouth

ALASKAN TALE
This haunting story shows the Inuits' respect for the beauty and fragility of life in the harsh Arctic environment. It was told to the Danish/Inuit ethnologist Knud Rasmussen by Pamik, an Inuit from the region of the Utokok River, Alaska, USA.

As it tumbled down the whale's throat, the raven thought it must surely die. But then it found itself in a house, a neat, snug house full of light and warmth. It was a whalebone house, built and furnished like the houses of men. On a bed sat a young woman tending a glowing lantern. She welcomed the raven, saying, "Make yourself at home. But please, never touch my lantern." The raven promised never to meddle with the lantern.

The raven promises not to touch the girl's lantern

HUNTING TO SURVIVE
In the freezing seas off the Greenland coast, an Inuit hunter throws a spear at a narwhal. Whale meat and other products are vital to the traditional Inuit way of life. Anyone killing a whale – especially one as large as the whale in this tale – would be admired and respected.

The young woman seemed very restless. She was always getting up and going out of the door, and then coming back in again.

"What's the matter?" asked the raven.

"Nothing," said the girl. "It is just life. Life and breath."

The raven grew curious about the girl and the lantern. So when she next slipped from the room, the raven touched the lantern's candle. Immediately the girl fell headfirst through the door and lay in a dead faint. The candle in the lantern went out.

It was too late for the raven to be sorry. The damage was done. The bright warm house was gone, and the raven was left in darkness, with the smell of the whale's fat and the whale's blood. It tried to find its way out of the whale's belly, but just kept going in circles, getting hotter and hotter and rubbing all its feathers off. The feathers swirled around so that the raven almost choked to death.

The girl was the whale's soul, and she slipped out through the door into the air whenever the whale drew breath. Her heart was the lantern with its steady flame. When the raven touched the lantern, it snuffed out the whale's heart's flame. Now the whale was dead, and the raven was trapped in its belly.

The raven fought for life in the blood and darkness, and at last it managed to haul itself out of the whale's mouth. Exhausted, it sat slumped on the floating carcass – a naked raven, smeared with grease and filth, on the back of a dead whale.

Eventually a storm came up and drove it towards land. The people saw the whale's carcass and rowed out in their kayaks

The meddling raven touches the lantern, its light goes out, and the girl faints away

to bring it to land. The raven saw them coming and changed itself into a man – a battered, ugly little man standing on a dead whale.

The raven did not say, "I meddled with a beauty I could not understand and destroyed it."

STORM LANTERN
The Inuit used whale oil to fuel lamps and to make candles. In this story, the candle flame, symbolizing the whale's heart, is protected from sudden draughts by a storm lantern.

When people come to see the whale's carcass, they meet an ugly little man shouting in triumph

Instead it crowed, "I killed the whale! I killed the whale!"
And the raven became a big man among men.

Beauty & the Beast

CLASSIC TALE
Although many
versions of "Beauty and
the Beast" have been
written down or told by
word of mouth, the one
that remains best
known – and which
forms the basis of this
retelling – is the classic
text of Madame Jeanne-
Marie de Beaumont
(above), first published
in 1756.

A DOG'S WIFE
"Beast-marriage" stories
are found all over the
world – the prince may
be a ram, a pig, a snake,
even a crocodile.
In an English version,
the bridegroom is "a
great, foul, small-tooth
dog". In Kentucky,
USA, a similar story is
called "The Girl that
Married a Flop-Eared
Hound-Dog".

ONCE THERE LIVED a rich merchant who had three sons and three daughters. He was especially fond of the youngest girl. She was so pretty that, when she was small, everyone called her "Little Beauty", and the name stuck. Her older sisters, who weren't quite so attractive either in looks or character, couldn't help being jealous.

Beauty's haughty sisters had plenty of suitors but declared that they wouldn't dream of marrying anyone who wasn't a duke or a count. Beauty just said to anyone who proposed to her, "Thank you, but I'm too young to marry, and besides, I couldn't leave my father."

One day the merchant's ship was lost at sea and with it his fortune. All he had left was a cottage in the country. He sadly told his children that they would all have to move there and work the land. Although

Beauty does all the work while her sisters complain of being bored

Beauty wasn't used to such hard work, she said, "Of course, father. Why, I'm sure it will be great fun." But her sisters moaned about having to give up their fine dresses and high-and-mighty ways. Poor Beauty ended up doing all the work, while her sisters did nothing but complain about being stuck in the boring country.

A year later, the merchant heard that his ship, of which he had given up all hope, had arrived safely in port after all, laden with goods. When he went to see about selling the cargo, he asked the girls what they would like best as a present on his return. The two eldest clamoured for jewels, dresses, and expensive trinkets. Beauty, who realized the sale of the cargo would scarcely buy everything her sisters wanted, kept quiet.

"Don't you want anything, Beauty?" asked her father.

"Just a rose," she replied gently.

He came upon the gates to a great palace

When the merchant reached the port, however, he found that the cargo had already been sold to pay off his debts, and he was as poor as ever. Very downhearted, he turned back the way he had come. The only thing that cheered him up was the thought of seeing his family again.

He was some way from home when a snowstorm blew up and he became lost in a forest. The wind howled and the snow swirled and he couldn't tell left from right or up from down. But just when he thought he must surely die, he came upon the gates to a great palace. He urged his poor horse on and reached the safety of the courtyard. Everything was prepared in the stable, but there were no other horses there, and no stable-lads either.

The merchant entered the palace. Still there was no one to be seen. But he found a table set with roast chicken and wine, so he helped himself to supper. Then he went upstairs, found a bed, and, exhausted, fell asleep.

In the morning, he found a fine suit of clothes laid out for him, to replace his weatherstained ones. Downstairs, breakfast had been laid. "This must be the house of some good fairy, who has taken pity on me," he mused.

Outside, the snow had melted, and beautiful flowers were blooming in the garden. The merchant remembered his promise to Beauty and went outside to pick a rose. As soon as he had done so, he heard a terrible roaring that made him go weak at the knees. He looked up. A hideous, snarling creature, half man, half beast, towered over him.

CASTLE IN THE WOOD
The beast's palace could well have looked like this castle in Saumur, France, which was designed to keep out unwelcome visitors.

The merchant is caught stealing a rose by the furious, roaring Beast

BEAUTY'S ROSE
The rose that may have caught the merchant's eye might have been similar to *Rosa centifolia*, rose of a hundred petals, which was much admired in 18th-century France. It was grown to imitate a rose from China that was so popular it was copied onto porcelain and silk embroideries.

THE HARPSICHORD
Before the advent of the piano, it was common to find harpsichords in French drawing rooms of the 18th century. A refined young lady much like Beauty would sit and play a stately air by the popular composers of the day, such as François Couperin or Jean-Philippe Rameau.

"Ungrateful wretch!" it boomed. "I welcome you into my castle, feed you and take care of you, and in return you steal my roses, which I love more than anything in the world. You shall die for this!"

The merchant threw himself to his knees. "Forgive me, sir, I beg you! I only plucked one rose, for my daughter, who asked me for one."

"Don't call me sir. My name is Beast, and I don't care who knows it. But now you tell me you have a daughter, I've a mind to let you go. On one condition. She must come here of her own free will, to die in your place. Otherwise, you must return yourself in three months."

Although the merchant had no intention of sacrificing one of his daughters to the Beast, he agreed, thinking, at least I'll be able to hold them in my arms before I die.

The Beast sent him home with a chest of gold coins, but a heavy heart. When he told everything to his daughters, the older ones said, "It's all Beauty's fault, asking for fol-de-rols like roses, instead of jewels and clothes."

Beauty's sisters, with the help of half an onion, weep at her departure

Beauty replied, "If it is my fault, I must mend it. I will go to the Beast and beg his mercy."

Beauty's father tried to stop her from going, but she refused to be persuaded. So they set out together for the Beast's palace. Beauty's father and brothers were weeping, and even her sisters managed a tear or two, with the help of an onion.

When Beauty and her father arrived at the palace, everything was as before, except this time two places had been laid for dinner. "The Beast must want to fatten me up before he eats me," thought Beauty.

After they had eaten, they heard a growl and the Beast appeared. The Beast asked her if she had come of her own free will.

"Yes," she said, in a trembling voice.

"Then you shall stay," the Beast replied. "But your father must go." The merchant protested in vain. Beauty remained behind, alone.

Upstairs, she found a bedroom with "Beauty's Room" in gold on the door. Inside there was everything she could desire, even a harpsichord. "Surely the Beast wouldn't have gone to all this trouble if he meant to eat me straightaway," she thought.

The Beast joined her at supper the following night and told her that as long as she stayed with him, she only had to ask for something and she should have it. "You are the mistress here," he said, "and I am the servant. Tell me, am I very ugly?"

Beauty enters her beautiful room

Beauty's father is expelled from the palace

At supper, the Beast asks Beauty to marry him

"Yes," said Beauty. "But you are also very kind."
"That's probably only because I'm so stupid," said the Beast.
"Not at all," said Beauty. "Really stupid people think they're very clever. You have a good heart, so you can't be stupid."
And the Beast replied, "In that case, Beauty, will you marry me?"
"No," said Beauty. "I will not."

LA BELLE ET LA BETE
This story has been dramatized many times, including as an opera by André Grétry, *Zémire et Azor*, and a 1991 Walt Disney cartoon. Perhaps the most atmospheric adaptation was the film *La Belle et la Bête*, (above), directed by Jean Cocteau in 1946. It starred Josette Day as Beauty and Jean Marais as the Beast.

POSH FROCK
This 18th-century silk brocade dress has supports called paniers at the hips. It would have made a fine gift for a gentleman like the Beast to offer his lady.

After that, the Beast asked Beauty every evening if she would marry him, and every evening Beauty turned him down.

Otherwise, they lived happily, but Beauty missed her father. She had learned from looking in a magic mirror that her brothers had joined the army, and that her two older sisters had married, so her father was all alone. She begged the Beast to let her visit him for just a week, and promised to return.

"Make sure you do," said the Beast, "or I shall die of sorrow."

In the magic mirror Beauty sees her father looking lonely and ill

Beauty's sisters envy her beautiful clothes and jewels and plot her downfall

When Beauty got home, she found her father lying in bed. He had never recovered from the shame of leaving her with the Beast.

"Father, there's no need to be sad," she said. "The Beast is good and kind. Why, just look at the beautiful dress I am wearing; that is just one of his gifts." So Beauty's father began to cheer up. But when her envious sisters, who had made poor marriages, saw how grand Beauty had become, they were beside themselves with spite. They decided to make the Beast so angry he would eat her after all. They begged and pleaded until Beauty agreed to delay her return by one more week.

On the tenth night, Beauty dreamed she was in the Beast's garden and he was lying dead at her feet. She awoke shaking. She realized how fond she had grown of him, and how much she missed him.

She went straight back to the Beast's palace, but he was nowhere to be found. She ran into the garden, and there, just like in her dream, was the Beast, lying on the grass. She threw herself down beside him, hugging him, and begging him to wake. She bathed his forehead in her tears. The Beast opened his eyes.

"You are too late," he croaked. "I am dying."

"Don't die!" said Beauty. "I want to marry you!"

The envious sisters are turned to stone

Beauty finds the Beast lying in his garden, dying

CUPID AND PSYCHE
This tale shows the influence of the Roman story of Cupid and Psyche, told by the poet Apuleius in the 2nd century AD. The beautiful Psyche is forced by the gods to marry a monster, who is really Cupid, god of love, in disguise. This 19th-century painting of the moment Cupid and Psyche meet face to face is by British artist Sir Edward Burne-Jones.

As she spoke, the palace exploded with light and music. The Beast was gone, and in his place was a handsome young prince.

"Beast, where are you?" called the anxious Beauty.

"Here I am," said the prince. "It was me all along, under a cruel spell. I had to find a girl who would love me for my good heart, not for my looks, or intelligence, or wealth. And now I have found you, I will never lose you again."

Beauty and the Beast were married and lived happily ever after. As for Beauty's sisters, the fairy who had enchanted the Beast turned them into statues to stand on either side of the palace doors. It was their punishment to see Beauty's happiness, and be unable to spoil it.

SAD ENDING
In a Portuguese version of the story, Beauty is tricked by her sisters and fails to return to the Beast in time. Beauty rushes back to the castle, but finds the Beast dead. She is so upset she pines away, and her jealous sisters are condemned to a life of poverty.

Three Magic Oranges

HOT JUNGLES
In Costa Rica's tropical jungles, where this story is set, the daytime temperature is 38° C (100° F) – hot enough to make anyone thirsty!

ONCE UPON A TIME an old king thought it high time his son was married. He invited princesses from far and near to a feast, but the prince didn't like any of them.

The king declared that his son had better find *himself* a wife. So the prince mounted his horse and rode off. Before long he reached a forest, at the edge of which was an orange tree with three golden oranges. He picked the oranges and went on his way.

It was a hot day, and the prince felt thirsty. He pulled out his knife and cut open the first orange. Wonder of wonders! From it sprang a beautiful maiden with eyes the colour of the sky and hair the colour of the sun. "Give me a drink of water, I beg you," she pleaded. But the prince had no water to give her, and the girl vanished.

The third time, the prince has water to give the girl and breaks a witch's spell

The prince finds three oranges

Twice he cuts open an orange; each time a maiden appears, begs for water, then vanishes

SAME GIRL
Though the girls in this tale look different, they are really the same person – there is only one enchanted maiden, not three.

The sun beat down and the prince cut open the second orange. Wonder of wonders! From it sprang a maiden with eyes the colour of a forest pool and hair the colour of a red hibiscus. She also begged him for water he did not have. Then she vanished.

At last the prince came to a spring and drank his fill. Feeling hungry, he cut open the third orange. Wonder of wonders! From it sprang a maiden with eyes and hair black as a raven's wing and a face as white as a jasmine flower. "Give me water, I beg you," she pleaded. He scooped some up for

The witch thrusts a pin into the girl's head – turning her into a dove

her to drink. And so the spell was broken, for a witch had imprisoned her in the magic oranges.

The prince and the girl were married and before long they became king and queen. But the witch discovered that the girl had been set free and went up to the palace, crying out, "Hairpins! Who'll buy my fine hairpins?"

The queen asked the old woman to come in. The witch took out a hairpin topped with a pearl. "Let me fix this in your hair," she said. The queen bowed down and the witch thrust the pin into her head. She was turned into a white dove, which flew away into the forest where the young king was hunting.

The dove is the prince's only comfort for the loss of his true love

The king caught the dove as a present for his wife. To his dismay, when he came home, she was nowhere to be seen.

Months passed. His only comfort was the white dove, a reminder of his lost love. One day, as he stroked the bird's head, he felt the pearl head of a pin. Who could have been so cruel? He pulled the pin out and – wonder of wonders! – there stood his beautiful queen.

The king ordered his men to bring the witch to the palace, but there was no need. That day, her hut caught fire and she was burned to death. The last anyone saw of her was a plume of smoke, blowing over the treetops.

AROUND THE WORLD This story is truly international, being popular in Europe, India, and North and South America. It also inspired the Russian composer Sergei Prokofiev (1891–1953) to compose the opera *The Love for Three Oranges* (above), first performed in 1921.

One day he finds a pin in the dove's head, pulls it out, and his lost wife appears again

The furious witch accidentally burns herself to death

Urashima & the Turtle

—— 🍃 ——

TIME SLIP
In folktales, days spent in fairyland are often the equivalent of years in the real world. When the Irish hero Oisin (pronounced "Isheen") wishes to leave *tir nan-Og*, the magical Land of Youth, to visit his home, his fairy wife lets him go on a white horse, but warns him never to get down from its back. He falls from the horse – and at once becomes an old man.

LONG AGO *THERE LIVED* a fisherman named Urashima. He lived at home with his mother, for he was unmarried. When she urged him to find a bride, he answered, "I can only catch enough fish to feed two, so while you are alive I will not marry."

One day, all he caught was a little turtle. "You will scarcely make a mouthful for mother and a mouthful for me," he said.

The turtle replied, "In that case, set me free! If you show me mercy, I will show you gratitude." Kind-hearted Urashima set the turtle free.

Several years later, when Urashima was out fishing as usual, a storm swept through the bay and capsized his boat. Like so many fishermen, he could not swim, and he seemed sure to drown. But as he splashed and spluttered, a huge turtle swam up from the depths. "I am the turtle whose life you once saved," it said. "Climb on my back."

The turtle did not take Urashima to the shore – it plunged down, down to Ryugu,

One day, all Urashima catches is a little turtle

the dragon king's palace at the bottom of the sea. "I am maid-in-waiting to the Dragon Princess Otohime," the turtle said. "She wishes to thank you herself for saving my life."

The giant turtle takes Urashima down to the bottom of the sea

As soon as they set eyes on each other, Urashima and the princess fell in love. She begged him to stay, telling him, "In this kingdom you will never grow old."

Three years passed and Urashima and the princess were very happy. Just one thing spoiled Urashima's contentment – worry about his mother. One day he asked Princess Otohime if he could visit her.

"If you go," she replied sadly, "you will not return." Urashima pleaded and at last she gave in. She placed a small casket in his hand, saying, "Keep this safe, and never open it. If you do this, the turtle will meet you at the seashore and bring you back to me."

Urashima promised not to open the box. He seated himself on the turtle's back and the creature took him back to the beach he knew so well. But everything had changed. As he walked through his village, Urashima could not see anyone or anything he recognized. Where his home had been, only the stone washbasin and the garden steps remained. After a while he asked an old man if he had ever heard of a fisherman named Urashima.

"Don't you know the legend?" the old man replied. "It's said that Urashima lived in this village three hundred years ago, but he went down to the dragon kingdom under the sea and never came back."

"What happened to his mother?" asked Urashima.

"She died the day he left," the old man replied.

ISLES OF THE DRAGON
The Japanese word for palace of the dragon king is *ryugu* or *ryukyu* – the same as the name given to a long chain of islands running southwest from the Japanese coast across the East China Sea. Perhaps the beautiful Ryukyu Islands, the "palaces" of Li, mythical dragon ruler of the deep, were the setting for Urashima's love affair with Li's daughter, the dragon princess.

The dragon king's palace   *Princess Otohime*   *Urashima*

Urashima opens the box – and his body crumbles to dust

Sad that Urashima must leave her, the princess gives him a box, which he promises not to open

A PARTING GIFT
As Japanese kimonos had no pockets, little boxes, tucked into a sash (*obi*) worn around the waist, were often used for carrying small items. This jewel box, inlaid with mother of pearl, dates from the 12th century AD.

Urashima could not believe his ears. "I am Urashima," he cried, "and I've only been away three years, not three hundred!"

He took out the box, saying, "Look, this was a parting gift from the dragon princess." In his haste, he forgot the dragon princess's warning, and opened the box. There was nothing in it but a puff of smoke. And as the smoke escaped, the weight of years fell on Urashima. His skin wrinkled, his legs gave way, and his body crumbled to dust.

Why the Sea Moans

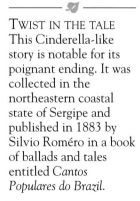

The queen's prayers are answered and she has a daughter, Maria, around whose neck coils a snake, Dona Labismina

---

TWIST IN THE TALE
This Cinderella-like story is notable for its poignant ending. It was collected in the northeastern coastal state of Sergipe and published in 1883 by Silvio Roméro in a book of ballads and tales entitled *Cantos Populares do Brazil*.

ONCE UPON A TIME there was a queen who had been married for a long time but had never had a child. She prayed, "Please God, let me give birth, if only to a snake!" God heard her prayer and she gave birth to a baby daughter. Around the child's neck, a snake was tightly coiled.

The princess was named Maria, and she made a friend of the snake, whose name was Dona Labismina. They used to walk along the seashore and the snake would leave Maria's neck and play in the waves; but if Labismina did not soon return and curl around her neck again, the princess would start to cry.

One day, the snake went into the sea and did not come back. But she told Maria that if she was ever in danger, she should call for her.

Some years later, the queen of a rich neighbouring kingdom fell ill. On her deathbed, she took a ring from her finger and gave it to her husband, the king. "If you ever marry again," she whispered, marry a princess whose finger fits this ring – not too slack and not too tight." With these words, she died.

The king, an old, ugly, evil-tempered man used to getting his own way, at once resolved to marry again. He sent the ring to all the princesses of all the kingdoms: but the ring didn't fit any of them.

At last only Princess Maria had not tried the ring. The old king called on her and roughly put the ring on her finger. To Maria's horror – but to her parents' delight, as the vile old king was immensely rich – it fitted just right. The king told Maria he would marry her without delay.

Maria was so unhappy; she cried all the time. She went to the seashore and called for Labismina, and the snake came. Maria told her what was wrong, and the snake said, "Don't worry. Tell the king you will only marry him if he gives you a dress the colour of the field with all its flowers."

Maria's parents

The king

The ring fits Maria's slender finger

The princess did as she was told, and the king was very annoyed. But so struck by her beauty was he that he told her he would search for such a dress. And, though it took him a long time, he found one.

Then the princess went to Labismina, who told her, "Tell him that you will only marry him if he gives you a dress the colour of the sea with all its fishes."

The princess did so, and the king was even more vexed than before. But though it took him a long time, at last he found one.

The princess went again to Labismina, who told her, "Tell him that you will only marry him if he gives you a dress the colour of the sky with all its stars."

She did so, and, though the king was angrier than anyone had ever seen him, he promised to look for one. He took even longer than before, but at last he found just such a dress.

ON THE SHORE
Sergipe is Brazil's smallest state. The beaches near its capital, Aracajú, may have helped inspire the seashore setting of parts of this tale.

Labismina

Fearing she will have to marry the ugly old king, Maria sails away, taking with her three beautiful dresses

LUSCIOUS BLOOM
A magical dress featuring all the country's flowers would feature many spectacular blooms, such as this orchid from central Brazil.

The desperate princess ran to the sea and boarded a ship, which Labismina had got ready. Labismina said, "Sail away in this ship, land wherever it takes you, and you will marry the prince of that kingdom. On your wedding day, come to the sea, and call my name three times. Then I will be disenchanted, and I will be a princess, too."

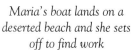

The palace

Maria's boat lands on a deserted beach and she sets off to find work

She is put in charge of the king's hens

When a festival is held, Dona Labismina makes sure that Maria makes a big impression

Maria

The prince

HARD TIMES
Northeastern Brazil, from where this story comes, has many very poor areas. Only in fairy tales would Maria have found work so easy to come by.

The prince sees Maria for the first time

The prince sees Maria for the second time

Maria, in her sea-coloured dress

So Maria left, and where her ship stopped she went ashore. She had nothing to live on, so she went to the palace and begged for a job – she was put in charge of the king's hens.

After a while, there was a three-day festival in the town. Everyone in the palace went, except Maria, who was told to mind the hens. But, after everyone had gone, she put on her dress the colour of the field with all its flowers, asked Labismina for a beautiful carriage, and went to the festival herself.

He falls deeply in love, but no one knows who the mysterious girl is

Everyone gasped and gaped to see such a pretty girl, for no one recognized her. The prince, the king and queen's son, fell head over heels in love. But Maria left before the festivities ended, and by the time the royal family had returned to the palace, she was back in her old poultry-maid's gown. She heard the prince say, "Mother, did you see that lovely girl at the festival? I wish I could marry her! Don't you think she looked rather like our poultry maid?"

PARTY DRESS
The wonderful dresses Maria wears to the fiesta are typical of the beautiful prints worn by many of the women of northeastern Brazil.

"That ragged, dirty creature?" replied the queen.

Later the prince went up to Maria and said, "Poultry maid, at the festival today I saw a girl who looked rather like you!"

"Oh! Prince, don't make fun of me," answered Maria.

Next day there were more festivities and Maria went again, wearing her dress the colour of the sea with all its fishes. The prince fell even deeper in love, but nobody could tell him her name.

On her wedding day, Maria is so very happy…

FIESTA!
In Brazil, festivals such as Carnival, with traditional music and samba dancing, often go on for several days. In smaller towns they are often held in the main square in front of the church.

On the third day, Maria wore her dress the colour of the sky with all its stars. The prince gave her a jewel on the church steps. When he returned to the palace, the love-sick prince took to his bed and refused to touch any food. Finally the queen asked the poultry maid to make him some broth.

The prince gives his love a jewel, which he later finds in some broth made by the poultry maid

Maria sent some to the prince, and placed the jewel he had given her in the bowl. When the prince stirred the broth, he found the jewel. He leapt out of bed crying, "I'm cured! I'm going to marry the poultry maid!"

The queen sent for Maria, who arrived wearing her dress the colour of the sky. Maria and the prince were married that very day.

Carried away by her own happiness, Maria forgot to go down to the seashore and call three times for her faithful Dona Labismina. So Labismina has never been freed from her enchantment.

And that is why the sea moans.

SOUND OF THE SEA
In a later version of this story by Elsie Spicer Ellis, published in 1917, Maria is given the name Dionysia. At the end, Labismina reproaches the forgetful princess by calling "Dionysia, Dionysia," a sound resembling waves breaking on a beach.

…that she forgets all about her faithful Dona Labismina

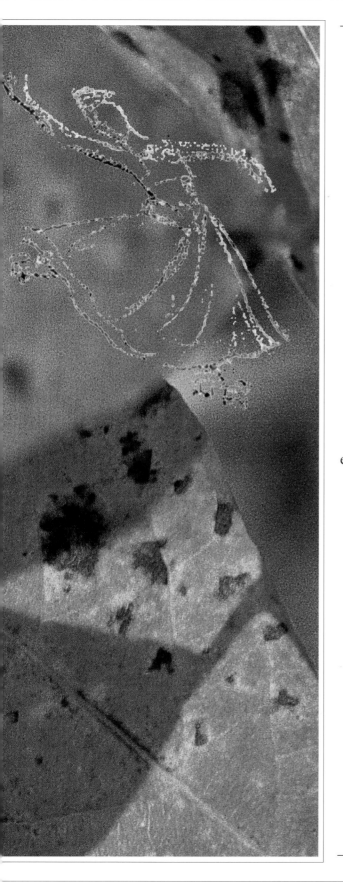

Riches & Rags

Fairy tales were originally told and listened to by poor people, and so it is not surprising that so many feature poor heroes hoping to make their fortunes. Sometimes they strike it rich through pure luck, like the fortune-teller Cricket, or by accidentally making a princess laugh, like Lazy Jack; sometimes they win through wit, like the heroine of "The Poor Girl Who Became Queen," or sly cleverness, like the Ash Lad in "That's a Lie!". More often, however, it is goodness, bravery, or fidelity that is eventually rewarded, usually by magic, as in "The Wonderful Brocade". Of course, as the drunken old skipper of "Easy Come, Easy Go" demonstrates, a chest full of money can be lost just as quickly as it can be won, while the grasping Fisherman's Wife emphasizes that even the best run of good luck can be pushed too far.

The Fisherman's Wife asks for too much and she and her husband find themselves back in their pigsty

Rumpelstiltskin

TALE SPINNING
The spinning and sewing rooms of castles and houses were storytelling centres. The work, done by women, was dull, and stories helped pass the time. So it is not surprising that so many tales mention spindles, spinning wheels, needles, and sewing.

FOOLS' GOLD
This 16th-century engraving shows alchemists at work, trying to change "base" material – perhaps lead or dung – into pure gold. Many noblemen employed alchemists in the vain hope of becoming rich. If only Rumpelstiltskin had been around to help!

A POOR MILLER ONCE boasted that his daughter could spin straw into gold. His wild words came to the ears of the king, who ordered the girl to be brought to the palace. He shut her in a room filled with straw and said, "Spin this straw into gold by morning, or I will have you put to death."

The poor girl burst into tears. Suddenly the door opened and a little man entered. "Why are you crying?" he asked.

"Because I have to spin this straw into gold," she sobbed. "And I can't do it!"

"What will you give me if I do it for you?"

"My necklace," said the miller's daughter eagerly.

The little man took her necklace and sat down at the spinning wheel… By morning all the reels were full of gold. When the king saw this, his heart filled with greed. He shut the miller's daughter in a bigger room filled with straw, and commanded her to spin all of it into gold before morning, if she valued her life.

The miller

The king orders the miller's daughter to spin straw into gold

A strange little man appears who offers to do the work for the girl if she gives him her necklace

Once again the girl burst into tears, and the little man appeared and asked, "What will you give me if I do it for you?"

"My ring," she replied.

The little man took her ring and sat down at the spinning wheel…

The king's heart leapt when he saw all the gold. He shut the girl in an even bigger room filled with straw and told her: "If you can spin all this straw into gold, I will make you my wife. But if you fail, you will be put to death."

Once more the little man came to the miller's daughter and asked her, "What will you give me if I do it for you?"

"I have nothing left to give," she sobbed.

The little man said, "Promise me that if you become queen, you will give me your first child, and I will spin the straw into gold."

The miller's daughter had no choice but to agree.

When, next morning, the king saw all the gold, he thought, "I'll never find a better wife!" So the miller's daughter became his queen.

THE CHANGELING
"A living soul is more precious than riches," says Rumpelstiltskin. It was once believed that fairies snatched away children. Sometimes a gloomy fairy child, called a changeling, would be left in the human child's place. If the changeling could be made to laugh, the fairies would return the stolen child.

The little man sets to work and fills reel after reel with gold thread. In the morning, the king is delighted

A year later, the queen gave birth to a fine boy. As she nursed him, she never gave a thought to the little man. But one morning, there he was, saying, "Give me what you promised."

"When I made that promise, I was poor, and had nothing else to give you," the queen replied. "But now I can make you rich beyond your dreams. What use is my baby to you?"

"A living soul is more precious than riches," replied the little man. "I will have what I was promised."

The king resolves to make the girl his queen

"Give me what you promised," says the little man

GNOME NAMES
Rumpelstiltskin goes by
many names in many
parts of the world,
including Panczimanczi
(Hungary), Purzinigele
(Austria), Whuppity
Stoorie (Scotland),
Ricdin-Ricdon (France),
Tom Tit Tot (England),
Trit a Trot or Even Trot
(Ireland), and Trwtyn-
Tratyn (Wales).

The queen begged and beseeched, and at last he said, "If in three days you can find out my name, you may keep your baby."

The queen lay awake all night thinking what the creature's name might be. When he came to her room the next morning, she asked, "Is your name Caspar?"

"That is not my name," the little man replied.

"Melchior?"

"That is not my name."

"Balthazar?"

"That is not my name."

She tried every name she had ever heard of, but the answer was always, "That is not my name."

On the second day she sent her servant out to look for unusual names. She tried them all, but the little man always replied, "That is not my name."

On the third day the servant came back and said, "I have not been able to find a single new name. But as I was walking through the forest, I came to a high hill. There I saw a hut. Nearby a fire was burning and a little man was capering about, singing:

"Today I'll brew, tomorrow bake,
After that the child I'll take.
I'll brew today and bake tomorrow;
The poor queen's heart will break from sorrow.
For I know neither sin nor shame,
And Rumpelstiltskin is my name."

Next morning the little man asked the queen, "Your Majesty, what is my name?"

"Is it Tom?"

"That is not my name."

"Is it Dick?"

"That is not my name."

"Is it Harry?"

"That is not my name."

"Well, could it be Rumpelstiltskin?"

"The Devil told you that!" the little man screamed, and he stamped his right foot so hard that his whole leg sank into the ground. In a terrible fury, he took his left foot in both hands and pulled so hard he tore himself in two.

*Rumpelstiltskin shouts out his name, unaware
that one of the queen's servants is watching*

✍ *Cricket, the Fortune-Teller* ✍

A BUTLER, A MAID, AND A COOK once stole a ring from a king. The king longed to get it back and put up a notice that read, "Fortune-Teller Wanted."

A poor, hungry sailor called Cricket saw the notice and thought, "That's a way to get three meals a day." He went to the king and claimed he was a fortune-teller. The king told Cricket about the missing ring and begged him to use his powers to find it.

Next morning, the butler brought Cricket breakfast. Cricket, who only had thoughts for his three meals, murmured, "Here's one!"

The guilty butler ran out. At midday, the maid brought Cricket's lunch. Cricket, who was still very hungry, said, "Here's the second one." The maid left, shaking with fear.

At dinnertime, the cook took Cricket his meal. Cricket said with satisfaction, "And here's the third!"

The cook flung himself at Cricket's feet. "Please, sir, have mercy! I'll give you fifty dollars if you don't tell the king we stole the ring!"

Cricket, who was a smart fellow when his stomach was full, laughed and said, "Give me the money and put the ring in the turkey's crop."

Then Cricket went to the king. "I know where your ring is," he announced. Come into the yard." When they got there, Cricket pointed at the turkey. "Cut off its head and look in its crop." When the turkey's head was cut off, there, sure enough, was the king's ring.

The king showered Cricket with gifts and threw a party so all his friends could meet his wonderful fortune-teller. "Ask him anything you like," said the king. "He's sure to know it."

One of the guests snatched up a cricket from the grass and, turning to Cricket, asked, "What do I have in my hands?"

Cricket had no idea. "Come on," said the king's friends.

"Th-that's t-t-too easy," he stammered.

"It better be," growled the king, "or the turkey won't be the only creature to lose its head today."

Cricket saw all was lost. "Poor Cricket," he sighed. The guest opened his hands and out jumped the cricket! The proud king made Cricket rich, and he had three meals a day for the rest of his life.

The wire bends,
And the story ends.

LUCKY GUESSES
This is a Trinidadian version of an international type of tale known as "Doctor Know-All", after a story by the Brothers Grimm. Stories of lucky guesses are popular all over the world – perhaps the poor people who told them could only imagine making a fortune by luck. Pictured above is a painting of Trinidad by Albert Goodwin.

Cricket

The king

The king's guest asks Cricket to tell him what he is holding in his hands

Mushkil Gusha

ONCE UPON A TIME there lived a thorn-cutter, his wife, and daughter. One day they had no food left, so the thorn-cutter went into the desert to cut thorns to sell. He did not return until late in the evening, when he found the door of the house tight shut. He was so tired he fell asleep outside by his bundle of thorns. Next morning he went back into the desert, and that night, too, came home late and had to sleep outside the door.

On the third night, he found the door tight shut again. By this time he was so wracked with hunger and thirst he sank to the ground. His head spinning, he thought he heard a man say, "Thorn-cutter, look! Out in the desert someone is giving away bread and rice!" The thorn-cutter staggered off into the desert, but could find no one, and when he got home, someone had set fire to his thorns and they were now just a heap of blackened twigs. He lay down and wept.

"What's the matter with you?" said a stranger. The thorn-cutter explained what had happened and the stranger said, "Say seven prayers, shut your eyes, and get up on my horse behind me."

The stranger rode to a place covered with pebbles of all shapes and sizes and said, "Pick up as many as you want."

The thorn-cutter didn't want any pebbles, but he filled his sack and pockets with them out of politeness.

LAND OF THIRST
The setting for this story is the harsh desert of Iran, where little grows but thorn bushes and the occasional acacia tree.

GUARDIAN ANGEL
This fairy tale mingles folk belief with religion. Mushkil Gusha, is a mysterious, magical horseman similar in appearance to the warrior above. He brings great good fortune but expects loyalty in return.

Mushkil Gusha

The stranger tells him to pick up pebbles from the desert and take them home

A thorn-cutter encounters a stranger, Mushkil Gusha

The stranger took him home and said, "Say seven prayers, open your eyes, and dismount. Never forget Mushkil Gusha, Remover of Difficulties. Every Friday, tell the story of Mushkil Gusha, and give away dates and raisins in his memory."

The thorn-cutter promised faithfully to do so. Then he dismounted and knocked at his door. His wife and daughter let him in and he told them what had happened. After he had dumped the pebbles in a pile in the corner of the room, he went to bed.

Later that night, the thorn-cutter and his wife were awoken by a bright light, like pure moonlight, coming from the pile of pebbles. To their amazement, the pebbles had turned into precious stones!

The next day, the thorn-cutter's wife took one of the gems to sell to a jeweller at the bazaar. The man said, "Ten gold coins." The wife, who had never owned anything worth so much as ten copper coins in her whole life, said, "Don't joke with me." So the jeweller offered her twenty gold coins. "Don't joke with me," said the wife. And so it went, till at last the exasperated wife said, "Just give me what it's worth!" The jeweller gave her a hundred gold coins.

After that, the thorn-cutter and his family wanted for nothing. When his daughter wanted to live in a palace, he built one for her, right opposite the palace of the princess.

SHOPPING CENTRE
The bazaar, where the thorn-cutter's wife sells jewels, is a feature of Middle Eastern towns. It is a street of stalls and shops that sell everything from antiques to foodstuffs. Bargaining over prices is all part of the fun.

The man's wife and daughter

The man's wife sells a jewel at the bazaar

The princess

The pebbles turn into jewels

The thorn-cutter builds a palace opposite that of the princess

The thorn-cutter's daughter

The princess

While swimming, the princess hangs her necklace in a tree

The listener

When the necklace is lost, the thorn-cutter is blamed – until a man listens to the story of Mushkil Gusha

The next day, the necklace is found and the thorn-cutter freed, thanks to Mushkil Gusha

LUCKY STORY
When this story was recorded, in 1919, poor women used to fast on a Thursday and tell the story of Mushkil Gusha to a child on a Friday evening for good luck.

The princess wanted to know who had built such a splendid palace opposite hers. She asked the thorn-cutter's daughter to come on a picnic. They rode out to a lake, ate lunch, and went for a swim. The princess hung her necklace in the fork of a tree and the two girls played in the water all afternoon.

Next morning, the princess missed her necklace. "The thorn-cutter's daughter must have stolen it," she said. All the thorn-cutter's possessions were confiscated and he was put in the stocks for everyone to mock.

"I haven't felt so miserable since the night Mushkil Gusha first came," he said to himself. Then he remembered with shame that it was a Friday evening, and that although he had promised to tell the story of Mushkil Gusha every Friday, he had never done so.

At his feet he noticed a copper coin. He held it out to passers-by, crying "Take this coin to buy dates and raisins, and hear the tale of Mushkil Gusha, Remover of Difficulties." Nobody would stop.

At last a man came along who was visiting the bazaar to buy a shroud for his dying son. The man thought, there is nothing I can do for my son; it will be an act of kindness to hear this poor wretch's tale. So he bought some dates and raisins with the thorn-cutter's coin and listened to the story of Mushkil Gusha.

When the man got home, he discovered that his son had miraculously recovered. And next morning a maidservant of the princess happened to go to the lake. Looking into the water, she saw the necklace. But when she put her hand in to grasp it, it vanished. Then she sneezed, and, raising her eyes, saw the necklace dangling in the tree, where it had been all the time. The thorn-cutter was freed and given back his riches and his palace.

May God, who granted the thorn-cutter's desire, grant also the desires of all mankind. Hail, Mushkil Gusha!

❧ *I Ate the Loaf* ❧

THREE MEN – two from the city and one from the country – set out on a pilgrimage to Mecca and agreed to share their food on the journey. But they didn't take enough with them, and at last all they had left was the flour to make one small loaf. As the loaf was baking, the men from the city fell to talking. "There isn't enough bread for three," said one.

"We need a plan," said the other. They put their heads together and then said to the countryman, "There isn't enough bread for all of us. So let us leave it till the morning, and the one who has had the most wonderful dream shall eat it." And the countryman agreed.

While the countryman bakes the loaf, the men from the city are scheming

However, when the two city-dwellers were asleep, the crafty countryman got up and ate the loaf.

In the morning, the countryman woke first, but lay as if asleep. He overheard the city dwellers muttering to each other. "I'll say I dreamed that two angels took me off to heaven," one said.

"And I'll say I dreamed that two angels took me off to hell," said the other.

Then the countryman pretended to wake. "What! Are you back so soon?" he exclaimed.

"What do you mean?" asked the city-dwellers.

"Why, I dreamed two angels came and took one of you to heaven and the other to hell. I didn't expect either of you to come back, so I ate the loaf!"

One man "dreams" of going to heaven

The other "dreams" of going to hell

The countryman "dreams" that both have died

HOLY CITY
Mecca, in Saudi Arabia, is the birthplace of the prophet Muhammad and the holiest city of Islam, the Muslim faith. Muslims, like the characters in this story, are expected to make a pilgrimage (*hajj*) to Mecca at least once in their lives. Pilgrims gather at the Great Mosque complex, pictured here.

———— ❧ ————

CROWD PLEASER
This tale comes from a medieval Latin collection by Petrus Alfonsus of Aragon. The story is also popular in both Arabic and in Jewish traditions, and is well known in many other cultures. It can easily be adapted so that the wily bread-eater is of the same background as the people listening to the story.

The Girl Who Combed Pearls

The girl's mother bequeaths her a magic towel and comb

Every time she uses the comb, pearls fall from her hair

Her sailor brother takes some of the pearls to show to the king of a faraway land

GOLDEN MOUTH
In other versions of this story, the girl has the gift of dropping gold or jewels from her mouth when she speaks. But from her jealous rival's mouth fall only toads.

THERE ONCE lived a woman who had a daughter and a son who was a sailor. One day the mother fell ill. She called her daughter to her and gasped, "I've nothing to give you but this towel and this comb. Use them and think of me." Then she died. From that day on the girl always dried herself with her mother's towel and combed her hair with her mother's comb. Each time she did so, pearls fell like tears from her hair and her skin. She told her brother, who declared, "I'll take these pearls on my next voyage and sell them."

He sailed to a faraway land and showed the pearls to the king. He also told him about his sister and her wonderful towel and comb.

"Not only do I want these pearls," the king exclaimed, "I want to see your sister, too. If what you say is true, I'll marry her. But if it's false, I'll put you to death."

The brother sailed home happily. His sister was so delighted she couldn't resist telling her witchy neighbour the news: "I'm going to be a queen!"

"Since you're going to be so grand," her neighbour replied, "you won't mind my daughter and me coming along, too."

On the voyage, the neighbour gave the girl poison and she fell down in a faint. Her heart was stilled; not a breath stirred in her body.

She was buried at sea by her brother, who wept bitterly.

"Without my beloved sister, we must turn back, or the king will have my head," he sighed.

"And lose a fortune?" snapped the neighbour. "Why not pretend my daughter is your sister? She can take the towel and the comb and the king need never know." Reluctantly, the brother agreed.

They reached port and went to the king's palace. The sailor presented the neighbour's daughter to the king, saying, "I have brought my sister to be your wife."

244

"First let me see her comb pearls from her hair," the king replied.

The neighbour's daughter took out the comb, but instead of pearls, showers of dandruff speckled the carpet. The furious king ordered the brother to be thrown into prison to await execution.

That day, the palace cook went down to the sea to catch fish. On the shore lay a dead whale. As he approached, he heard a voice crying, "Let me out!" He cut open the whale's belly – and out stepped a beautiful girl. She told the cook a strange story indeed. He didn't know what to think, so he hid her in an upstairs room at the palace. There she spent her time gazing sadly from a tiny window.

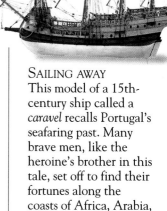

SAILING AWAY
This model of a 15th-century ship called a *caravel* recalls Portugal's seafaring past. Many brave men, like the heroine's brother in this tale, set off to find their fortunes along the coasts of Africa, Arabia, the Orient, and the spice islands of the East Indies.

The palace cook cuts open the dead whale's belly – and a beautiful girl crawls out

One day she saw her brother's dog, Cylindra. "How is my brother?" she called. "Waiting to die," the dog replied.

Cylindra, the dog

From her window at the palace, the girl sees her brother's dog, and asks it for news of him

The girl confided in the cook, who told the king everything.

Next day, he and the king hid and waited. They heard the girl ask, "Cylindra, how is my brother?" This time the dog replied, "He will die today."

Then the king asked the girl to comb her hair with her mother's magic comb. When she did so, pearls cascaded onto the floor. The king married her and set her brother free.

The scheming neighbour and her daughter were killed in his place.

WHALE OF A TIME
Being swallowed by a whale is a fate the heroine of this story shares with the wooden puppet Pinocchio. Created by Italian Carlo Collodi in 1883, he is pictured here by Charles Folkard.

"That's a Lie!"

PRIZE LIE
Lying contests are a staple of folktales the world over, but this particular kind is especially common in Scandinavia. In England, the story goes that a certain village held a lying contest. A bishop, passing by, scolded the competitors, saying, "For my part, I never told a lie in my life." They immediately gave him the prize!

CHEESE-MAKING
A Scandinavian woman strains digestive juices from a calf's stomach to ferment milk into cheese. Cheeses made by traditional methods were tiny in comparison with those mentioned by the fibbing hero and heroine of this tale.

ONCE UPON A TIME a king had a daughter who was a terrible fibber. The king said that if any man could out-fib her and get her to say, "That's a lie!" that man could have her for his wife, and half the kingdom besides. Many young men came to try their luck, but their feeble stories just prompted the princess to wilder and wilder lies of her own.

At last there came three brothers, who all wanted to have a go. The first went into the castle boasting and came out in a sulk; the second went in bragging and came out in a temper. The princess hadn't listened to a word they had said, but just sat there spinning stories.

Finally the youngest brother, the Ash Lad, strolled into the magnificent castle yard. Presently the princess came.

"Not much of a place you've got here," the Ash Lad said to her.

"Well I bet you've nothing to match it," she snapped. "Why, when two shepherds stand at opposite ends of this yard and blow their ram's horn trumpets, one can't hear the other!"

"Oh, ours is far bigger," said the Ash-lad. "When we've sheared a sheep we just make it walk around the yard and by the time it gets back, it's ready to be sheared again!"

The Ash Lad and the princess are soon trading tall stories in the castle yard

"I dare say!" said the princess. "But at least you haven't got such a huge ox as ours. You can sit a man on each horn and they can't touch each other with a shepherd's crook!"

"That's nothing," said the Ash Lad. "If two men sit on *our* ox's horns and blow ram's horn trumpets, they can't hear one another!"

"I dare say," she said, frowning, "but you don't have as much milk as we do, I'll be bound. We've so much, we milk our cows into great pails, empty them into huge tubs, and make cheeses as big as carts!"

"Do you?" replied the Ash Lad. "We milk our cows into great tubs, put the tubs in carts, empty them into great brewing vats, and make cheeses the size of houses. We used to have an old brown mare to tread the cheese while it was making, until she fell in and we lost her. But it was all right, because after we'd been eating that cheese for seven years, we found her inside it, alive and kicking. Her backbone was broken, but I took a fir sapling and made her a new backbone out of that, so she was right as rain. Well, that sapling grew into a fine fir tree, and I climbed right up to heaven by it. And when I got there, I saw the Virgin Mary sitting and spinning the foam of the sea into pig's-bristle ropes. Just then, the fir tree broke, and I couldn't get down; so the Virgin Mary let me down by one of the ropes, and I slipped straight down into a fox's hole. Who should I find there but my mother and your father, cobbling shoes! Just as I stepped in, my mother gave your father such a box on the ear it made his whiskers curl."

"That's a lie!" said the princess. "My father never did any such thing!"

And that's how the Ash Lad won the princess for his wife, and half the kingdom besides.

The Virgin Mary

The Ash Lad

The Ash Lad's mother gives the princess's father a bang on the ear

The Ash Lad slips down the Virgin Mary's pig's-bristle rope and slips straight into a fox's hole

❧ *The Boat That Sailed on Land* ⚐

THERE WAS ONCE an old couple with three sons. The king proclaimed that whoever could make a boat that could sail on land could marry his daughter, so the eldest son set off for the forest to build his ship. There he met an old woman who asked what he was making. "Wooden plates, witch," he snapped.

"You are, too," said the old woman. And however hard he worked, all he made were wooden plates. The second brother rudely told the old woman he was making wooden spoons, and that was all *he* made. When the youngest brother, Jean, went to the forest, the old woman asked him the same question.

"I'm making a boat that can sail on land," he said politely.

"I wish you well," she answered, and wandered off.

Jean set to work. The old woman came by at sunset just as he was hammering in the last nail. "The boat is finished," he cried.

"But there are no sails," she said.

Jean didn't know where to find sails, but the old woman said, "Gather all the rags you can find and bring them to me tomorrow."

Next morning, she turned the rags into glorious sails and Jean went sailing over land to the king's palace.

On the way he met a man lying by a dried-up spring.

"What are you doing?" asked Jean.

"I've drunk this spring dry and I'm waiting for it to fill," came the reply. "My name is Bold Drinker."

"Come and sail with me," said Jean.

With her magic wand, the old woman turns Jean's rags into sails

---

⚐

IMMIGRANT STORY
This story was collected in French patois from the Old Mines area of Missouri by Joseph Médard Carrière in 1934. The French-speaking residents are descended from immigrants that came from Acadia in Canada to old Louisiana in the 18th century. In Europe the tale is also known as "The Extraordinary Companions" and "Six Go Through the Whole World". In some versions the boat flies.

The king's palace

Hoping to marry the princess, Jean sails his magic boat to the king's palace with his companions – Bold Drinker, Greedy Eater, Sharp Hearer, Fast Runner, and Great Blower

Soon they met a man who was licking stones.

"These stones used to be part of an oven, and you can still taste the bread," said the man. "My name is Greedy Eater."

"Come and sail with me," said Jean.

Then they met Great Blower, who was blowing right across the ocean to turn a windmill's sails, and Sharp Hearer, who was listening to corn growing, and Fast Runner, who was running races with rabbits. They all went with Jean to see the king.

The king was not keen to give his daughter to a raggedy young fellow like Jean. He said that first Jean must find a man who could drink his cellar dry. Bold Drinker emptied every barrel!

Then the king challenged Jean to find someone who could eat a feast laid for a hundred. Greedy Eater did so and still wasn't full!

Then Jean had to find someone who could race the princess to the spring and back. Fast Runner set off, and was halfway back before the princess had even reached the spring. So he lay down for a little rest. Jean said, "Where's he got to?" Sharp Hearer put his ear to the ground and said, "I can hear him snoring. He's fallen asleep and the princess has passed him."

RIVERBOAT QUEEN Steamboats still operate on the Mississippi River to this day. Now they only ferry tourists, but in the 19th century "Riverboat Queens" were a vital mode of transport. Perhaps the big wheel helped to inspire the amphibious boat of this story.

Bold Drinker

Greedy Eater

Sharp Hearer

Great Blower

Fast Runner

No challenge is too great for Jean's friends: Bold Drinker drinks the king's cellar dry; and Greedy Eater eats enough for a hundred!

Great Blower said, "Leave it to me." He blew the princess right back to the spring, and woke up Fast Runner.

Jean and the princess were married, and Bold Drinker, Greedy Eater, Fast Runner, Sharp Hearer, and Great Blower lived with them for the rest of their days.

If Jean wants to marry the princess, she must be defeated in a race: Sharp Hearer, Fast Runner, and Great Blower see to that!

Lazy Jack

SILVER COIN
Until the mid-17th century, pennies were made of silver, not copper, so Jack's wage of a penny a day would have been reasonable.

Lazy Jack drops his penny in a stream

A BOY NAMED Jack lived with his mother on a dreary common. They were very poor. The old woman earned a little money sewing and mending, but all Jack did was sit by the fire in winter and laze in the sun in summer. At last she told him, "Work for your porridge, or you'll get none!"

So Jack hired himself to a farmer for a penny for the day. But on the way home Jack dropped the penny as he crossed a stream and lost it. "You stupid boy!" said his mother crossly when he told her what had happened. "You should have put it in your pocket."

"I'll do so next time," said Jack.

Next day, Jack hired himself to another farmer to look after the cows. This farmer gave him a jug of milk for pay, and Jack put the jug in his pocket, as his mother had told him. But as he walked home the jug jiggled in his pocket and milk slopped everywhere. "You ninny!" said his mother. "You should have carried it on your head."

"I'll do so next time," said Jack.

The jug of milk spills in Jack's pocket

Jack's mother scolds her ninny of a son

WRONG AGAIN!
This tale of a simpleton who always gets things wrong has been widely told, especially in Europe. More than a hundred versions have been collected in Ireland and Finland. It has also been found in Asia and Africa. This version comes from Yorkshire, England.

Next day, Jack went to another farmer, who gave him a cream cheese for his day's work. Jack put the cheese on his head, as his mother had told him. But by the time he got home, the soft cheese had run all over his hair. "You featherbrain!" said his mother. "You should have carried it in your hands."

"I'll do so next time," said Jack.

The soft cheese runs all over Jack's hair

Next day, Jack hired himself to a baker, who paid him with a tomcat. Jack carried it carefully in his hands, but before he was halfway home the cat had scratched so much that he had to let it go. "You dolt!" said his mother. "You should have tied it with a string and dragged it along after you."

"I'll do so next time," said Jack.

Next day, Jack hired himself to a butcher, who paid him with a leg of mutton. Jack tied the mutton with a string and dragged it after him. By the time he got home, it was filthy with dust. "You halfwit!" said his mother. "You should have carried it on your shoulders."

"I'll do so next time," said Jack.

Next day, Jack hired himself to another farmer, who gave him a donkey for his trouble. Now Jack was a strong lad, but even so he found it hard to lift the donkey onto his shoulders, and he huffed and puffed as he carried it.

On his way home, Jack passed the mansion of a rich man, whose beautiful daughter had never laughed. The rich man had promised that anyone who could make her laugh could marry her.

The rich man's daughter was looking glumly out of the window when Jack trudged by with the donkey on his shoulders, its legs sticking up in the air. The rich man's daughter couldn't help herself. She hooted with laughter, till people round about came running to see what was the matter. She and Jack were married, and they lived happily in the mansion with her father and Jack's mother, and Jack never had to go to work again.

The tomcat scratches so much that Jack has to let it go

Jack drags the leg of mutton behind him in the dust

Jack trudges by with a donkey on his shoulders

When she sees Jack, the rich man's daughter hoots with laughter

THE LAUGHING BRIDE
A rich girl who has never laughed also appears in "The Golden Goose," by the Brothers Grimm. The hero, Dummling, finds a golden goose. Everyone who touches the goose (except Dummling) becomes stuck to it or each other. When the girl sees Dummling leading a weird procession, she bursts out laughing, and later becomes his bride.

Prince Nettles

FIT FOR A KING
Vajdahunyad Castle,
Budapest, would make a
suitably splendid home
for King Yellow
Hammer in this tale.

THERE WAS ONCE a miller who was so proud he thought an egg should feel honoured if he stepped on it. He had a fine mill, but he thought it wasn't good enough for him, so he set off to look for a better one.

He wandered over seven times seven countries, and at last came to a tumbledown mill on the banks of a river. It was covered in nettles, but the miller began to rebuild it. He worked until his clothes were rags. Then he waited in his marvellous mill for people to ask him to grind their flour. He waited and waited, but no one came.

One day, some huntsmen were chasing a fox. The fox ran up to the miller, crying, "Hide me!" The miller threw an old sack over the fox, and when the hounds came sniffing after it he chased them off. The fox came out from under the sack and said, "Thank you. Now I'll do *you* a good turn. How would you like to get married?"

"But I've only these miserable rags to wear," sighed the miller. "How can I hope to win the hand of *any* girl?"

"I'll find you a bride," the fox said.

The fox travelled over seven times seven countries to the court of King Yellow Hammer. "Your majesty," declared the fox, "I am the ambassador of Prince Nettles. He wishes to marry your daughter

The fox takes a lump of gold to King Yellow Hammer and tells him that Prince Nettles, his master, wants to marry his daughter

A miller waits and waits, but no one wants him to grind their corn

One day the miller saves a fox from hunters

The king's daughter

and sends this gold as a token of esteem. The prince is sorry to send you such a great lump of gold, but it's the smallest piece he has."

"Tell Prince Nettles we can't wait to see him," said the king.

So the fox went back to the miller and said, "Remember, you are Prince Nettles from now on. Come with me, and you shall be married." When the castle of King Yellow Hammer came in sight, the fox said, "That is the home of your bride."

The fox told the miller to take off all his clothes and bathe in the river. Then he ran to King Yellow Hammer and said, "Your majesty, Prince Nettles set out in a carriage so overloaded with gold and jewels that it has toppled into the river and sunk. I have only just managed to rescue the prince naked from the water!"

So King Yellow Hammer sent servants with fine clothes and a carriage to collect Prince Nettles, and after a month the miller and the king's daughter were married. Then the king's daughter said, "My love, take me home to your own castle."

The miller was worried at this, but the fox said, "Leave it to me."

They travelled home through the rich lands of Vasfogu Baba the witch, and everywhere they went, the fox had been before them, bribing the peasants to say that the land belonged to Prince Nettles. Meanwhile the fox visited Vasfogu Baba's castle.

"Tell me why I should not crush your bones as small as poppyseed," said the witch.

"Because the French army is coming!" the fox cried. "We must all hide. Come, I know a place where they will never find you."

The witch went with the fox to a bottomless lake. He pushed her in and she is probably still falling through its black, endless waters. Then the fox returned to the miller and declared, "You were born under a lucky star, for you are the sole heir of Vasfogu Baba, the witch."

And Prince Nettles, his bride, and the fox lived happily ever after.

HELPFUL CAT
This story is similar to the tale of "Puss in Boots" (illustrated here by a 19th-century postcard), which was first published by Frenchman Charles Perrault in 1697.

ON THE DUNGHEAP
In longer versions, an ungrateful Prince Nettles orders the fox to be thrown on a dungheap. But the fox threatens to reveal his secret and the prince asks for forgiveness.

The king's carriage

The fox tricks the king into thinking that Prince Nettles has had an accident

The witch dives into the lake and Prince Nettles takes her castle

❧ The Fly ❧

The rich man says a fly can be the witness to the deal he makes with the boy

VILLAGE ATMOSPHERE
This detail from a 1958 painting by Vietnamese artist Nguyen Van Ty perfectly conveys the village atmosphere of this tale. The humbling of a rich bully is a popular theme all over the world.

ONCE THERE WAS a rich man who lent money to all the poor people in the area at unfairly high rates of interest.

One poor peasant was heavily in debt. So the rich man went to see if he had any valuable possessions to confiscate.

When the rich man got to the peasant's hut, he found the man's little son playing in the yard. "Are your parents at home?" he asked.

"No," said the boy. "My father has gone to cut living trees and plant dead ones, and my mother is at the market selling the wind and buying the moon."

The rich man cajoled the boy and threatened him, but he always answered in the same words. So finally the rich man said, "Look. If you will tell me what you mean, I will forget the debt they owe me, as heaven and earth are my witness."

"Heaven and earth cannot talk," said the boy. "Some living thing should be our witness."

The rich man pointed to a fly that had settled on the door frame. "That fly can be our witness," he said.

So the boy told him, "My father has gone to cut down bamboos and make a fence with them, and my mother has gone to sell fans to buy oil for our lamps."

The rich man laughed. "You are certainly a clever boy," he said.

But a few days later the rich man came back to demand his money. The boy said, "Father, you need not pay." But the rich man denied he had ever made such a promise.

So the case came before the local landowner. The rich man said that he had never *seen* the boy, let alone made him any promise, and the boy said that he had. "It's one person's word against another's," said the landowner. "I can't judge either way without a witness."

"But there was a witness," said the boy. "A fly heard every word."

"A fly!" said the landowner. "Are you making fun of me?"

"No," said the boy. "There was a fly – a big, fat one, sitting on this gentleman's nose."

"You little liar!" shouted the rich man. "It wasn't on my nose, it was on the door frame!"

"Nose or door frame, it doesn't make any difference," said the landowner. "You *did* make the promise, so the debt is paid."

The Endless Tale

ONCE UPON A TIME there was a king who had a very beautiful daughter. Now this king was very fond of stories, and he said that she should marry the man who could tell him an endless tale. Anyone who could not tell an endless tale would be beheaded.

Many rich young men tried to tell an endless tale, but one by one they ran out of story, and one by one they lost their heads. At length a poor man came to court and said he wanted to try his luck.

"By all means," said the king.

The poor man began his tale and this is what he said: "There was once a man who built a barn that covered many acres of land and reached almost to the sky. He built it so well that there was only one hole in the roof, through which a single locust might creep. Then he filled the barn full of corn to the very top. When he had filled the barn, a locust came through the hole in the top and fetched a single grain of corn."

Another locust came...

and another locust came...

and another locust came...

and another locust came...

and another locust came...

and another...

"Call that a story?" cried the king. But the poor man hadn't finished.

"And then," he said, "another locust came and fetched another grain of corn." And the man went on saying "another locust came and fetched another grain of corn" until the whole court was heartily sick and weary of it.

Another locust came and another locust came and another locust came. The king had had enough. "Isn't this story ever going to end?"

"No, your majesty," said the poor man.

"In that case," said the king, "you had better marry my daughter."

And he did, and his beautiful bride made him promise never to tell his endless tale again.

---❧---

NEVER-ENDING STORY
This version of "The Endless Tale" comes from Nottinghamshire, England. Similar stories have been found in many countries. In one from Japan, rats, not locusts, are counted. In another, from Italy, a shepherd carries sheep over a stream.

The poor man's endless tale proves to be truly endless

Shoes That Were Danced to Pieces

A KING HAD A DAUGHTER who wore out seven pairs of shoes every night. He vowed that whoever found out why would win both the princess and half his kingdom; but anyone who tried and failed would die. Many tried, but none succeeded.

One day, a poor boy from the city asked his mother to bake him three loaves of bread for the journey and set out to try his luck. His mother put poison in the loaves, thinking, "It's better he should die on the way, than be cruelly put to death by the king!"

On the way he met a man who asked him for one of the loaves, and in return gave him God's blessing. That was St Anthony. Then he met a woman, who asked him for one of the loaves, and in return gave him a coat of invisibility. That was the Virgin Mary. And lastly he met an old man who asked him for the last loaf and in return gave him a whip. That was God himself.

The king told him to sleep that night in a room next to the princess's. But instead he put on his coat of invisibility and tiptoed into the princess's room. He saw her take six spare pairs of shoes from a wardrobe and slip out of the room. He followed close behind as she stole down the main staircase and out of the palace.

First she came to a gold bush. "Good evening, gold bush," she said.

"Good evening princess, and to your friend," the bush replied.

"I am alone," frowned the princess. She picked a flower and fastened it to her coat and the invisible boy did likewise. Next she came to a silver bush, then to a copper bush, and each time she

RELIGIOUS DIFFERENCE
The Cape Verde Islands were a Portuguese territory and this story reveals Portuguese origins by its mention of Catholic icons such as St Anthony and the Virgin Mary (above). The princess, who dances with "devils", clings to pagan ways; for this reason the boy refuses to marry her.

HILLSIDE HOUSES
The city boy of this story might well have lived in a house like the ones pictured above.

The princess

The princess takes out six pairs of shoes, watched by the invisible boy

The boy's shadow

She picks a flower from a gold, copper, and silver bush

claimed she was alone and each time first she, then her invisible companion, picked a flower.

The princess jumped on a white horse, which took her across a river. But the boy cracked his whip and was there before her.

They arrived at a palace full of devils dancing the night away. The princess danced a waltz and wore out her first pair of shoes; then she danced a mazurka, a reel, a strombolica, a contra-dance, a tango, and a sarabande, until all seven pairs of shoes were worn out. Then she rode on the white horse back to her father's palace. But the boy cracked his whip and was there before her. He rushed up to his room and lay down.

DANCING GIRLS
Tales similar to this have been recorded all over Europe. The Brothers Grimm tell a version titled "The Twelve Dancing Princesses".

A white horse carries the princess across a river

The boy follows her to a palace, where she wears out her shoes dancing with devils

The princess looked in, saw the boy asleep, and felt sure her secret was safe.

In the morning, the king asked his guest if he knew why his daughter wore out seven pairs of shoes every night. To his amazement, the boy replied, "Yes!" And to prove his tale he showed the king the flowers from the gold, silver, and copper bushes.

The king promised he could marry the princess.

"I'll marry no girl who dances with devils," the boy replied, "but give me half your kingdom, and me and my mother will be happy the rest of our days!"

The flowers prove the boy's story, but he throws them away – and the princess, too!

The Wonderful Brocade

FINE THREADS
The Chinese have excelled at brocade work – weaving raised designs onto cloth – since ancient times. This 19th-century example shows a phoenix on a robe belonging to Empress Dowager Tz'u-hsi.

CHINESE LOOM
Weaving in China began c.2500 BC. Weaving was done using both small hand looms and also large machines like the 19th-century one above.

ONCE UPON A TIME there lived an old widow with three sons. She supported her family by weaving brocades. The animals, birds, and flowers she wove almost seemed alive.

One day when she went to town to sell her work, she saw a wonderful picture in a shop. It showed a big house set in a lovely garden. Just looking at it made her feel happy. Instead of buying rice to eat, she bought the picture.

When she got home, she showed it to her sons. "Look at this beautiful place!" she said. "That's where we should live."

"Only in our dreams," said her eldest son.

"Or perhaps after we die," said her second son.

"If we can't live there, mother," said her youngest son, "why don't you copy the picture? While you're weaving, you'll feel as if you're there."

The widow buys a wonderful picture and decides to weave a copy of it for herself

So his mother took her brightest silk thread and started to weave the wonderful picture in brocade. Day after day she worked, determined to do her best work. Her first two sons were not at all pleased. "We're tired of gathering firewood to buy the family's rice," they grumbled. "Stop this foolishness. Make some brocades to sell!"

"Leave her alone," her youngest son said. "This picture means everything to her. If you're too tired to gather firewood, I'll do it."

The eldest comes upon a mysterious stone horse

So from then on the two boys lounged around all day while their young brother collected firewood and their mother wove.

She worked all day and all night. Weaving in the evening by the flickering fire made her old eyes hurt, but she never stopped. After a year, her tears fell like rain upon the cloth, and where they landed she wove a little river and a pond. After two years, blood fell from her

The widow finishes her brocade, but a breeze snatches it away

The youngest son

Her oldest sons do nothing while the youngest works to support the family

The widow begs her three sons to find her wonderful brocade

eyes onto the cloth, and where it landed she wove a red sun and many flowers. After three years, the brocade was finished.

How beautiful it was! The house had turquoise walls, red pillars, and blue tiles on the roof. There was a garden full of flowers, and in the middle of the garden was a pond full of fish. On one side was an orchard full of fruit and singing birds; on the other a vegetable plot just ready to harvest. Rice and corn grew tall in the fields. A sparkling stream ran past the house and a red sun shone above it.

Delighted with her work, the old woman took the brocade outside to admire it in the sunshine. Suddenly a fierce gust of wind snatched it away and the wonderful brocade disappeared into the sky.

"Find my brocade," she begged her sons. "It means life itself to me!"

Her eldest boy put on his straw sandals and set off eastwards, in the direction the brocade had gone. After a month he came to a mountain cave. A stone horse stood outside, its mouth wide open as if it wanted to eat the red berries that grew on a tree nearby. An old woman appeared and he asked her if she had seen the brocade.

STEED OF STONE
Stone horses like the one in this story are a feature of ancient Chinese royal tombs. This one is at the tomb of Emperor Yang Ding Ging, in Gan Xian.

NATURE SPIRITS
Fairies in Chinese tales are female and beautiful – like the nymphs of Greek mythology. They have some magical powers, such as causing a wind to steal the widow's brocade in this tale. They may be mischievous, but are generally gentle and friendly. In stories, a lucky hero may win a fairy as a bride.

MYSTERIOUS PEAKS
This story is told by the Zhuang of the Guangxi region of southern China. The region has some spectacular "fairy-tale" scenery, such as the huge, teeth-like rocks towering over rolling farmland in this picture.

"It has been stolen by the fairies of the Sun Mountain," came the reply. "To find them, you must pull out two of your teeth and put them in the stone horse's mouth. It will eat the red berries from yon tree and carry you over the Fire Mountain and the Sea of Ice to the Sun Mountain. But if you flinch while crossing the Fire Mountain, you'll be burned to a flake of ash; and if you shiver while crossing the Sea of Ice, you'll be frozen solid!"

The eldest son flinched and shivered even as she spoke, and the old woman said, "Don't go. This is too hard for you. Take this box of gold and spend it wisely."

He took the box of gold, but did not go home, because he didn't want to share it with his family.

Then the middle son set out, and the same thing happened to him as to his brother.

The horse carries the boy through the flames of the Fire Mountain

Finally, the youngest son set out, though he hated to leave his mother alone, lying in bed like a shrivelled stick. When he reached the cave and the old woman offered him a box of gold, he said, "No. I must find my mother's wonderful brocade."

He knocked out two of his teeth and put them in the horse's mouth. The animal immediately came to life and ate the red berries. It carried the boy across the Fire Mountain. Though the fierce flames licked around him, he did not flinch. It carried him across the Sea of Ice. Though the bitter waves lashed him, he did not shiver. And so they came to the Sun Mountain, where he found the fairies in their hall, making a copy of the wonderful brocade. "You can have your mother's brocade back when we have finished," they said.

When darkness fell, the fairies hung from the ceiling a pearl that gave as much light as the sun. The prettiest fairy finished her work and stood back to compare their copy with the widow's work. She saw at once that the copy was not nearly as good and quickly stitched a little picture of herself onto the widow's brocade.

A moment later the youngest son picked up his mother's brocade and galloped away on the magic horse. They crossed the Sea of Ice and the Fire Mountain and soon found themselves back at the cave. The old woman took the teeth from the horse and put them back in the boy's mouth. The horse became cold stone once more.

The boy was soon home again. "Mother! I've got your brocade," he called. "Come outside and see!"

His mother was lying in bed as fragile as a wisp of tinder, but she dragged herself out into the sunshine. As she unfolded the brocade, a gentle breeze billowed under it. The wonderful brocade spread out, growing longer and wider until it covered the ground as far as the eye could see. The family's poor cottage vanished and they found themselves outside the big house from the picture, with its gardens and rich land. A beautiful girl was there with them.

"I am a fairy from the Sun Mountain," she explained. "I embroidered myself onto your brocade because I longed to live in this marvellous place."

So the widow and her youngest son settled down in the big house, and the son married the fairy.

One day, two ragged beggars came to the edge of this magical land. They were the oldest brothers, who had wasted their gold in the

The brocade becomes real and a fairy appears

city. When they saw the beautiful place that had grown from their mother's brocade, they were too ashamed to enter. They stumbled away, dragging their sticks in the dust.

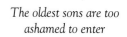

The oldest sons are too ashamed to enter

Easy Come, Easy Go

A shipwrecked old skipper catches a gull

ONCE THERE WAS an old skipper who went to sea, but a whale came and broke his ship to pieces. The old skipper managed to keep afloat by clinging to the broken mast, and after a while the whale came back and threw him onto the beach. There the old skipper found a seagull that had lost its way. He caught the gull and shoved it underneath his jersey.

A farmer came riding along the dyke and saw the old skipper shivering on the shore. "Go up to the farm house," the farmer shouted, "and my wife will give you something to eat and let you dry yourself by the fire."

When the old skipper reached the farmhouse, the farmer's wife was already entertaining the parson, so she wasn't pleased to have an old sailor dripping water all over the place. "You can dry off in the attic," she said. "But I've no food in the house."

However, when the old skipper peeped through a crack in the attic floorboards, he saw the farmer's wife bring out roast meat and three bottles of wine and set them on the table. He then heard her say to the parson, "Bread and water's good enough for my old man, but only the best will do for you."

Just then the farmer came home. His wife hid the meat in the pantry and the wine in the scullery, and the parson scrambled into a chest by the door. The farmer came in and asked, "Where's the old skipper?"

"Upstairs," his wife replied. "He wanted to be in the attic."

"Skipper, come down here!" called the farmer.

The skipper came downstairs with the gull still hidden beneath his jersey. He gave the gull a pinch and it cried out.

"What's that noise?" asked the farmer.

"It's a fortune-teller," said the old skipper. "It says there's roast meat in the pantry."

"Nonsense," said the farmer. "I haven't had roast meat for years." But when the farmer looked, he found a delicious roast.

The skipper gave the gull another pinch, and it cried out again. "What's it saying now?" asked the farmer.

"It says there are three bottles of wine in the scullery."

HIGH-FLYING BIRD
The soaring seagull, a popular symbol of freedom, is a suitable helper for this story's free-spirited sailor.

WATERY LAND
Dykes are a feature of the Dutch countryside, helping to drain the low-lying land or keep the sea at bay.

"Nonsense," said the farmer. "It's so long since I had any wine, I can't remember what it tastes like." But when the farmer looked, he found three bottles of the best wine money could buy.

"Wherever can that have come from?" his wife said nervously.

"The fortune-teller must have put it there," cried the farmer. "What will you take for it?" he asked the old skipper.

"A horse and wagon and that chest," the skipper replied.

The farmer helped the old skipper load the chest, in which the parson was still hiding, onto the wagon. The old skipper gave the farmer the gull and set off in the wagon. As he drove along the dyke, he said aloud, " This chest is no use to me. I'll throw it in the sea."

Inside the chest, the parson groaned. "Now it's making horrible noises," said the old skipper. "I shall definitely throw it in the sea."

"Don't! Please don't!" the panic-stricken parson shrieked. "I'll fill this chest with money if you'll let me out!"

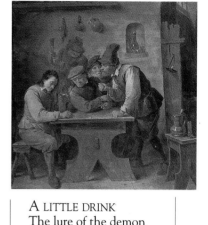

A LITTLE DRINK
The lure of the demon drink, by tradition the ruin of many a sailor, proves too much for the skipper, who celebrates in an inn similar to the one pictured here by David Teniers.

The farmer

The parson in the chest

The old skipper

The parson is so relieved to be let out of the chest that he fills it with money

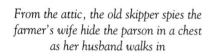

From the attic, the old skipper spies the farmer's wife hide the parson in a chest as her husband walks in

The old skipper swaps his "fortune-telling" gull with the farmer for a horse and wagon and the chest

The old skipper opened the chest and let the parson out, and the parson filled the chest with money. "With all this money, I can buy myself a new boat," the skipper said to himself.

But on the way to buy the boat, he passed an inn. "I'll just have one drink to celebrate," he thought. One drink led to another and, after a week, the old skipper was down to his last penny.

"Ah well," he sighed. "Easy come, easy go."

The old skipper fritters away all the money on beer

❧ *The Fisherman & His Wife* ❧

The fisherman and his wife live in a pigsty

One day the fisherman hooks a giant talking flounder

GOOD-LUCK CHARMS
Fish have ancient associations with good luck and were linked by the first Christians with Jesus, who miraculously fed five thousand people with "five loaves and two fishes". The mosaic above is from a church built near the site of this miracle, near the Sea of Galilee, Israel.

THERE WAS ONCE a fisherman and his wife who lived in a pigsty by the sea. Every day the fisherman went fishing, and the wife stayed at home in the pigsty.

One day the fisherman was sitting with his rod, staring down into the clear water. Suddenly his line dipped down, down into the depths. When he hauled it in, he had caught a huge flounder. The flounder looked him in the eye and said, "Don't kill me. I am not a flounder, but an enchanted prince. Put me back in the water, please."

The cottage

First the flounder gives the fisherman and his wife a cottage to live in, then a castle

The castle

The fisherman had never before heard a fish talk, and he willingly let it go free.

When he got back to the pigsty, he told his wife all about the talking flounder.

"What reward did you ask for?" she said.

"Why, nothing," he replied. "What could we want?"

"Somewhere better to live than this stinking pigsty for a start!" shouted his wife. "You go back this minute and ask that flounder to give us a cottage!"

The fisherman trudged down to the sea and called:

"Flounder, flounder, in the sea,
Come, come, come to me
For my wife, named Ilsabel,
Wants what I want not myself."

The flounder came swimming from the green and yellow waves and said, "What does she want?"

"She wants a cottage. She's fed up with living in a pigsty."

"Go home," said the flounder. "She has it already."

And sure enough, when the fisherman got home, there was his wife sitting on a bench outside the door of a neat little cottage.

For a fortnight the fisherman and his wife lived happily in their new home. But one morning the wife said, "This cottage is so poky. There's scarcely room to breathe. I think the least that flounder could have done, considering you set him free, was to give us a castle."

The fisherman was sent back to the sea to ask for a castle. The water was dark and foaming, but the flounder granted the wish.

When the fisherman got home, he found his wife standing on the steps of a great stone castle. Inside, the floors were paved with gleaming marble and the walls hung with rich tapestries. The furniture was of gold, and liveried servants were everywhere.

The next morning when they awoke and looked out of the window, the fisherman's wife said, "Look at all that country out there. There's no reason why we shouldn't be king of all that. Go and tell the flounder we want to be king."

So the fisherman went back to the sea. This time dark grey waves were breaking on the shore.

"What does she want now?" asked the flounder.

"She wants to be king," said the fisherman, shrugging his shoulders.

"So be it," said the flounder. "She is king already."

When the fisherman got home, his wife was living in an even grander castle, with yet more servants and guards to do her bidding. She was sitting on a high, golden, diamond-studded throne, with a golden crown on her head and a golden sceptre in her hand.

BIG FISH
This popular story, illustrated above by German artist Paul Hey, emphasizes that even the best luck can be pushed too far!

LAP OF LUXURY
This beautiful sitting room in Germany's Neuschwanstein Castle would have satisfied the fisherman's wife's wildest demands – at least for a little while.

The fisherman's wife wants to be king – and her wish is granted

GONE TO POT
This story was contributed to the Grimms' collection by the painter Philipp Otto Runge. Similar tales are found in Scandinavia, Eastern Europe, France, England, and Italy, but the story is most popular in Germany and Russia. In some versions, the couple starts – and ends – living not in a pigsty (above), but in a potty!

"Now you are king," said the fisherman. "Let that be an end to it."

"Nonsense," snapped his wife. "For now I am king, I find time hanging heavy. I want to be emperor." So the fisherman went and asked the flounder to make her emperor. The sea was black and curdled, but the flounder granted the wish.

Soon, even being emperor wasn't grand enough. "I want to be pope," she cried. The fisherman went back to the sea, which was boiling and roaring. "Oh, dear," he said. "The flounder must be sick of granting wishes." But the flounder agreed to make his wife pope.

When he returned, he saw a cathedral surrounded by palaces. Inside was his wife, dressed in gold and sitting on a great throne. All the emperors and kings of the world were lining up to kiss her feet.

"You couldn't ask for anything more," said the fisherman.

"Perhaps not," she replied.

That night, the fisherman slept soundly, but his wife tossed and turned, wondering if there was something even more wonderful she could have asked the flounder for. She woke her husband up at sunrise and declared, "I want to be god."

"You're already pope!" he protested. But she screamed, tore her hair, kicked him, and chased him out of the palace. He ran down to the sea.

A storm was raging and the sea seethed with huge black waves. The sky was a violent, angry red.

Shouting to be heard above the wind, the fisherman cried:

"Flounder, flounder in the sea,
Come, come, come to me,
For my wife, named Ilsabel,
Wants what I want not myself."

"What does she want now?" said the flounder.

"She wants to be god," stammered the fisherman.

"Go to her," said the fish. "You'll find her back in the pigsty." And they are living there still.

The fisherman finds his wife back in the pigsty

The Poor Girl Who Became Queen

THERE WAS ONCE a poor cottager who lived with his daughter. She said he should go to the king and ask for a plot of land so they could grow enough food to live on. "If you will come with me, I will," he said.

So father and daughter set off for the king's palace. The king granted their request right away. Perhaps he was sorry for the poor cottager, or perhaps he liked the sparkle in the daughter's eye.

The cottager and his daughter lived happily on their little farm, till one day they dug up a golden mortar. The man said, "I should take this to the king."

His daughter replied, "Don't. For he will only demand the pestle to go with it."

"Nonsense," he said. "The king will be mighty glad to have the mortar alone!"

How wrong can a person be? The king made a great fuss about the missing pestle, accused the man of stealing it, and threw him in prison. After two days, the jailer came to the king and begged him to let the cottager go. "He's making my life a misery wailing all day and all night 'If only I'd listened to my daughter! If only I'd listened to my daughter!'"

The puzzled king had the cottager brought before him, and the cottager explained how his daughter had warned him what would happen. "Go home," said the king, "and send your daughter to the palace."

When the king met the daughter again, he remembered the sparkle in her eye, and decided to test her to see if she was as clever as she seemed. So he said, "Come back here tomorrow neither clothed nor unclothed, and neither riding nor walking nor being carried."

Next day he waited for her, and soon he heard the distant braying of a donkey. When the donkey came into view, it was pulling a great bundle of fishing nets behind it.

PEASANT QUEEN
Known in the fairy tales of the Brothers Grimm as "The Peasant's Wise Daughter", this retelling is based on a tale collected by Patrick Kennedy in County Wexford (above). More than 680 versions of this story have been collected in Ireland

The wise girl advises her father not to take the golden mortar to the king

267

After passing the king's test, the poor girl becomes his queen

DONKEYS OF IRELAND
Donkeys have been specially bred in Ireland for centuries and were commonly used for carrying goods and hauling loads. This one is pulling a cart that dates back to the mid-19th century.

HUNG OUT TO DRY
The shallow waters around the Irish coast have traditionally been excellent fishing grounds. Nets like those shown drying in this 19th-century photograph would have been ideal for the girl of this story to dress up in.

Wrapped in the nets was the cottager's daughter, naked but perfectly decent, and neither walking nor riding nor being carried.

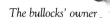

The bullocks' owner

The bullocks' owner refuses to return the man's foal, saying it is their child. The foolish king agrees

She was standing on the net and the donkey was dragging her along. "Brave girl!" laughed the king. "You're the bride for me!" And he married her, just like that.

One day two countrymen came to the palace. One had a horse, a mare, and a foal, and the other had two bullocks. The foal got in among the bullocks, and when its owner tried to get it back, the other man wouldn't let him. "This foal belongs to the bullocks," he said. "Why, you can see how fond they are of each other. It would break those bullocks' hearts to take their child away from them."

The man with the horse and mare complained to the king, but the king, who had never been a farmer, believed the man with the bullocks and let him keep the foal.

The man with the horse and mare remembered that the queen was a cottager's daughter, and he went to her with his problem...

Next day, while the king was out for his morning walk, he found the countryman on his hands and knees in the road, casting a net in the dust. "What are you doing?" he asked.

"Fishing," the man replied.

"You'll not catch any fish on the high road," laughed the king.

"I will, Your Majesty," said the man. "Or, at least, as many fish as you'll get foals from a pair of bullocks."

"Who put you up to this?" roared the king. The man confessed that the queen had told him what to do and say.

Now the king felt that the queen had shown him up to be a fool. He was so angry that he told her, "I can see you're more at home with peasants' quarrels than the duties of a queen, so back to your cottage you shall go. But, since you've been a good wife, I will let you take with you whatever you value most in the palace."

"All right," said she. "But let's have one last meal together."

When the king woke up after that meal he thought he was in a damp, dark prison cell. He called in alarm for his servants, but none came. He called louder still. In came the queen, his wife.

"Where am I?" he asked.

"Why, with me, in the cottage where I was born," she laughed. "You told me I could take whatever I valued most from the palace, so I gave you a sleeping draught and brought *you* along with me!"

Then the king saw what a headstrong fool he had been.

"You are not just clever," he said, "but wise as well. Come home with me and be my queen again."

And back they walked to the palace, arm in arm.

POOR FAMILY'S HOME
Parts of Ireland still contain tumbledown cottages similar to the one the king finds so dismal in this tale. Irish peasants lived hard lives scratching a livelihood from the soil. When crops failed – as in the Potato Famine of the 1840s – disaster and death often followed.

Later, the king finds the man fishing by the roadside, and learns that the queen has made a fool of him

Banished to her bare cottage by the king, the girl turns the tables on him – by tricking him into coming with her!

KINGS OF THE CASTLE
Rich Irish landowners had imposing homes, none more so than Kilkenny Castle. Occupied for centuries by the Butler family, it is one of the most spectacular castles in southeastern Ireland, and would have been a fitting home for the king in this story.

Heroes & Heroines

Courage and steadfastness are two of the most important qualities of a fairy-tale hero and heroine. They are the ones who do and dare. If a magic beanstalk sprouts outside their window, they unhesitatingly climb up it to see what is at the top. If they find themselves married to a murderer, or persecuted by a wicked stepmother, or threatened by a monstrous flying head, they keep their nerve and their wits about them. Though some people think fairy-tale heroines are weak and simpering dolls, this could not be further from the truth. Many tellers of fairy tales were women, and the heroines of many stories are as resourceful and brave as any man – even if, as in "The Girl Who Pretended To Be a Boy", some have to wear boy's clothes to prove it.

Soliday bravely lures the monstrous Man-Crow down from its tree and lets fly with an arrow

Little Red Riding Hood

WISE WORDS
Charles Perrault was the first to write this story down, in 1697. He saw the tale as a warning to children not to talk to strangers, concluding: "From this story one learns that children, Especially young lasses, Pretty, courteous and well-bred, Are wrong to listen to any sort of man."

DOWN IN THE WOODS
This story makes it plain that dangers may be lurking even along the prettiest woodland path, such as this one in the Fôret de Compiègne in northern France.

THERE WAS ONCE A pretty little village girl. Everyone loved her, especially her grandmother, who had made her a red cloak with a hood that she wore so often people used to call her Little Red Riding Hood.

One morning, her mother baked some bread and said to her, "Go and see how your poor old grandmother is, and take her a loaf and a pot of butter."

Straightaway Little Red Riding Hood set off to visit her grandmother, who lived in a village on the other side of some woods. Walking through the woods, she met a wolf.

*On the way through the woods to her grandmother's cottage,
Little Red Riding Hood meets a wolf*

He asked her where she was going, and the poor girl, who did not know that it is dangerous to stop and chat with wolves, said, "I'm taking this loaf and pot of butter to my grandmother."

"Is it far?" asked the wolf.

"She lives in the first house in the village beyond the trees."

"I'd like to meet her, too," said the wolf. "You take the path on the left, I'll take the path on the right, and we'll see who gets there first."

With that, the wolf bounded off down the right-hand path, which led straight to the village. Little Red Riding Hood dawdled along the longer path, stopping to pick her grandmother a pretty little bunch of wayside flowers.

The wolf soon arrived at grandmother's house. He knocked – rat! tat! – on the door.

"Who's there?"

"It's your granddaughter, Little Red Riding Hood," said the wolf, in a high-pitched voice. "I've brought you a loaf and a little pot of butter that my mother has sent you."

The grandmother, who was in bed as she wasn't feeling well, called out, "Lift the latch and let yourself in."

The wolf went into the cottage, leapt upon the poor old woman, and gobbled her up. Then he closed the door and tucked himself up in bed, to wait for Little Red Riding Hood.

Soon she came, and knocked – rat! tat! – at the door.

"Who's there?"

When Little Red Riding Hood heard the wolf's hoarse voice, she was frightened, but then she remembered that her grandmother hadn't been well. Thinking that she must have caught a bad cold indeed, she replied, "It's your granddaughter, Little Red Riding Hood. I've brought you a loaf and a little pot of butter."

The wolf called out, "Lift the latch and let yourself in."

Little Red Riding Hood went into the cottage. The wolf, who was hiding under the bedclothes, shouted, "Put the loaf and butter in the bread bin, and get into bed with me."

So Little Red Riding Hood climbed into bed with the wolf.

"Grandmother! What big arms you have!" she said.

"All the better to hug you with, my dear," came the hoarse reply.

"Grandmother! What big legs you have!"

"All the better to chase you with, my dear!"

"Grandmother! What big ears you have!"

"All the better to hear you with, my dear!"

"Grandmother! What big eyes you have!"

"All the better to see you with, my dear!"

"Grandmother! What sharp teeth you have!"

"All the better to eat you with!"

And the wolf leapt upon Little Red Riding Hood and gobbled her up.

A TASTE OF GRANNY In earlier word-of-mouth tellings, the wolf tricks the heroine into eating some of her dead grandmother. In the end, she escapes by saying she has to go to the lavatory – outside the cottage! In other versions, the wolf is killed by a hunter. However in the 1984 film *A Company of Wolves*, above, the wolves come out on top.

Little Red Riding Hood scrambles into bed with "Grandmother"

The Dancing Water

THERE WERE ONCE three sisters who made their living by spinning thread. The king of the country used to go out after dark and listen at doors and windows to hear what his people were saying. One night he chanced to listen outside the very house where the sisters lived.

The oldest sister said, "If only I could marry the king's butler, I could drink as much as I wanted." The middle one said, "If only I could marry the king's valet, I could have as many clothes as I wanted." And the youngest said, "If only I could marry the king himself, I would bear him three children: two sons with apples in their hands, and a daughter with a star on her brow."

Next day the king summoned the girls and asked them to tell him honestly what they wished for. They did so, and he married the eldest to his butler and the middle one to his valet. Then he turned to the youngest and asked, "Will you marry me?" And she said yes.

Once she was queen, her sisters grew jealous. It no longer seemed enough to be married to the king's butler or the king's valet. They hid their hatred behind smiles.

While the king was away fighting a war, the queen gave birth to two boys with apples in their hands and a girl with a star on her brow. But the jealous sisters stole away her babies and put puppies in their places. When the king heard rumours that his wife had given birth to three puppies, he ordered her to be put on a treadmill as punishment.

The sisters abandoned the babes in the countryside, thinking they would be eaten by wild animals. But instead three fairies found them. "What beautiful children," said the first fairy. "I will give them a deer as a nurse."

"I will give them a purse that is always full of money no matter how much is taken out of it," said the second fairy.

"And I," said the third fairy, "will give them a ring that will change colour when any misfortune befalls one of them."

The deer looked after the children until they were grown up. Then the first fairy came to visit and advised them to rent a house opposite

*The queen's babies are
stolen by her jealous
sisters, who put puppies
in their places*

the king's palace. They did so, and were soon recognized by their mother's jealous sisters, for the boys still had apples in their hands, and the girl a star on her brow.

Fearing that the children might be planning revenge on them, the two sisters pretended to be friendly. The eldest said to the girl, "You have such a lovely house. It's such a shame it lacks the three things that would make it perfect."

"What are they?" asked the girl.

"Why, the Dancing Water, the Singing Apple, and the Speaking Bird," the other sister replied. "But if your brothers really love you, they will get them for you."

The eldest brother set off in search of the Dancing Water. On his way he met three hermits – the three fairies in disguise. They told

The Dancing Water ... *A giant*

The Dancing Water is protected by four giants and four lions. All the while the eldest boy searches for it, his poor mother is walking the treadmill in prison

him, "Climb the mountain, and you will come to a palace with a gate guarded by four giants with swords in their hands. If the giants' eyes are closed, enter. If they are open, do not. Inside, you will find four lions, guarding the Dancing Water. If their eyes are open, bide your time. When they shut their eyes, you can take the water."

WILD CHILD
Legends and stories abound of children being raised by animals. The children in this tale are brought up by a deer; a wolf nursed Romans Romulus and Remus. But perhaps the most famous "wild child" of all is Mowgli (above, played by Sabu in a 1942 film), hero of Rudyard Kipling's *The Jungle Book*.

The Dancing Water dances from one golden basin to another

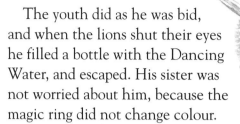

The youth did as he was bid, and when the lions shut their eyes he filled a bottle with the Dancing Water, and escaped. His sister was not worried about him, because the magic ring did not change colour.

When he came home, he put two golden basins in the garden and poured the Dancing Water into one of them. The water leaped constantly from one basin to the other in a beautiful arc, all the colours of the rainbow.

Next the second brother went in search of the Singing Apple. The hermits told him to climb to the palace. Inside he would find a tree where the Singing Apple hung. "The tree sways back and forth, but if you bide your time, it will be still for a moment, and you can pluck the apple."

When the tree stops swaying, the second son plucks the Singing Apple

He did as the hermits advised and plucked the apple. He took it home and placed it in the garden, where it trilled all day like a nightingale. Now only the Speaking Bird was needed, and the house would be perfect.

The elder brother set out once more. The hermits said, "Climb the mountain and enter the palace. You will find a garden full of statues. In a basin in a fountain is the Speaking Bird. If it speaks to you, do not reply. Pick a feather from its wing, dip it into a jar you will find there, and anoint all the statues, and all will be well."

The brother climbed the mountain, and found the bird. It said, "Your aunts have sent you to your death, and your mother is imprisoned and on the treadmill."

"My mother on the treadmill?" exclaimed the boy, and instantly he turned into a stone statue.

At home, the sister saw her magic ring change colour from blue to red. "Something has happened to our brother!" she said. So the younger brother set out; but the same thing happened to him. Waiting at home, the girl saw her magic ring turn from red to black.

She met the hermits, climbed the mountain, reached the palace with its garden full of strange statues, and found the Speaking Bird. It said, "Are you here, too? Then you will suffer the same fate as your brothers. Do you not see them? One, two, and you make three.

SICILIAN HILLS
This story evokes the distinctive landscape of Sicily with its many hills and mountains. In summer, the hot, dry *sirocco* wind dries up all rivers and streams, making the Dancing Water appear doubly miraculous and beautiful.

Your father is at the war. Your mother is imprisoned and on the treadmill. Your aunts are rejoicing."

But the brave girl did not reply. Instead she picked a feather from the bird's wing, dipped it in the jar, and anointed her brothers' statues. Instantly, they came to life again. They anointed all the other statues, and brought them all back to life. Then they returned home with the Speaking Bird.

The king had recently arrived home from the wars, and the brothers with apples in their hands and the sister with a star on her brow invited him to a banquet. When he saw them, he was amazed. He said, "If I did not know my wife had given birth to three puppies, I would think these were my children."

The king admired the ever-changing glories of the Dancing Water and the exquisite music of the Singing Apple. Then he said to the Speaking Bird, "Do you have nothing to say?"

YACKETY-YACK! The Speaking Bird could have been based on travellers' tales of the mynah bird of Asia (above). One of the bird world's finest mimics, this member of the starling family excels at imitating human speech.

Stone statues

With a touch of the Speaking Bird's feather, she brings her brothers back to life

The girl's ring changes colour – something has happened to her brothers!

The Speaking Bird

The bird replied, "These are your sons, with apples in their hands. This is your daughter, with a star on her brow. The queen, your wife, is on the treadmill, reduced to skin and bone."

And so the king learned the truth. He rescued his wife from the treadmill, and loved her truly from that day on. But her sisters he ordered to be thrown into a cauldron of boiling oil.

The treadmill

The king rescues his wife from the treadmill

The Girl who Pretended to be a Boy

EQUAL OPPORTUNITY
This Romanian story of a girl who dresses up as a fully armoured knight to protect her father's kingdom is also told in Greek, Italian, Czech, and Russian versions.

ONCE UPON A TIME there was an emperor who conquered countries all over the world. Every time he conquered a new one he made its king send one of his sons to serve him for ten years as the price of peace.

The king of one country held out for many years, but at last he, too, had to submit. But how could he ask for peace? He had no son; only three daughters. They saw that he was unhappy and asked him the reason. "If only one of you were a boy!" he sighed.

"We may be girls, but we are not useless," they cried.

"Oh, yes," said the king, "you can spin, sew, and weave. But can you wield a sword and face down your enemy on the field of battle?"

"I can try," said the eldest, springing to her feet. "For am I not a princess and the daughter of a king?"

She dressed in man's clothes and mounted the most spirited horse in the stable, with eyes of flame and a coat of shining silver, and set out to prove her courage.

Unknown to his daughters, the old king was a magician. He hid beneath a bridge in the shape of a huge grey wolf, and when his daughter approached, he sprang out, baring his fangs and uttering a fearsome growl. The terrified girl turned tail and did not stop until she was back home in the palace.

The king used his magic to be there before her. When she dismounted, he hugged her and said, "Thank you for trying, my dear, but flies do not make honey."

Then the second daughter tried, but she could not face the wolf either. Then it was the youngest daughter's turn. The king said, "Do you think you are braver than your sisters, little one?"

"No," she replied, "but for your sake, father, I would cut the devil into pieces or become a devil myself. I will not fail."

His youngest girl is determined to show she is as brave as any boy

The old king wishes he had a son to make peace with a warlike emperor

278

The girl went into the stables, but instead of the silver stallion, she chose her father's ancient warhorse, Sunlight. Old and worn-out as he was, she knew she could trust him with her life.

When the wolf sprang at her, its claws like saws and its mouth as wide as an oven, she drew her sword, charged straight at it,

The girl defeats a wolf, a lion, and a many-headed dragon to prove her bravery, and the king sends her to the emperor as his son, Fet-Fruners

She dresses in armour and chooses her father's old warhorse, Sunlight

and the animal whined and slunk away. At the next bridge the king waylaid her in the shape of a fierce lion, but again she charged it down.

At the third bridge, the king met her in the shape of a dragon with twelve writhing heads breathing fire. She sliced off one of the heads with her sword and the dragon turned into her father. "Well done!" he said. "You are the best and bravest daughter, and wise, too, for you have chosen the right horse, who will give you good advice. Go to the emperor with my blessing. Tell him you are my son, Prince Fet-Fruners."

When she had ridden a few miles, she saw a curl of golden hair lying like sunshine on the road. "Should I pick this up, or let it lie?" she wondered.

Sunlight the horse spoke up, "If you pick it up, you will regret it. But if you let it lie, you will regret that, too. So take it."

The golden curl

BIBLICAL MONSTER
The dragon Fet-Fruners fights may have been inspired by the Hydra, destroyed by the Greek hero Heracles, or by the seven-headed serpent in the Book of Revelation in the Bible (above, a 15th-century illustration).

MAGNIFICENT EMPIRE
This story, with its mention of an all-conquering emperor, reflects the fact that from the 15th to the early 20th century most of what is now Romania belonged to the Ottoman Empire. The most famous emperor was Suleiman I (above), nicknamed the Magnificent. The empire was not popular and Romanian lords frequently rebelled.

UGLY MUG
As hideous as this 15th-century portrait, ogresses are gigantic women with a taste for human flesh. The one in this story has stilt-like legs for striding over the ocean and ape-like arms for swinging through the trees.

The princess hung the curl safely around her neck. Sunlight told her, "That golden curl belongs to the Princess Iliane, the most beautiful girl in the world."

The princess reached the court of the emperor, and told him her name was Prince Fet-Fruners. She was so cheerful and willing to undertake any task that she was soon the emperor's favourite among all his pageboys, each of whom was the son of a king.

One day, the emperor noticed the golden curl and asked Fet-Fruners about it. She replied, "This curl belongs to Princess Iliane, the most beautiful girl in the world."

"I am the most powerful man," said the emperor, "so the most beautiful girl should be my wife. If you do not bring her to me, you shall lose your head."

Fet-Fruners asked Sunlight for advice. The horse replied, "Ask the king for a ship filled with treasure, and sail to the island where an ogress keeps Princess

Fet-Fruners   The emperor

The emperor orders Fet-Fruners to bring him Princess Iliane, the most beautiful girl in the world, whom he wishes to have for a wife

Iliane captive. Pretend to be a merchant and ask the princess to come aboard to see your goods. Then you can steal her away."

Fet-Fruners did as Sunlight advised. As she sailed away with the princess, the ogress chased the ship. With each stride, one of the ogress's legs reached up to heaven while the other plunged through the waves to the bottom of the sea. When the ship reached land, the ogress was right behind.

Sunlight was waiting on the shore, and Fet-Fruners and the princess jumped on his back. Sunlight said, "Put your hand in my left ear, take out a stone, and throw it behind you."

Fet-Fruners did so and the stone became a mountain. But the ogress clambered over it with ease.

Sunlight told Fet-Fruners to take a brush from his left ear and throw it

An ogress pursues Fet-Fruners and Princess Iliane

behind. It became a forest, so tangled not even a wren could pass through it. But the ogress climbed a tree and swung from branch to branch like a hideous ape.

At last Sunlight said, "Take the ring from Princess Iliane's finger and throw it behind you." The ring turned into a tower of stone. The ogress leaped to the top, fell down inside the ring, and broke into pieces at the bottom. Then Fet-Fruners put the ring back on the princess's finger.

The emperor was delighted when they arrived at court, but the princess said, "I have sworn only to marry the man who brings me the flask of holy water that is kept in a little church by the river Jordan and guarded by a hermit."

The emperor never did anything for himself; it was second nature to him to bark, "Fet-Fruners, go and fetch it!"

With Sunlight's help, Fet-Fruners managed to steal the water. As they made their escape, the enraged hermit called down a curse upon them: "If you are a man, may you become a woman; but if you are a woman, may you become a man!"

So Fet-Fruners turned into a real prince.

When they returned with the flask, the emperor said to the beautiful Princess Iliane, "Now will you marry me?"

"No," she replied, "for Fet-Fruners has brought me the holy water, not you."

The emperor was so angry he choked to death. Fet-Fruners gained his empire, married the princess, and they lived happily ever after.

On the emperor's orders, Fet-Fruners steals a flask of holy water and is turned into a man by an angry hermit

When the princess wants to marry Fet-Fruners, the emperor chokes to death from rage

Man-Crow

JUNGLE LAIR
This story is set amid the lush, tropical jungle of Jamaica's hilly interior. It is here that the monstrous Man-Crow has his lair.

ONCE THERE WAS a giant bird in the wood, called Man-Crow. When Man-Crow spread his wings, the world was cast into darkness. The king offered a great reward to anyone who could kill Man-Crow and make the world light again. He also promised that the victor could marry one of his daughters. Thousands of men went into the wood to kill Man-Crow. They found him, perched on one of the tallest trees, but they couldn't kill him.

One day a poor boy called Soliday said to his grandmother, "I am going to see if I can kill Man-Crow."

His grandmother answered, "Don't be stupid, boy!"

But Soliday went to Kingston to buy a bow and six arrows and then set out. When he found Man-Crow, he sang, "Good morning to you, Man-Crow, good morning to you, Man-Crow, good morning to you, Man-Crow, how are you this morning?"

And Man-Crow jumped down to the first branch and answered "Good morning to you, Soliday, good morning to you, Soliday, good morning to you, Soliday, how are you this morning?"

Soliday shot an arrow at Man-Crow, and two of his feathers flew out. He sang his song again, and Man-Crow jumped down to the second branch, and answered as before. Soliday shot a second arrow, and two more of Man-Crow's feathers flew out. And so the singing and shooting went on. At every song, Man-Crow moved down one branch, and Soliday fired an arrow.

Soliday sang the song for the sixth time, and Man-Crow jumped down one more branch. Soliday shot his last arrow and Man-Crow fell to the ground, dead. Anancy saw it all from a tree.

Anancy

Soliday

Soliday fires an arrow at Man-Crow

MAN-CROW  Jamaican

Soliday cut out Man-Crow's golden tongue and golden teeth, put them in his pocket, and went straight home to tell his grandmother.

Anancy came down from his tree, heaved Man-Crow's body over his shoulder, and walked across the bush to rap at the king's gate.

"Who's there?"

"It's me, Anancy. I've killed Man-Crow."

The gate was thrown open and the king welcomed Anancy into his house. Cunning Anancy immediately wed the prettiest of the king's daughters and everyone started feasting to celebrate the death of Man-Crow. Only Anancy couldn't really enjoy the feast, because he had one eye on the door, in case Soliday should come.

Suddenly there was a knock at the gate. "Excuse me a moment," said Anancy, and, when everyone else went to see who was outside, he stole away from the table. Another knock rattled the gate's hinges.

"Who's there?" everyone shouted.

"It's me, Soliday. I've killed Man-Crow!"

"That's not possible. Anancy has killed Man-Crow."

Soliday showed them the golden tongue and teeth. The king looked in the mouth of dead Man-Crow, and saw that its tongue and its teeth had indeed been cut out. He then noticed that the door to his own house was shut fast. He shouted for Anancy.

The king looks in Man-Crow's mouth and realizes that Soliday has told the truth

"Just coming!" Anancy called from within.

After a minute or two, the king shouted for him again.

"Won't be a moment!" called Anancy. "I don't feel well."

All this time, while the king waited angrily outside, Anancy was making a hole in the roof. He was so ashamed. At last, the king lost patience and kicked down the door. Anancy was nowhere to be seen.

Some say he's still lost, up there in the rafters.

So the king married his prettiest daughter to Soliday instead, and made him one of the richest men in the world.

ANANCY

Anancy is a happy-go-lucky rogue who relies on cunning to fool the powerful. He is lazy and loves to claim praise when he has not earned it, as in this story. Stories of this trickster, who frequently takes the form of a spider, originally came from Ghana in West Africa, and were adopted and added to by the Afro-Caribbean peoples of the West Indies.

SEAPORT CAPITAL

This print of Kingston, the town where Soliday buys his bow and arrows, dates from the 19th century, when Jamaica was under British colonial rule. A thriving port since the 1690s and the capital of Jamaica since 1872, Kingston is situated on the southeastern coast of the island.

Kahukura & the Net Makers

SPECTACULAR COAST
With its many islands, fjords, and bays, the New Zealand coast is a perfect setting for this story of a young man's encounter with fairy fishermen.

IN THE OLD DAYS the people used to catch fish one at a time with hooks and lines. Sometimes they had to go hungry, because not enough fish were caught.

One time a clever young man named Kahukura was travelling up the coast. As he walked along the beach, he came to a spot where a huge catch had been landed. Nearly a thousand fish had been caught, but, to his amazement, there were only enough footprints for a few people. He realized that this enormous catch must belong to the patupaiarehe, the fairies. But how had they made it?

Kahukura hid near the beach, determined to find out the answer. Night came on and he heard voices out on the water, singing:

"Pull in the net! Work with a will!
The harvest of the sea writhes and twists
This way and that! Pull in the net!"

Kahukura had no idea what the song could mean – no one had ever used a net to catch fish before!

As he watched from the darkness, he saw moonlight glisten on the pale bodies of a group of patupaiarehe. They began pulling on a rope dangling over the side of their canoe, singing their song once again, for the patupaiarehe were cheerful people, and they were in good spirits that night.

Now Kahukura was a fair-skinned man, like the patupaiarehe, and as they were hauling their

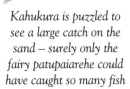

Kahukura is puzzled to see a large catch on the sand – surely only the fairy patupaiarehe could have caught so many fish

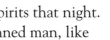

That night, he hears voices singing out on the water

net up the beach, he joined them at their work. In the darkness he looked like them, and they did not notice him. All night long he worked, till the patupaiarehe had once more caught upwards of a thousand fish.

Towards dawn, the patupaiarehe began to divide up their catch. "Hurry up," their leader called, "and finish before the sun comes up." For if the sun touches the pale bodies of the patupaiarehe, they die.

Kahukura tried to string his share of the fish onto a length of flax like the others, but the knot kept giving way so that all the fish fell off. This happened so many times that he delayed the patupaiarehe until dawn. As the first light came into the sky, they saw that he was a man, and they fled, shivering and shouting, into the sea. They left all their fish behind, and their precious net. And Kahukura saw that their canoes were not canoes at all, but just sticks of flax.

SEA PEOPLE
The sea plays a prominent part in Maori folklore. The Maoris were originally a seafaring people – they first came to New Zealand in canoes from the islands of Polynesia. Fishing was essential to their livelihood, and they found plenty of fish, such as snapper and tarahiki, around the coast.

Keen to discover the fairies' fishing secret, Kahukura helps them haul in their catch

In the dawn light, he is spotted

The patupaiarehe flee, leaving their fish, and their precious net, behind

And this is how men learned to fish with a net, so that many fish can be caught, instead of just a few.

THE CHIEF'S STORY
This tale was narrated to Sir George Grey, a former governor of New Zealand, by the warrior-chief Te Wherowhero, pictured above in an 1844 painting. It was first published in Grey's *Polynesian Mythology* in 1855.

The Demon in the Jug

THE BAAL SHEM TOV
This story is from Jewish Hasidic tradition, which often uses fairy tales to convey spiritual messages. The foolish man is helped by a holy teacher, the Baal Shem Tov, which means "Master of the Good Name". This title was bestowed on Israel ben Eliezer (1700–1760), who founded modern Hasidism.

FALLEN ANGELS
The evil spirit of this story resembles the demons, or *jinn*, of Arabic mythology and the *Arabian Nights* tales. *Jinn* are fallen angels that can assume animal or human shape. Some are beautiful and good, others hideous and evil. The frightening one above was painted by René Bull.

ONCE UPON A TIME a man became lost while walking through a forest. He sat down on a hollow log to rest and, reaching inside it, found a sealed jug. Thinking it might contain something to drink, he pulled out the cork. Instead of liquid, a cloud of smoke poured out. It billowed into the air and shaped itself into a huge spirit, roaring with laughter.

The man was very afraid, but also hopeful, for he had heard stories of men who had been well rewarded for freeing such spirits.

The spirit spoke, as if reading the man's thoughts. "I owe you thanks for releasing me from that jug, in which I was imprisoned long ago by my enemy. In return, I will grant you three wishes."

Overjoyed, the man cried, "My first wish is to go home, for I have been wandering, lost in this forest."

A man finds a jug, pulls the cork, and smoke pours out …

He forgot to ask who the enemy was who had imprisoned the spirit. If he had, he would have learned that it was that holy man the Baal Shem Tov who, when only a boy, had faced down this *jinni* – in truth, a wicked demon – sealed it in a jug, and hidden the jug deep in the forest.

All the man could think of was what to ask for as his final two wishes. Should it be riches, or power, or both? When they reached his home, the spirit said to him, "I advise you to sleep on the matter. You do not want to waste your wishes!" And the man agreed.

When he awoke next morning, however, he found he could barely move! His bed was only half its normal size – and the same was true of everything else in the house. Even the money in his purse was only half what it had been. He went into the kitchen and there, sitting at the half-size table like some hulking great lad, was the demon.

"Make everything in my house its proper size and never meddle with it again!" the man shouted.

"Your wishes are my commands," cackled the demon. It waved its hand, and everything went back to normal.

"What do you mean, wishes?" the man exclaimed.

"Why, you asked me to make everything its proper size, and I have done so," said the demon. "You also asked me never to meddle with it again and I will not. Those were your two remaining wishes. And as you have had three wishes, it's only fair I should have one. I wish that this house should be mine from now on!"

The man knew then what sort of a creature it was he had set free. He went to the Baal Shem Tov and begged him to help.

The Baal Shem Tov gave him holy amulets to hang in every room of the house. When the man hung up the last one, a kind of whirlwind swept out of the window; it was the demon, who could not bear to stay in a holy place.

The next day, the Baal Shem Tov came himself to make sure the demon was gone. He searched everywhere, even in the cracks in the walls. Then he saw that the lid of the water barrel was ajar. He lifted it, and at once the whirlwind rose from the barrel.

The Baal Shem Tov said, "Take your own shape, you creature of the dark!" And the whirlwind shaped itself, not into a laughing spirit, but a snarling demon. Then the Baal Shem Tov said, "Once before I confined you to a jug. Now I do so again. Begone, and never trouble this world again!"

The Baal Shem Tov walked towards the demon. Step by step, as he drew nearer, it grew smaller and smaller, until it was just a tiny, wailing figure, beating its wings against the sides of the jug. This the Baal Shem Tov quickly sealed.

The smoke shapes itself into a demon, who grants the man three wishes

But the demon cheats, shrinking everything in the man's house

With the help of a holy man, the Baal Shem Tov, the man drives the demon from the house

Holy amulet

The snarling demon is no match for the holy powers of the Baal Shem Tov, who imprisons it in a jug once more

Baba Yaga

THE WORST WITCH
Baba Yaga, shown here in a 1900 Russian illustration, is the best known witch in Russian folklore. A hideous hag, sometimes described as having tusks, she preys on children and flies using a magic pestle and mortar instead of a broomstick. Luckily for the heroine of this tale, Baba Yaga, like most witches, is unable to cross running water.

PRETTY SCARVES
Peasant life may have been hard, but Russian women still found time to create beautiful embroidered kerchiefs, like the one mentioned in this story. They were mostly worn on festive occasions, as depicted above in a 1902 painting by Andrej Rjabuschkin.

O*NCE UPON A TIME* a widower remarried and his new wife hated his daughter. She did everything she could to make her life a misery. One day when the father was away, the stepmother said, "Go to your aunt, my sister, and ask her for some sewing thread." Now the stepmother's sister was Baba Yaga Bonylegs, the witch who lives in the forest in a hut that stands on chicken's legs, so the girl suspected that her stepmother meant trouble.

The girl's stepmother sends her to visit the witch Baba Yaga, whose hut stands on chicken's legs

When she got to Baba Yaga's hut, she asked to borrow some thread. Baba Yaga said, "Of course. But while I'm looking for it, sit and do some weaving." Once the girl was sitting at the loom, Baba Yaga called her maid and said, "Run my niece a bath, and make it good and hot. I want to eat her for breakfast."

The girl overheard this, begged the maid not to make the water too hot, and gave her a pretty kerchief as a reward. Then the girl heard Baba Yaga say to the cat, "You can scratch out my niece's eyes." But the girl gave the cat a piece of ham, and in return the cat gave her a comb and a towel. "Run," said the cat. "If you hear Baba Yaga on your tail, throw these behind you."

The girl ran out of the house. Baba Yaga's dogs leapt up at her as if to tear her to pieces, but she threw them some bread and they left her alone. Baba Yaga's gate tried to bang shut on her, but she oiled its hinges and it let her through. The birch tree outside the gate tried to lash her eyes, but she tied it back with a ribbon and it let her pass.

Meanwhile, the cat sat at the loom and wove instead of her, and whenever Baba Yaga called, "Are you weaving, dear?" the cat would reply, "I am weaving, Aunt." Soon, however, Baba Yaga came to see what was going on, and when she saw the terrible tangle the cat had made of the weaving, she flew into a rage. She beat the cat, but the cat said, "In all the years I have served you, you have never given me so much as a fish bone, but your niece gave me a piece of ham."

Baba Yaga's maid, cat, and dogs look on as their cruel mistress pursues the girl

Baba Yaga in her magic mortar

Racing across the sky, the witch seems sure to catch the girl – but the cat's magic gifts protect her

Baba Yaga beat her maid, and her dogs, and her gate, and her birch tree, but they all told her that her niece had treated them better than she ever had. So Baba Yaga mounted her magic mortar, and using her pestle to whip it on, set off in pursuit of her niece.

When the girl heard Baba Yaga close behind, she threw the towel behind her, and it turned into a wide, wide river. Baba Yaga gnashed her teeth with rage, for she could not cross running water. She flew back home and fetched her oxen. The oxen drank the river dry and then she could cross.

The girl heard Baba Yaga close behind her once more. She threw down the comb and it became a great, dark forest. Howling with fury, Baba Yaga began to gnaw through the trees, her sharp and twisty teeth cutting through trunks and branches. But just as the witch struggled out of the forest, the girl reached the door of her own house and slammed it shut behind her.

After that her father sent the wicked stepmother away, and he and his daughter lived together in happiness and prosperity.

The towel changes into a wide, wide river – but Baba Yaga's oxen drink it dry

The comb turns into a forest

The girl's house

Can the girl get home before Baba Yaga, with her twisty teeth, gnaws through the trees?

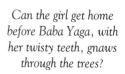

❧ The Flying Head ❧

BEYOND THE TREES
This tale was first recorded in 1902. It is told by the Iroquois peoples of northeastern North America, a region of rivers, lakes, and dense woods (above). Many Native American nations have stories of monsters that once preyed on humans.

POWERFUL MEDICINE
The power of the spirit world is reflected in this Iroquois mask, but here the power is for good, not evil. Carved from a basswood tree, this mask once belonged to a member of the False Faces, a group of healers. Each spring and summer the False Faces would visit longhouses exorcising evil spirits and curing ailments.

The Flying Head gulps down red-hot rocks and screams in agony

I N THE PAST, human beings were at the mercy of many terrible monsters and spirits. By day, the strong sun kept them at bay, but at night, and in storms, these spirits came out from their lairs to prowl the earth. The most terrible of all was the Flying Head. It was just a huge head without a body, four times as tall as the tallest man, with wings sprouting from its cheeks. It would fly up into the sky and then swoop down and seize some unlucky person in its terrible fangs. Its hair was filthy and matted, and its mouth was set in a snarl of rage.

One night a young Iroquois woman was sitting alone with her baby in the longhouse. Everyone else had fled for fear of the Flying Head, but the young woman had said, "We cannot let our children live in fear of this monster. Someone must make a stand."

She waited until the Flying Head appeared at the longhouse door. Then she pretended to be busy cooking a meal, picking up red-hot rocks with a forked stick and bringing them up to her face. The Flying Head couldn't see that she was dropping the rocks behind her, not eating them. She kept smacking her lips and exclaiming, "No one has ever tasted meat like this!"

The Flying Head rushed in and gulped down the rest of the fiery rocks. The rocks burned its throat, and it flew away, screaming, across the land. It screamed so loud the earth trembled, and the leaves fell from the trees.

When the last screams had died away, the people took their hands from their ears and went back to the longhouse, where they found the brave young woman calmly feeding her baby. And the terrible Flying Head was never seen again.

Jack & the Beanstalk

A POOR WIDOW HAD an only son, called Jack. Every morning she milked their cow, Milky-White, and Jack took the milk to market. But one morning Milky-White was dry and not one drop of milk fell into the pail.

"I'll get work," said Jack.

"Nobody would take a lazybones like you," his mother said. "There's only one thing for it. We must sell Milky-White."

So Jack set off for town with the cow. He hadn't gone far when he met a funny-looking man. "Good morning, Jack. And where are you off to?" asked the man.

"I'm going to market to sell our cow," replied Jack, wondering how the man knew his name.

"And you've the look of a proper businessman about you," the man smiled. "I bet you know how many beans make five."

"Two in each hand and one in the mouth," said Jack.

"I knew we could do business," the man said. "Because here they are, the very beans." The funny-looking man held out some funny-looking beans. "I'll let you have these beans for that cow."

"Milky-White's worth more than five beans!"

"Just as you like," said the man. "If you don't want my magic beans, I dare say others will."

"I didn't know they were *magic* beans!" Jack exclaimed. He took the beans and placed Milky-White's halter into the man's hand…

"Back already, Jack?" cried his mother. "And you've sold Milky-White! Good lad! How much did you get?"

"You'll never guess," said Jack. "I've done better than we ever thought!"

FULL OF BEANS
This woodcut is from the earliest-known printed version of the story, dating from 1730, in which Jack has several fantastic adventures at the top of the beanstalk.

A man offers Jack a handful of magic beans for Milky-White the cow

Bean sprouting

SOWING IN THE RAIN
Jack's magic bean might have been a runner type, the fastest growing and tallest bean. The story does not say what the weather was like when Jack's bean sprouted, but it is likely to have been wet if an English proverb is to be believed: "Sow beans in the mud, and they'll come up like a wood."

SPITTING
The fact that Jack's mother spits the magic bean out of the window may be significant. For, despite being frowned on in polite circles, spitting is supposed to bring good luck. This superstition is found all over the world.

"Oh, oh!" Jack's old mother gasped. "Let me sit down. Is it fifty pounds?"

"No," grinned Jack.

"A hundred?"

"No," Jack laughed.

"Surely not a thousand?!"

"Better than that, Mother. I got five magic beans!" Jack held out his hand. The beans jiggled on his palm.

The magic begins when Jack's mother spits one of the beans out of the window

"Dolt! Nincompoop! Brainless ninny! A cow for a handful of beans! Off to bed! Not a sip shall you drink, not a bite shall you eat!" Poor Jack went hungry to bed. His mother tossed four beans on the fire. The last one she popped in her mouth and spat out of the window.

When Jack awoke next morning, the room was filled with a strange green light. Outside, a beanstalk reached up into the arching blue as far as he could see. Jack swarmed up this living ladder till he reached the sky. There he found a broad road leading to an enormous house. Standing on the doorstep was an enormous woman.

"Morning," said Jack. "Could you spare me a bite of breakfast?"

"Breakfast?" the woman cried. " You'll be breakfast if you don't scarper. My man's a giant, and partial to broiled boy!"

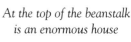

At the top of the beanstalk is an enormous house

But the giant's wife had a kind heart, so she took Jack into the kitchen and gave him bread and cheese and a jug of milk. Before Jack could finish his meal, thump! thump! thump! the house began to shake. "Quick!" she hissed. And she bundled Jack into the oven, just as the giant came in.

He was a big one to be sure. He pulled three calves from his belt and threw them on the table. "Broil these for breakfast," he grunted. "As we haven't any boy." Then his nose twitched and he bellowed: "Fee fie fo fum, I smell the blood of an earthly man. Be he alive or be he dead, I'll grind his bones to make my bread."

The giant's wife

"Nonsense, dear," said his wife, "you're dreaming. Or perhaps you smell the scraps of that little boy you had yesterday."

After the giant had breakfasted, he went to a chest and took out two bags of gold. Then he sat and slowly counted his gold pieces. After a while his head began to nod and his gigantic snores were soon rattling the kitchen pots and pans.

The giant counts out his money

Jack tiptoed from the oven, seized a bag of gold, and tucked it under his arm. He ran out of the house, reached the beanstalk, and climbed down. His mother was waiting anxiously at the bottom. "I told you they were magic beans," Jack laughed.

Jack escapes with a sack of gold

Jack and his mother lived in fine style thanks to the giant's gold, but at last every piece was spent, so Jack decided to climb the beanstalk again. When he reached the sky, he found the road and the house and the giant's wife, just as before.

"'Morning," said Jack, bold as brass. "What's for breakfast?"

"You're the youngster who was here before," frowned the giant's wife. "My man missed a bag of gold that day."

"Did he?" said Jack. "I daresay I could tell you something about that, but I'm so hungry I can't speak."

The gold spent, Jack tells his mother that he will climb up the beanstalk again

The giant's wife took him in and gave him some food, then thump! thump! thump! came the giant's footsteps. Jack hid in the oven once more.

A GOLDEN HEN
While, of course, no
one has ever owned a
hen that lays gold eggs,
a good egg-laying hen
was much prized in
bygone times. Special
breeding for egg-laying
did not begun until the
19th century.

GOLDEN DONKEY
The giant's hen that
lays golden eggs is
echoed in other tales,
including one collected
by the Brothers Grimm
in which the young
hero acquires a magical
donkey. At the
command "Bricklebrit,"
it spits out gold pieces.

"Fee fie fo fum!" the giant roared. "Wife, bring me
my hen that lays the golden eggs." When she had
brought it, he said to the hen,
"Lay!" and it laid an egg of
solid gold. After a while
the giant fell into a doze
and began to snore. Jack
crept out of the oven
and tucked the hen
under his arm. He raced
to the beanstalk, with
the hen clucking loudly:
"Cack cack-a-dack, cack
cack-a-dack!"

The giant stirred and mumbled,
"Wife, what are you doing with my
hen?" But Jack was already slithering
down the beanstalk. He showed his
mother the hen. "Lay!" he said, and the hen
laid another gold egg.

Still Jack was not content.
Though his mother begged him
not to go, once again he swarmed
up the beanstalk. This time he
hid until the giant's wife
came out of the house to
hang up her washing. Then
he sneaked in and hid in the
empty washtub. Before long,
thump! thump! thump! in
came the giant, followed
closely by his wife.

"Fee fie fo fum, I smell the
blood of an earthly man,"
roared the giant. "I smell
him, wife, I smell him."

"Do you, dear?" said his
wife. "Well, if it's that
rogue who stole your

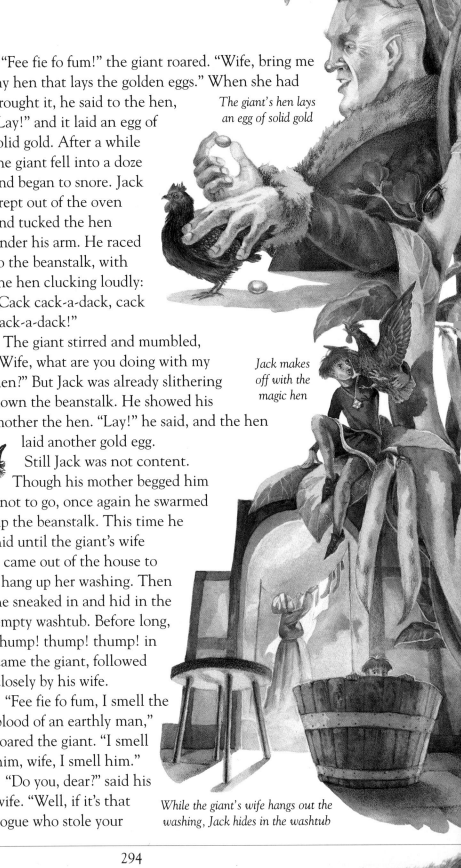

*The giant's hen lays
an egg of solid gold*

*Jack makes
off with the
magic hen*

*While the giant's wife hangs out the
washing, Jack hides in the washtub*

gold and your hen, he's sure to be in the oven." But Jack wasn't in the oven, and the giant's wife said, "There you are again, with your fee fie fo fum. You must be smelling the boy you caught last night, the one I've just broiled for your breakfast!"

The giant sat down at the table, but every now and then he muttered, "Well, I could have sworn..." and got up and searched the kitchen. Jack's heart fluttered like the washing in the wind, but the giant didn't think of looking in the washtub.

After breakfast he called, "Wife, bring me my golden harp!" She placed it on the table before him. "Sing!" he said, and the harp poured forth a stream of golden notes.

Soon the giant's head began to nod, and the harp's beautiful music was drowned by his thunderous snores.

Jack crept out of the washtub, grabbed the harp, and ran. But the harp cried out, "Master! Master!" and the giant woke up. He spotted Jack scrambling down the beanstalk clutching the harp.

The giant

When Jack grabs the golden harp, it cries out, "Master! Master!"

The giant jumped onto the beanstalk after Jack. The beanstalk shook with the giant's weight. As Jack reached the bottom he shouted, "Mother, help me!" His mother ran to the woodshed for the axe. Jack seized the axe and hacked at the beanstalk until it toppled over. And as it fell, it flung the giant far away. He tumbled into the sea and was drowned.

Jack hacks down the beanstalk and the giant, in hot pursuit, tumbles into the sea

Jack and his mother now had the hen to lay them golden eggs and the harp to sing them golden songs; and if they've not lost them, they have them still.

THE HARP
The harp is one of the oldest stringed instruments, dating back over 4,000 years. The giant's magic harp plays itself, but, ordinarily, harps are played with the thumb and fingers of both hands. Early harps were small enough to fit under Jack's arm. It is hard to imagine him escaping down the beanstalk with a heavy, 170 cm–high (5.5-ft) modern version!

GIANT KILLER
The theme of a huge, powerful character being outwitted and defeated by a far weaker one is central to many stories, including "Jack & the Beanstalk". This 17th-century painting by Orazio Borgianni shows David killing giant Goliath.

A Magic Whistle

A JOLLY SWAGMAN
Damper is a "swagman" – not a tramp, but a worker who travelled from farm to farm shearing sheep, harvesting, or fruit picking. A swagman travelled light, carrying ("waltzing") his belongings in a pack called a "bluey" or a "Matilda". He cooked using cans called "billies", pictured above. All these things are mentioned in the song "Waltzing Matilda", which Damper sings.

WANDERING STARS
This tale is set in the outback of New South Wales, Australia, once famous for its swagmen, trappers, bushmen, and bushrangers.

ONCE IN THE AUSTRALIAN BUSH there was a young swagman named Damper. He was called that because he always said that damper bread, cooked in the ashes of an open fire under the stars, was the best food in the world.

One night as he lay on his back letting his supper go down, the darkness was suddenly lit up by a host of glow-worms and fireflies and Damper saw a troop of little figures, some dressed in black, some in gold, and some in white. He gave himself a punch or two on the head, muttering, "I'm not seeing straight." But when he looked again, the figures were still there.

Soon the tiny people began to dance, so fast it set Damper's senses reeling. But he noticed that two of them, the grandest of all, had fallen out of the dance. He decided that they must be the king and queen of this fairy host, so he tried to hear what they were saying.

He finds the whistle under a tree

The fairy king said, "I've hidden the magic whistle where no one can find it, under the roots of that old eucalyptus tree."

"Good," replied the queen. "For whoever found that whistle would be able to control any animal, bird, or man. For when it is played, any creature listening to it just has to dance."

In the morning Damper wondered if it had all been a dream. He decided to check under the roots of the old eucalyptus tree. There, sure enough, was a reed whistle, about six inches long, with a mouthpiece of pure gold.

Damper hears fairies talk of a magic whistle that can make every creature dance

Damper put the whistle in his bluey and went along the road. Soon he saw a cart coming in the other direction. A fat, angry woman was swaying on the cart, scolding a little man walking beside the horse.

Damper went up to the woman and asked her for a little food.

"Be off with you, you loafing rascal," she said.

Damper took out the whistle and began to play a lively jig. The fat woman threw herself from the cart and began to leap and cavort in the road, while the little man laughed fit to burst. After a bit Damper put down the whistle and she flopped down in the dust. When he raised the whistle to his lips again she begged him, "Stop, for mercy's sake! Take all the tucker in the cart."

Damper helped himself to a little of their tucker and went on his way, singing "Waltzing Matilda" at the top of his voice. But he swallowed his song when a big, bearded bushranger loomed up from nowhere, yelling, "Halt, or I'll fire."

Damper pulled out his whistle and began to play. The bushranger's horse started to galumph about the road with the bushranger hanging on for dear life. "Please, no more!" the bushranger begged. " I'll fill your pouch with gold."

"Not a bit of it," said Damper. "You'll hand over all of your ill-gotten treasure, and your horse as well, or you shall dance again!"

WILD COLONIAL BOYS Bushrangers were armed robbers who preyed on travellers. The most notorious was Ned Kelly, above, who terrorized northeastern Victoria with his gang in the 1870s. Other legends include Frank Gardiner, "King of the Bushrangers", Fred Ward, "The Thunderbolt", and "Gentleman" Matthew Brady.

When Damper plays the magic whistle, he makes a mean woman dance till she drops and persuades a bushranger to give up all his ill-gotten gains…

The bushranger began to curse, so Damper blew a single note on the whistle. "Stop! I agree," the bushranger cried. He handed over his revolver, his money belt, his boots, and his horse, and ran off. Damper looked in the belt. It was filled with gold. As he mounted the horse, he was the happiest boy in all Australia – and one of the richest, too.

… even his horse! The bushranger runs off into the bush, leaving Damper whooping with joy

Bluebeard

NO TIME TO LOSE!
This first page of a
17th-century retelling
of "Bluebeard" by
Charles Perrault shows
Bluebeard about to kill
his wife. Meanwhile
her brothers rattle
across the castle
drawbridge to the
rescue. Will they be
in time?

THERE WAS ONCE a rich man called Bluebeard who possessed
grand houses in the town and country, and everything his
heart could desire, but no wife. A noble lady living nearby
had two daughters, and Bluebeard asked her if one of them would
consent to marry him. Neither of the girls wanted to marry a man
with a blue beard, especially when they heard rumours that he had
been married several times before, and no one knew what had become
of any of his wives.

Nevertheless the girls agreed to go to his house in the country for a
party that was to last a whole week, with nothing to do but hunt, fish,
dance, picnic, and play games. It was all great fun and, by the end of
the week, the younger daughter had stopped worrying about the
colour of her host's beard. As soon as they got back to town, she and
Bluebeard were married.

*Bluebeard throws a week-long party
at his splendid country house*

Bluebeard's future bride

*Bluebeard is very
attracted by the young
ladies and decides to
make one of them his wife*

After a month,
Bluebeard told his wife that he
had to go away on business.

*The guests picnic, play games, and hunt —
and one young girl falls in love*

"But there's no need for you to get bored," he said. "Ask your sister Anne to come and stay with you and enjoy the country air."

He gave her a large bunch of keys and told her what they were all for. This one would open the strongbox and that one the safe. There was just one tiny key that she must not use. That was for the door to a little room at the end of the great gallery, and he forbade her to open it. "If you do, you will rouse my anger."

She promised to do as she was told, and he went on his way.

Despite having her sister Anne to stay and all the marvellous things in Bluebeard's house, the young wife could not enjoy herself, for she was eaten up by curiosity about what lay behind the door of the little room. She could think of nothing else. One afternoon, while Anne was busy at the other end of the house, she took the tiny key, opened the door, and entered the forbidden chamber.

FATAL CURIOSITY
In fairy tale, curiosity is often a female trait – and almost always has dire consequences! Bluebeard, here illustrated by Gustav Doré, tells his new wife about the key as a cruel test of her obedience. Little does she know that the penalty for failure is death. As Charles Perrault wrote in 1697: "Curiosity… often brings with it serious regrets."

REAL BLUEBEARDS
Various historical figures have been cited as models for Bluebeard. These include 15th-century French nobleman and murderer Gilles de Rais, whose victims numbered 140, and the English king Henry VIII, responsible for the deaths of two of his six wives. Another candidate is Comorre the Cursed who, in 6th-century Brittany, killed four wives when they became pregnant. His fifth wife, Tryphine, escaped and told all.

Before he leaves, Bluebeard warns his new wife never to use the tiny key…

…but she cannot resist a look in the forbidden chamber

As her eyes grew used to the gloom, she realized that the floor was sticky with clotted blood. She peered closer, then drew back in horror. Reflected in this crimson pool were the corpses of several women, hanging up along the walls of the forbidden chamber. These were Bluebeard's wives, whose throats he had cut, one after the other.

KEY CHANGE
In love stories, tiny keys have romantic associations, as the expression "key to my heart" testifies. This tale, however, cleverly turns this idea on its head, making a little key a frightening symbol of guilt.

The bloodstained key

Bluebeard sees blood on the key and realizes his wife has discovered his terrible secret

BAD NAME
Such was the fame of "Bluebeard" throughout Europe that mothers used to frighten their children by saying that Bluebeard would get them if they didn't behave. Even today, the media often call any man accused of killing his wife or lover a "Bluebeard".

She thought that she would die from fear. The key of the room fell from her hand onto the floor. Trembling, she picked it up and, locking the door behind her, went back to her bedroom, where she fell down in a faint.

When she awoke, she noticed that the key was stained with blood. She scrubbed and scrubbed, but the blood would not come off.

That evening, Bluebeard returned unexpectedly early from his travels and in the morning he asked her for his bunch of keys. When she brought them to him, he immediately noticed that one key was missing. A single glance at her pale face, her trembling hand, told him what had happened.

"Where is the key to the little room?" he asked.

"I must have left it upstairs," she replied.

"Bring it to me," he ordered.

Reluctantly, she fetched him the tiny key. As he took it, he glowered at her from behind his blue beard. "Why is there blood on this key?" he thundered.

"I'm sure I don't know," she whispered.

"Well I do," he raged. "You couldn't resist going into that room when I told you not to. Well, since you wanted to go in there, you shall. You shall hang alongside the others!"

She flung herself at her husband's feet, begging for mercy. She might have wrung pity from a stone; but Bluebeard's heart was harder than any stone.

"You must die," he declared grimly. "Your last hour has come."

"At least give me a quarter of an hour," she pleaded, "so that I can say my prayers."

"If you must," frowned Bluebeard.

When she was back in her room, she called for her sister Anne and told her what had happened. "Sister, I beg you, go to the top of the tower and tell me if you can see our brothers coming. They promised to come and see us today." So Anne climbed to the top of the tower.

The wife called, "Anne, sister Anne, do you see anything coming?"

And Anne replied, "Nothing but the dust made gold by the sun, and the green of the grass." Bluebeard set foot on the first stair, his huge cutlass in his hand.

"Anne, sister Anne, do you see anything coming?"

"Nothing but the dust shining gold in the sun, and the green grass growing." Bluebeard set foot on the second stair.

"Anne, sister Anne, do you see anything coming?"

"I see a cloud of dust in the distance," Anne replied.

"Is it our brothers?"

"No, sister, only a flock of sheep." Bluebeard set foot on the third stair.

"Anne, sister Anne, do you see anything coming?"

"I see two riders approaching," she replied. "God be praised! It is our brothers. Oh, hurry! Hurry!"

Bluebeard entered the room.

His wife once more begged for mercy. "Be quiet," he said. "You must die." He seized her by the hair, his cutlass at her bare throat.

At that moment her two brothers burst in, swords in their hands, and ran Bluebeard through the heart. Their poor sister lay on the floor, sobbing with terror and relief.

Bluebeard left no heirs, so his wife inherited all his wealth. She gave some money to Anne, so that she could marry her true love, and some to her brothers, so that they could become officers in the army. The rest she shared with her second husband, a good man, who helped her forget the terrible time she had spent with Bluebeard.

Sister Anne

The terrified wife calls out to her sister as Bluebeard approaches

Bluebeard climbs the stairs

The brothers

As Bluebeard prepares to murder his wife, her brothers rush to the rescue

STAIRWAY TO FEAR
This story is full of the classic ingredients of the horror story: a charming, but evil, villain, a terrible secret, and an innocent young heroine. The ending also features a superb suspenseful scene as the villain slowly climbs a flight of stairs towards his cowering victim. This situation has since featured in any number of spine-tingling tales and movies.

The Twin Brothers

A WOMAN ONCE gave birth to twin boys called Mavungu and Luemba. They were almost full-grown, and each boy brought his own luck into the world with him. About this time, the daughter of Chief Nzambi was ready to be married. The leopard, the gazelle, the pig, and every other animal offered themselves in turn, but Nzambi's daughter refused them all.

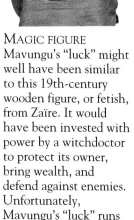

MAGIC FIGURE
Mavungu's "luck" might well have been similar to this 19th-century wooden figure, or fetish, from Zaïre. It would have been invested with power by a witchdoctor to protect its owner, bring wealth, and defend against enemies. Unfortunately, Mavungu's "luck" runs out in this story!

Mavungu

Chief Nzambi

Nzambi's daughter

The witch

Nzambi's daughter refuses all the animals and wishes to marry Mavungu

Mavungu sees a village in a mirror, travels there, and is killed by an old witch

When Mavungu heard of this girl, he determined to marry her. He asked his luck for help and, after many days travelling, arrived at Nzambi's village. As soon as Nzambi's daughter caught sight of him, she ran to her mother and said, "I have seen the man I love, and I shall die if I do not marry him."

So they were married, and after the wedding they were led to a fine hut, while all the village danced and sang for gladness.

In the morning Mavungu saw that the hut's walls were hung with mirrors; each mirror was covered with a cloth. He asked Nzambi's daughter to uncover them so that he might see himself in them. She uncovered the first, and in it he saw the reflection of his own village. As she uncovered the others, he saw reflected all the villages he had passed through on his journey. But she refused to uncover the last one. "It shows the village from which no traveller

VILLAGE LIFE
Though most Zaïrians now live in cities, in the country there are still many villages of small, thatched, dried-mud houses similar to the setting of this tale.

returns," she said. But Mavungu insisted on seeing it. And then he said, "I must go there," and she could not dissuade him.

When Mavungu reached the village, he met a witch. He asked for fire to light his pipe, and she killed him. He just vanished into the air.

Now Luemba was getting worried about his brother, and decided to follow him. When he reached Nzambi's village, Nzambi himself rushed to meet him, shouting "Mavungu, you have returned!"

Luemba tried to explain that he was Mavungu's twin brother, but Nzambi would not listen, and took him straight to Mavungu's hut.

AFRICAN PIPES
Pipe smoking has long been popular with men and women in Africa. The evil old woman kills Mavungu when he is looking forward to a relaxing puff after his long journey.

Mavungu's twin brother, Luemba, finds and kills his brother's murderer

Luemba brings his brother back to life by touching his bones with his luck

That night, Luemba prayed to his luck and Mavungu's wife went straight to sleep still believing Luemba was her missing husband.

In the morning, Luemba saw the covered mirrors, and learned of the village from which no traveller returns. "I must go there," he said.

"What, again?" said Nzambi's daughter.

Luemba travelled to the village and encountered the witch. He asked her for fire, and, before she could move, struck her dead.

Then Luemba gathered up his brother's bones, touched them with his luck, and they came back to life. Then the two brothers collected all the bones that lay scattered in that village of death, and each used their luck to bring them back to life. So now the two brothers had hundreds of devoted followers.

They returned to Nzambi's village, and then everyone could see that there were two brothers after all.

BROTHERLY HATE
This story of the Fjort people of Congo and Zaïre does not always end happily. Another ending tells that the brothers argued about their followers. Mavungu said they were his, because he was the elder; Luemba said they were his, because he had brought Mavungu back to life. Mavungu killed his brother, but Luemba's horse stayed with his body, touched him with his luck, and brought him back to life. Then Luemba rode after Mavungu and killed him. When the people heard the whole story, they all said that Luemba had done right.

An Eating Match with a Troll

EVENTYR
The folk tales of
Norway, known as
eventyr, have been
passed on by word of
mouth since medieval
times. This one was first
recorded by Peter
Christen Asbjørnsen
and Jørgen Moe in
Norwegian Folk Tales,
the first volume of
which was published
in 1845.

MOUNTAIN KINGS
Norway's Dovrefjell
mountains are a famous
haunt of trolls and
fairies. Trolls vary in
temperament from kind
to evil, and in size from
gigantic to dwarfish.
Although they may
have more than one
head, they are not
usually very bright.
They avoid sunlight and
live in Scandinavian
mountain caves, where
they keep hoards of
treasure.

A POOR OLD FARMER had three idle sons. He was deep in debt, and sadly decided that the old wood his father had left him would have to be cut down and sold for firewood.

He told his eldest son to cut down the trees and the lad went off in a very bad temper. Deep in the wood he found a mossy old fir tree. As he raised his axe, the rumbling voice of a huge troll boomed, "This is my wood. If you chop down that tree, I will kill you!"

The lad dropped his axe and ran all the way home.

"You chicken," his father grumbled. "In my younger days, I would never have let a troll frighten me."

He sent his second son off to the wood and the same thing happened. The troll shouted; the boy ran.

"Who would have thought I could have sired two such fainthearts," cried the old farmer. "In my younger days, no troll would ever have stopped me from chopping down my own trees!" And, shaking his head, he sent his youngest son off to the wood.

This son was called the Ash Lad, because he spent all his time dozing by the fire.

"You'll soon be back with your tail between your legs," his brothers jeered.

"We'll see," the Ash Lad answered. He asked his mother to give him some cheese curds, which he put in a leather wallet around his waist.

To the troll's amazement, the lad squeezes water from a "stone"

When the Ash Lad came to the wood, the troll appeared, shouting. But the Ash Lad said, "Hold your noise, troll, or I'll squeeze the breath out of you like water from a stone."

"What do you mean, water from a stone?" asked the troll.

"This," said the Ash Lad. He took the curd cheese out of his wallet; it looked just like a white stone. He squeezed it in his fist, and clear whey spurted out.

Trolls aren't the most intelligent of creatures, and this one was frightened out of what wits he had. So the Ash Lad said, "If you help me cut down these trees, I'll not harm you."

When they had cut down all the trees, the troll invited the Ash Lad to supper. When they arrived at the troll's house, the troll helped himself to some water from two enormous iron pails. But the Ash Lad said, "There's not enough water in these finger-bowls to quench my thirst. Where's your spring? I'll go and fetch that."

The troll was more alarmed than ever. "Don't!" he blurted. "I need that spring! I'll fetch you as much water as you want."

Then the troll cooked a great cauldron of porridge. "The two of us will never eat all this," he said.

"Let's have an eating contest," cried the Ash Lad, and the troll agreed. The troll dug into the porridge with a huge spoon and so did the Ash Lad. But while the troll was eating, the Ash Lad was spooning his porridge into the leather wallet at his waist.

At last the troll said, "I'm so full I couldn't eat another mouthful."

"Same here," said the Ash Lad. "Let's make some room." And he took his knife and ripped a gash in the leather wallet, so that the porridge spilled out."

"Doesn't that hurt?" asked the troll.

"Not a bit," said the Ash Lad. "Why don't you try?"

The foolish troll took a knife to his belly and killed himself. And the Ash Lad took the troll's gold home to his father, who paid off all the family's debts with it.

GIANT KILLER
Similar events occur in the old English tale "Jack the Giant Killer", pictured above. Jack, like the Ash Lad, is the resourceful hero of a series of exciting, bloodthirsty battles with various giants. He defeats them all, saves King Arthur's kingdom from ruin, and rescues knights and ladies.

The Ash Lad appears to slit open his own stomach, letting the porridge spill out

The foolish troll tries the same trick – and kills himself. The lad escapes with the troll's treasure

The Ash Lad and the troll begin an eating contest

INNOCENT VICTOR
This story of an innocent girl's triumph over a vain queen's jealousy was collected by the Brothers Grimm and published in 1823 under the title "Snow-drop". Similar tales are told throughout Europe, in Turkey, and in North and West Africa. In some versions, Snow White's rescuers are robbers, not dwarfs.

THE THREE BEARS
Snow White's discovery by the dwarfs is similar to the famous tale of "Goldilocks and the Three Bears", here illustrated by Arthur Rackham in 1933.

Snow White

ONCE UPON A TIME a queen sat sewing at a window. Snow was falling and some flakes landed on the window's ebony frame. Suddenly the queen pricked her finger with her needle and three drops of blood fell upon the snow. She said to herself, "If only I had a child as white as snow, as red as blood, and as black as ebony."

Soon afterwards the queen had a daughter called Snow White, with skin white as snow, lips red as blood, and hair black as ebony. When she was born, the queen died.

After a year, the king remarried. The new queen was proud and vain. Every day she asked her magic mirror,

"Mirror, mirror, on the wall,
Who is the fairest of them all?"
And the mirror would reply,
"You are, O queen."
But one day, when Snow White was seven years old, the mirror replied, "Snow White is."

The spiteful queen told her huntsman, "Take Snow White into the forest and kill her. Bring me her liver and lungs as proof."

The huntsman took the child into the forest, but he hadn't the heart to kill her. He shot a young boar instead and took its lungs and liver to the queen. She had them made into a stew and ate them.

Snow White's mother

After Snow White's mother dies, a proud, vain beauty becomes queen

Alone and afraid, Snow White ran through the forest. At last she came to a cottage. Inside, on a table, were seven plates and cups, and upstairs were seven beds. Snow White ate from each plate, and drank from each cup. Then she lay down on each of the beds. Some were too long and some were too short, but the seventh was just right, and she lay down to sleep.

At nightfall, the owners of the cottage came home. They were seven dwarfs who mined silver in the mountains. First one and then the other asked, "Who's been eating from my plate?"

"Who's been drinking from my cup?"
"Who's been sleeping in my bed?"
Then the seventh dwarf looked in his bed and saw Snow White sleeping there. Not wanting to disturb her, he slept the night turn and turn about with the other six – one hour with each.

The next day, Snow White told the dwarfs all about her stepmother

Snow White happily agrees to cook and clean for the seven dwarfs

The dwarfs' cottage

and the huntsman. They said, "If you'll look after us, we'll look after you."
So Snow White kept house for the seven dwarfs.
One day the queen asked her magic mirror,

The huntsman

Disobeying the queen's orders, the huntsman spares Snow White and kills a wild boar instead

DISNEY'S DWARFS
Walt Disney's *Snow White and the Seven Dwarfs* (1937) was the first full-length animated movie. One of Disney's most amusing touches was to give the dwarfs names reflecting their personalities: Grumpy, Sneezy, Doc, Bashful, Happy, Sleepy, and Dopey.

"Mirror, mirror, on the wall,
Who is the fairest of them all?"
"Snow White!" the mirror replied.
"So the child lives still," the jealous queen thought grimly. She disguised herself as an old woman selling brightly coloured laces and went from door to door searching for Snow White.

At last the queen arrived at the dwarfs' cottage. The dwarfs had told Snow White not to open the door to anyone, but she couldn't resist seeing the old woman's pretty laces.

The old woman said, "I'll lace you up." She laced Snow White up so tightly that she fainted.

The old woman has pretty laces to sell

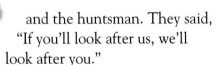

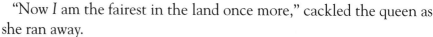

The dwarfs take the poisoned comb from Snow White's hair and she comes back to life

THE TEMPTING APPLE
Offering an apple used to be a declaration of love. However the fruit is also linked with deceit and death. In this scene from Walt Disney's *Snow White*, the queen, transformed into a horrible hag, tempts Snow White with a poisoned apple.

"Now *I* am the fairest in the land once more," cackled the queen as she ran away.

When the dwarfs came home from the mines, they found Snow White. At first they thought she was dead, but when they cut her laces, she began to breathe, and soon she was herself again.

The next time the queen asked her mirror who was the fairest of them all, to her astonishment she once again received the answer, "Snow White." Disguised as an even older woman, she went back to the dwarfs' cottage.

This time, Snow White would not let her in. "Look at my pretty combs," the old woman said. Snow White leaned out of the window to see, and the old hag said, "Let me put this comb in your hair."

The comb was dipped in poison; as soon as it touched Snow White's hair, she fainted away.

That night, the dwarfs again thought Snow White was dead, but when they took the comb from her hair, she revived. They warned her to watch out for any more of her stepmother's tricks.

Meanwhile, the queen asked her mirror the question, and once again received the reply "Snow White". So, disguised as a farmer's wife, she went back to the cottage. She took with her a beautiful apple, white on one side and red on the other. However, the red side of the apple was poisoned.

Snow White would not let her in, but the old woman said, "Why not share my apple? I shall have the white side, and you shall have the red." As soon as Snow White bit into the apple, she fell dead. The queen laughed a cruel wicked laugh and walked away.

That night, the dwarfs tried everything, but they could not wake her. After weeping for three days, they put her in a glass coffin, with her name on it in golden letters: Princess Snow White.

They placed the glass coffin on top of a hill, and one of them was always there to grieve and watch over it. The birds, who had been

The old woman gives Snow White the poisoned half of the apple

very fond of Snow White, also came to weep for her: first an owl, then a raven, then a dove.

Snow White lay in her glass coffin, and as the years passed she grew into a young woman, her skin still white as snow, her lips red as blood, and her hair black as ebony.

One day, a prince came by. As soon as he saw Snow White, he fell in love with her. "Please let me have the coffin," he cried. "I'll pay you well for it!"

"We wouldn't sell it for the world," one of the dwarfs said.

"But I cannot live without Snow White!" sighed the prince.

SAD VIGIL
The dwarfs watch over Snow White in her glass coffin while she grows into a beautiful young woman in this 1903 German engraving by Alfred Zimmerman.

The seven dwarfs

A prince sees Snow White in her coffin and falls in love at first sight

The dwarfs relented and gave him the coffin. As his servants were carrying it, one of them stumbled, the coffin tilted, and the piece of poisoned apple fell from Snow White's mouth. At once she awoke. "Where am I?" she cried.

"Safe with me!" said the prince. "Live with me and be my queen!"

Everyone was invited to the wedding, even Snow White's stepmother. At first she thought she wouldn't go, but she couldn't resist. As soon as she arrived, the prince's guards seized her.

Iron slippers had been placed in the fire to get red hot. They were brought to her, and she stepped into them, and danced and danced until she dropped down dead.

The coffin tilts suddenly and Snow White awakes

The evil queen sees the red hot shoes and realizes her time has come

True Love Conquers All

In fairy tales, it is love, not money, rank, or power, that makes the world go round: a prince may wed the family servant, Cinderella, or a witch's prisoner, Rapunzel. Even those who proudly protest they will never marry are not proof against love's spell; their fate is to lose their hearts – not to humans – but to elusive fairies, such as the selkie or snow wife, and suffer inevitable sadness. For lovers, the road from "Once upon a time…" to "…happily ever after" can be long and hard, but, as stories like "The Black Bull of Norroway" and "The Snake Prince" make clear, there are no hardships or terrors that those inspired by true love cannot endure and eventually overcome.

The slipper fits Cinderella's foot – and the prince realizes that, despite her shabby clothes, she is his true love

Cinderella

ORIENTAL TALE
The most famous retelling of "Cinderella" is Charles Perrault's of 1697. He invented the fairy godmother, the pumpkin coach, and the glass slipper. The story originated in China, where a small foot was a mark of beauty. The first known version, "Yeh-hsien", dates from the 9th century AD.

ONCE UPON A TIME there was a man whose wife died, leaving him to bring up their only daughter; so he married again. His second wife was a sharp-tongued, stuck-up sort, and she had two daughters of her own who were just as bad. The man's own daughter was as gentle and good-natured as her mother had been.

It wasn't long before the stepmother and her two daughters began to make the poor girl's life a misery. They were always mean to her, and treated her just like a servant. The only place she could find any peace was in the chimney-corner, among the cinders: so they laughed at her, and called her Cinderella. But Cinderella in rags was still far prettier than her stepsisters, for all their finery.

Now the king's son decided to give a ball, and he invited all the fine folk for miles around. There were to be two evenings of dancing and festivities. The sisters were thrilled. They could think and talk of nothing else, and they soon had Cinderella waiting on them hand and foot to make sure they looked their best. Cinderella even dressed their hair for them, and although she was as gentle as could be, they kept snapping, "Don't tug, girl," and "It's a good job you're not invited to the ball, you clumsy oaf!" Anyone else would have tangled their hair, but Cinderella was too kind-hearted for that.

When at last the sisters had squeezed themselves into their new dresses and set off for the ball, Cinderella sat down among the ashes, all alone. Then she began to cry.

When she looked up from her tears, an old lady was standing there. She had a kind face and was holding a wand in her hand. "Why are you crying?" she asked. "Tell me. I am your fairy godmother." So Cinderella told her godmother how much she longed to go to the ball.

"And so you shall," said her godmother. "Fetch me a pumpkin."

Cinderella's stepmother and stepsisters treat her like a servant

Cinderella went into the garden and picked the largest pumpkin she could find. Her godmother scooped out the insides, tapped it with her wand, and in an instant it had turned into a beautiful, gilded carriage. Then she looked in the mousetrap and found six live mice. When she touched them with her wand, they turned into six handsome dapple-grey horses.

"Now we need a coachman," said the godmother, looking around for something suitable.

"I'll see if there is a rat in the rat trap," said Cinderella excitedly. There were three, and one of them had the finest whiskers you've ever seen. "He'd make a good coachman," said Cinderella. So her godmother tapped the rat with her wand, and he turned into a fat coachman with an enormous moustache.

The fairy godmother weaves her magic…

…and turns a pumpkin into a coach, a fat rat into a coachman…

…six mice into horses…

…and six lizards into footmen in livery

"Now," said the godmother. "Behind the watering-can you will find six lizards. Bring them to me." When she tapped the lizards with her wand, they turned into six footmen, dressed in livery. "There – now you can go to the ball!"

"In these rags?" cried Cinderella.

So her godmother tapped Cinderella with her wand, and instantly her ragged clothes became a gown of silver and gold, embroidered with pearls; and her worn-out shoes turned into glass slippers.

With a wave of her magic wand, the fairy godmother transforms Cinderella's sorry rags into a ball gown fit for a princess.

FAIRY GODMOTHER
Perrault's "fairy
godmother" (shown
above in a reversible
drawing by Rex
Whistler, c. 1935) is
true to the spirit of
earlier, oral versions, in
which the Cinderella
figure is helped by the
spirit of her dead
mother, sometimes in
the form of a fish, a
cow, or a tree.

BOX-OFFICE APPEAL
"Cinderella" has been
adapted for the stage, as
a ballet (1945) with
music by Sergei
Prokoviev, and also for
the big screen, as a Walt
Disney cartoon (1950),
and *The Slipper and the
Rose* (1976), above.

As Cinderella climbed into the carriage her godmother told her, "Remember to leave the ball before midnight. For then the spell will end, and all these enchanted things will return to their true forms!"

When Cinderella arrived at the palace, no one could take their eyes off this beautiful stranger, who surely must be a princess. The prince himself danced with her all night. But at a quarter to twelve, she slipped out of the ballroom, and back to her carriage.

The next day, the sisters were full of excited talk about the ball, and especially about the princess who had arrived so unexpectedly, and vanished so suddenly. Whoever could she be?

"Oh, I wish I could see her," said Cinderella. "Please, won't one of you lend me a dress – just an everyday one – so that I can go to the ball?"

"Certainly not!" said the sisters. "You'd disgrace us in front of the prince. And what would the lovely princess think, seeing us with a grubby creature like you?"

That night, when the sisters had left, Cinderella's fairy godmother transformed the pumpkin, rat, mice, and lizards

At the ball, Cinderella and the prince soon fall in love

again and sent her to the ball in her glass slippers and an even grander dress. "Don't forget to leave before midnight," she said.

Cinderella and the prince danced together all night. They laughed and talked, and he whispered sweet nothings in her ear. She quite forgot the time. When she heard the chimes of midnight, Cinderella fled. The prince ran after her, but all he found was one glass slipper. He questioned the palace guards, but they had not seen a princess leave – just a peasant girl, dressed in rags.

Cinderella, meanwhile, made her own way home, with no carriage, no horses, no coachman, no servants, no fine dress. All that remained of her finery was a single glass slipper.

The prince, who was head over heels in love,

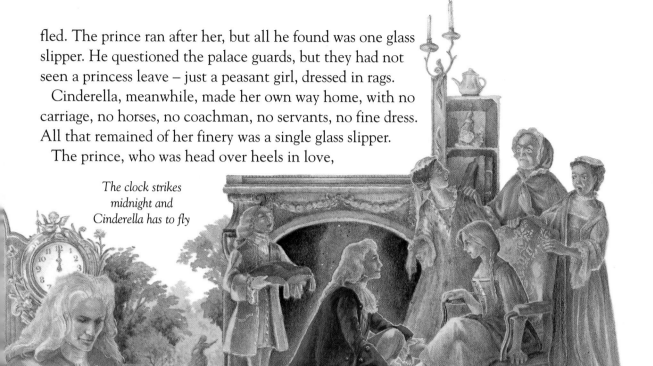

The clock strikes midnight and Cinderella has to fly

Cinderella

The prince finds Cinderella's glass slipper

The prince tries the slipper on Cinderella's foot and it fits perfectly, to the dismay of her stepmother and stepsisters

proclaimed that he would marry the girl whose foot fitted the glass slipper. He visited every house in the kingdom in search of her.

At last the prince arrived at Cinderella's house. The two sisters tried as hard as they could to squeeze their big feet into the glass slipper, but in vain. "Is there no other girl in the house?" asked the prince.

"No," the sisters replied. "Unless you count Cinderella, but she's just a grimy little good-for-nothing."

"Nevertheless," said the prince, "let her try on the slipper."

So Cinderella came out from the chimney-corner. Her foot slid as neatly into the glass slipper as a sword into its sheath. As she stood there, in her tattered dress all smeared with dust and ashes, the prince still thought she was the most beautiful girl in the world.

So Cinderella and the prince were married and lived happily ever after. And Cinderella, who was as good as she was beautiful, forgave her sisters and took them to live with her in the palace, where they married two great lords of the court.

GRIMM ENDING
In the Grimms' version of "Cinderella", the stepsisters each cut a piece from one foot to make it fit the slipper. Their attempts to fool the prince are thwarted by two pigeons cooing:
"Turn and peep, turn and peep,
There's blood within the shoe,
The shoe it is too small for her,
The true bride waits for you."
Later, at Cinderella's wedding, the same pigeons peck the sisters' eyes out!

Rapunzel

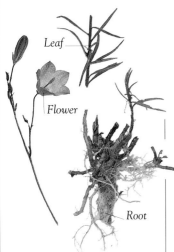

RAMPION
"Rapunzel" is the German for rampion, a type of harebell with delicate blue flowers. Its first-year roots and young leaves can be used in salads.

HERB GARDEN
This 14th-century book illustration shows a doctor selecting herbs in a herb garden. At that time, herbs were much more important for medicinal purposes than for cooking, and anyone specializing in making medicines or potions – a witch, for example – would be likely to maintain a well-stocked herb garden.

A MAN AND WIFE yearned for a child and at last God granted their wish. One day, the wife was standing at a window, looking down on the garden of their neighbour, who was a witch. The garden, which was full of flowers, herbs, and vegetables, was surrounded by a high wall. The wife gazed longingly at a bed of fresh green rapunzel and called out to her husband, "I must have some of that rapunzel or I will die."

At dusk her husband climbed the garden wall, snatched a handful of rapunzel, and took it to her. She ate it greedily, but it tasted so good that her craving grew. She now wanted rapunzel more than ever. Once again her husband crept into the witch's garden. But this time the witch was waiting.

The witch catches her next-door neighbour stealing rapunzel from her garden

"How dare you steal my rapunzel?" she hissed. "You'll pay for this!"

"Have mercy," begged the man. "My wife saw your rapunzel from our window, and said she would die if she did not have some!"

"If what you say is true," the witch replied, "take as much rapunzel as you like. But on one condition: when your wife gives birth, you must give me the child." The terrified man agreed, and, when a baby girl was born, the witch carried her off.

"Her name shall be Rapunzel," she said.

Rapunzel grew to be the loveliest child under the sun. When she was twelve, the witch took her into the forest and shut her in a tower that had neither stairs nor door, only a window at the top. When the witch wanted to come in, she stood below and shouted, "Rapunzel, Rapunzel, let down your hair!" Rapunzel had long, long hair, fine as spun gold, and, when she heard the witch's cry, she would unfasten her braids, twist them around the window hooks, and let her tresses fall to the ground for the witch to climb up.

A few years later, the king's son chanced to ride through the forest. As he passed the tower, he heard a voice singing so sweetly that he had to stop and listen. The prince longed to see the owner of the voice, but the tower had neither door nor stairs, so he rode home. But every day he returned to listen.

One day, the prince was standing behind a tree when the witch arrived and he heard her call, "Rapunzel, Rapunzel, let down your hair!"

Rapunzel undid her braids, and the witch climbed the ladder of golden hair. "So that's how it's done," he thought. Next day, towards evening, he came to the tower and called, "Rapunzel, Rapunzel, let down your hair!"

She did so and the prince climbed up. Rapunzel had never seen a man before, but the prince spoke so gently to her that she soon lost her fear. He told her that he had been captivated by her singing and couldn't rest until he had seen her. And then he asked if she would be his bride.

She saw that he was young and handsome and thought, "He will love me more than my old godmother does." So she answered yes, and put her hand in his. "Bring a skein of silk with you every time you come," she added. "I can weave a ladder from it. When it is done I shall climb down and ride away with you."

The witch hides Rapunzel in a high tower

The tower

When the witch visits Rapunzel, she tells her to let down her hair

The prince

The prince sees the witch climb up tresses of golden hair

When the prince reaches the top of the tower, he is captivated by Rapunzel's beauty

DARK FORESTS
Over a quarter of Germany is forest, and for centuries forests such as this one in north-eastern Germany have provided suitably atmospheric settings for the country's rich store of fairy tales and legends. The dense forest in "Rapunzel" cuts the heroine off from the outside world. Only when she escapes it does she find happiness.

After several years apart, Rapunzel and the blind prince meet again in her desert home

They agreed that he should visit her every evening, for the old witch came only by day. The witch suspected nothing, until one morning Rapunzel asked her, "Godmother, why is it that my dresses no longer fit?" For she had fallen pregnant to her husband, the prince.

"Wicked child!" cried the witch. "I thought I had shut you away from the world, but you have deceived me!" In her anger, she cut off Rapunzel's beautiful hair – snip! snap! Then she took Rapunzel out into a desert, and left her there.

That evening, when the prince came to the tower and called, "Rapunzel, let down your hair," the witch lowered the cut braids. The prince climbed up.

"Aha!" glowered the witch. "The bird has flown the nest. She won't be singing any more; the cat has got her. And the same cat will scratch your eyes out. You will never see your Rapunzel again!"

Determined to trap the prince, the witch cuts off Rapunzel's golden hair

In despair, the prince leapt from the tower. As he fell, thorns scratched his eyes and made him blind. He stumbled away, weeping.

The prince wandered for several years, until at last he came to the desert where Rapunzel was living, with the twins she had borne – a boy and girl. He heard a voice sweetly singing, and when he came closer, Rapunzel recognized him. She hugged him close, and wept, and as she wept, two tears fell on his eyes and his eyesight returned.

The prince took Rapunzel and their children back to his kingdom, where they were welcomed with joy, and lived in happiness and contentment.

Rapunzel's children

❧ *The Heart's Door* ❧

ONCE THERE WAS a young man named Severi who set out to seek his fortune. He walked over hills and meadows, and through deep woods, until at last he came to the sea. There he saw a little rowboat on the shore.

Severi got into the boat and set out across the ocean. The boat was tossed by the winds and lashed by the rains, and at last a huge wave washed Severi overboard. But he did not lose heart. He swam night and day until he reached a white beach at the foot of a black cliff. Dangling from the cliff top was a rope, so Severi climbed up.

At the top of the cliff, Severi found a path that led him down into the heart of the hill. At the bottom he came to a golden door, which opened for him. He stepped through into a magic world of green meadows, beautiful flowers, and trees hung with golden fruit.

There, Severi met an old man with long white hair who asked him who he was and where he was going. "My name is Severi," he replied, "but I do not know where I am going."

"Then stay here," said the old man, "and be my servant."

So Severi went to live with the old man in his copper castle.

The next morning, the old man said that he must go away on a long journey. "Here are the keys to the castle," he said. "There are twenty-four keys for twenty-four rooms. Feel free to go into all the rooms except the last. If you go in there, you go at your own risk."

When Severi was left alone in the castle, he began to explore the twenty-three rooms. Each one was more wonderful than the last. One was all gold, another all silver, another black ebony, another polished marble. But at last he had seen all of them, and then he was sad. "Now all my adventures are over," he said. "There's nothing left to see. I might as well go home."

But when he woke up next morning, Severi found the key to the twenty-fourth room clutched tight in his hand. "It's a sign," he thought. "I shall open the twenty-fourth door, and take the risk."

MAGICAL CASTLE
Though built of stone, not copper like the one described in this story, Olavinlinna's lakeland setting helps make it one of Finland's most impressive castles. Situated in Savonlinna in the east of the country, it dates from 1475.

Severi steps into a magical, enchanted world

Severi sees Vappu, the loveliest girl in the world, sitting on a golden throne

When he opened the last door, he saw in the middle of the room a high throne, and sitting on it was the loveliest girl in the whole world.

"Who are you?" asked Severi.

"My name is Vappu," said the girl, "and I have been waiting for you for the longest time." Her voice rippled through the air like the notes of a harp.

Severi and Vappu lived happily together in the copper castle for a whole month. They used to sit by the silver stream and feast on the golden fruit from the old man's garden with never a care in the world. But one day they fell asleep beside the stream, and when Severi awoke, Vappu was gone.

Severi called and called for her. "Vappu! Vappu!" But the only answer was the twittering of the red and golden birds that flitted through the trees.

GOLDEN DAYS
Summer is short in Finland, but for about four weeks the sun never sets and the countryside is transformed into something like the golden paradise described in this tale. Then, like a door closing, winter returns.

Vappu vanishes, but the old man's magic brings her back. To keep her, Severi must win a game of hide and seek. The old man whispers a magic spell

The old man came home to find Severi deep in misery. "I warned you not to open the twenty-fourth door," he said.

"I am man enough to make my own choices," replied Severi.

"And now you have made them, are you wiser for it?"

"My sorrow has made me older," said Severi, "and wiser, too."

Then the old man muttered a magic spell, and Vappu reappeared, radiant as a sunbeam.

"Never leave me again!" said Severi.

"I will not," said Vappu, "on one condition. You must hide from me so that I cannot find you. I will give you three chances."

Severi did not know how to outwit clever Vappu, but the old man whispered a magic charm to him that he said would help.

First Severi hid among the wild rabbits, but Vappu tracked him down. Then Severi tried to hide among the wild bears, but Vappu tracked him down.

At last, Severi resolved to hide in Vappu's heart. He said, "Three times I knock at your door, dear heart.

Let me in, heart's jewel, let me in."

Vappu looked all around. "It is strange," she said. "One minute Severi was standing beside me. Now he is gone."

So Severi called to her, "Can you not find me, my golden one?"

"No, I cannot," said Vappu. "Where are you?"

"I am here, in your heart," said Severi.

FIRESIDE STORY
In Finland, fairy tales were traditionally told around the fire in a tupa, a peasant's hut. This story's beautiful imagery would have cheered listeners on long winter nights.

He hides among the rabbits and hides among the bears. Each time Vappu finds him

"Then my heart is yours," said Vappu.

Severi came out from her heart, and the two lovers embraced. They lived happily ever after in the copper castle in that kingdom, beside the silver stream, beneath the golden trees.

Then he finds the perfect place to hide – in her heart

The Goodman of Wastness

ISLAND OF SELKIES
There are many selkie stories in Orkney and Shetland, an area well known for seals. Wastness is probably modern-day Westness, on the coast of the Orkney island of Rousay. A similar Irish tale tells of a man who captures a beautiful, green-haired merrow, a sea fairy, by stealing her magic diving cap.

MERMAID
Similar to the selkie, and also with a sweet singing voice, is the mermaid (above), which, according to the accounts of lonely sailors, has a woman's head and body and a fish's tail.

THE GOODMAN OF WASTNESS was a handsome bachelor. All the girls of Orkney set their caps at him, but he would have none of them. "I'm happy as I am," he said.

One day the goodman went walking by the sea. There he saw a band of the selkie folk, the seal people who live in the ocean in those parts. They were naked, having set aside their seal skins in the warm sun. They were playing and laughing, and diving off rocks into the sea. But although the water was deep enough for diving on the ocean side, on the shore side it was just a shallow pool. The goodman crept through this pool and snatched one of the skins.

The selkies grabbed their skins and fled. They swam out to sea and turned to stare at the man who had dared to sneak up on them. Each head was the head of a seal, except for one.

The goodman walked away. He was not even back on dry land before he heard a girl sobbing and pleading

The goodman seizes the selkie's seal skin, and she is forced to follow him

behind him. It was the poor girl whose skin he had taken. "Man, if there is any mercy in you, give me back my skin!" she begged. "I cannot, cannot, cannot live in the sea without it. I cannot, cannot, cannot live with my own folk without a seal skin. Have pity on me, as you hope for pity yourself."

Now the goodman did indeed pity the girl, but no sooner did he feel pity than he also felt love. And of the two emotions, love was the stronger. So he kept the skin. He argued, and higgled, and haggled, until the girl agreed to marry him and live on the land.

So they were married and in time the sea-girl bore her husband seven children, four boys and three girls. She had a laugh that rippled like the waves of the sea and you might have thought her happy. But when no-one was watching, she used to gaze out to sea, and she taught her children mournful songs that nobody had ever heard the like of before.

In all this time, she had had never so much as an inkling of where her seal skin might be hidden. One day, the goodman took his three oldest boys fishing, and the wife sent three of the other children to collect whelks on the seashore. Only the youngest girl stayed at home, because she had a sore foot. As soon as the others were gone, the wife began to search the house, as she did every time she was left alone. She looked everywhere; but she couldn't find the seal skin.

"What are you looking for?" asked her youngest.

"For a seal skin to wrap up your sore foot."

"I know where it is," said the girl. "I once saw father take one down from the space between the wall and the roof. He looked at it a minute, then put it back."

The wife rushed to the place and pulled down her long-lost skin. "Farewell, peerie buddo!" she cried. "Farewell, little darling!" She ran to the beach, put on the seal skin, and dived into the sea.

The goodman was coming home in his fishing boat as a seal swam past him. It was his wife. She uncovered her face and sang:

"Goodman of Wastness, farewell to thee!
I liked you well, you were good to me,
But better I love my man of the sea!"

He never saw his beautiful seal-wife again.

The goodman marries the mysterious selkie and in time they have seven children

The youngest child tells where her father hid the selkie's seal skin

The selkie wife puts on her skin and joyfully returns to the sea, leaving husband and children behind

❧ The Snake Prince ❧

GREEN FIRE
The necklace in the tale could have resembled this one, made of emeralds and enamelled gold sections. Called a *satratana*, each of its seven jewels represents a planet in Indian astrology.

O NCE IN A CITY in India there lived a poor old woman who had nothing to eat but a little dry flour. She took a brass pot down to the river to collect water to mix with the flour so she could make some bread.

She left the brass pot on the bank while she bathed. A little later when she came to fill it with water, she lifted the cloth cover and saw inside the glittering coils and flicking tongue of a deadly snake!

She replaced the cloth, saying, "Better to die from snakebite than hunger. I will take you home, shake you from the pot, and then all my troubles shall be at an end."

But when she upturned the pot on her hearthstone, instead of a snake, out fell a necklace of flashing jewels.

The old woman took the magnificent necklace to the rajah, who rewarded her with enough money to keep her in comfort for the rest of her life.

Soon afterwards the rajah was invited by a neighbouring rajah to celebrate the birth of a baby girl. The rajah said to his wife, the rani, "Now is your chance to wear that beautiful necklace." The rani went to her jewel chest to fetch the necklace, but when she opened the lid, instead of a necklace, she found a fat little baby boy, crowing and shouting. The rani, who had no children of her own, picked him up, crying, "You are more precious than any necklace."

She takes the necklace to the rajah, who rewards her

The necklace turns into a baby boy, who becomes the rajah's son

The old woman

After bathing in the river, the old woman finds a snake in her brass pot

So the rajah sent to his neighbour, and said that he could not come, for he must celebrate the birth of his own baby boy.

In time, it was arranged that the two children should marry and, when they were grown, the wedding took place with much rejoicing. But the neighbouring rajah and rani had heard rumours that there was something odd about the prince's birth. They told their daughter not to speak a word to her husband after the wedding. "When he asks you what is the matter," urged her mother, "tell him you will never speak to him unless he tells you the secret of his birth."

After the wedding, the prince begged his wife to speak to him.

"Tell me the secret of your birth," she said.

He replied, "If I did, you would regret it till the end of your life."

And so the days passed in brooding silence. The prince's secret lay between man and wife like a cloud between the sun and the earth.

At last the prince could bear it no longer. "At midnight, you shall have your wish," he said. "But I warn you, you will regret it." His wife paid no heed to his warnings.

At midnight, they rode down to the river, where the old woman had gone with her brass pot. The prince said, "Do you still insist on learning my secret?"

"Yes!" answered his wife.

"Then," said the prince, "know that I am the son of the king of a far country, who was turned by enchantment into a sna..."

The prince marries a princess – who refuses to speak until he tells her the secret of his birth

GREAT KING
The subcontinent of India was once ruled by rajahs such as the Maharajah ("Hindi for Great King") of Lahore (above). A rajah's wife is called a "rani".

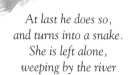

At last he does so, and turns into a snake. She is left alone, weeping by the river

Even as the prince said the fateful word, he turned back into a snake and slid into the river. By the light of the moon, the princess saw ripples on the black water as the snake swam away. And then she was alone on the riverbank.

The princess wept and tore her clothes. She ordered her servants to build her a little house of black stone by the river, and there she lived, mourning for her lost husband.

A long time passed. Then one day, when the princess awoke, she saw a trail of fresh mud on the carpet of her bedroom. She summoned her guards, but they swore that no one had entered. The next night, the same thing happened. On the third night, the princess was determined to stay awake. She took a knife, cut her hand, and rubbed salt into the wound so the pain would keep her from sleeping.

At midnight, a snake slithered into her room, leaving a trail of mud at it went. It crawled towards her bed, raised its flat head onto the mattress and stared at her.

"Who are you? What do you want?" she whispered, trembling with fear.

*The princess mourns the loss of her
prince in her house of black stone*

*Because of the pain of her cut hand, the princess is wide awake when
her snake husband slithers to her bedside at midnight*

FRONTIER TALE
This story comes from
Firozpûr, on the Indian
side of the border with
Pakistan.

The snake replied, "I am your husband." The princess began to weep. The snake continued, "Did I not tell you that if you forced my secret from me, you would regret it?"

"I do regret it," she said. "I regret it every day. If only there was something I could do to make things right again."

"There is something," said the snake, "but it is very dangerous. Tomorrow night, place a large bowl of milk and sugar in each of the four corners of this room. All the snakes in the river will come to drink, and the one that leads the way will be the queen of snakes. You must bar her way at the door and say, 'Queen of snakes, queen of snakes, give me back my husband!' If you show no fear, you will win my freedom. But if you flinch, you will never see me again."

That night, the princess put out the bowls of milk and sugar and waited. At midnight she heard a great hissing from the river, and soon the whole riverbank was seething with snakes. At their head was a huge hooded creature with gleaming, shimmering scales.

The princess's guards ran in terror.

The guards

SERPENT GODS
Snakes are especially important in Hindu culture as symbols of fertility. Semidivine creatures called *nagas* (above, a 12th-century bronze), half human, half snake, inhabit bejewelled palaces in underworld kingdoms. They are associated with water, especially wells, rivers, and lakes.

The princess bravely faces the snakes, and wins back her husband

But the princess stood in the doorway and commanded, "Queen of snakes, give me back my husband."

The rustling, writhing snakes seemed to hiss "Husssband! Husssband!"

The snake queen's head swayed to and fro, fixing the princess with wicked, beady eyes. But the princess did not flinch. "Queen of snakes, give me back my husband," she repeated.

The snakes, led by their queen, crawl from the river

"Tomorrow!" said the snake queen. "Tomorrow!"

Then the princess stood aside, and the snakes flooded into her room, jostling greedily over the bowls of sweet milk.

The next morning the princess dressed in her most beautiful sari. She filled the house with flowers and waited. At midnight, the prince came walking through the door and they fell into each other's arms. There were never any secrets between them again.

WINDOW DRESSING
This woman, like the princess at the end of this tale, is dressed in her "most beautiful sari". She is sitting in a window of the Jaisalamer Palace, Rajasthan, India.

Falling Star

CAMPFIRE STORY
This Native American tale is especially popular among the Cheyenne, who once pitched their buffalo-hide tepees (above) on the vast North American plains.

UP A TREE
In this story, Brightest Star takes on the form of a porcupine to lure First Girl up into the sky world. Porcupine meat is edible, which helps explain why First Girl pursues it. The North American porcupine frequently climbs pine trees to feed on bark.

ONE SUMMER'S NIGHT two girls lay outside their tepee looking up at the stars. "Look at that one!" said First Girl. "It's the brightest of them all. I would like to marry that star."

Next day, the two girls were gathering wood when they saw a porcupine climbing a tree.

"I'll fetch him down," said First Girl, scrambling up the tree after him. The porcupine kept climbing, always just out of reach, but First Girl kept climbing, too.

"Come down! Come down!" begged Second Girl, but soon First Girl was too high to hear.

The pine tree went up and up until it reached the sky world. First Girl began to weep with fear because she had climbed so high. Then a voice said, "Don't cry. I am Brightest Star, and I would like to marry you."

So First Girl and Brightest Star were married. Brightest Star said that she could do anything she liked in the sky world, but if she dug up any of the white turnips that grew there, something bad was sure to happen.

They lived happily together, and soon had a child. But First Girl couldn't help being curious about the white turnips and one day she dug one up. It left a hole in the sky world through which she could see the earth far below. Longing to see her home again, she wove some grass into a rope. It looked long enough to reach the ground, so First Girl began to climb down through the hole, her baby in her arms.

She is met at the top by Brightest Star

She follows a porcupine up a tree

First Girl longs to marry the brightest star

First Girl longs to visit her home on earth

She climbs down with her baby, but the rope is too short and she falls

The boy soon learns to run as fast as the larks fly

The baby is rescued by a meadowlark

SHARP SHOOTER
The bow and arrow was the Cheyenne's principal weapon. Arrows were tipped with buffalo bone; a hide quiver, decorated with dyed porcupine quills, held about 20. The bow was of hardwood, and only about 1 m (3 ft) long, making it easy to use on horseback. The bowstring was a twisted buffalo sinew.

But when First Girl reached the end of the rope, the ground was still far below her. She clung on desperately, but at last her strength gave out and she fell…

She died, but her baby, who was made of star-stone, survived. A meadowlark carried the child to her nest, and looked after him alongside her own fledglings. She called him Falling Star.

The boy grew quickly and could soon run fast enough to keep up with the flying birds. But the meadowlark was sad he had no wings. When winter approached, and it was time for the larks to fly south, she knew he could not make such a long journey on foot.

"Make me a bow and arrows, and I will look after myself," said Falling Star.

With the bow and arrows the larks made for him, he walked along a river, and so came to the tepees of his mother's people. He said to an old woman there, "Grandmother, I am thirsty."

"I can't give you water," she replied. "There's a monster in the river that swallows up anyone who goes near!"

But Falling Star's throat was so parched he borrowed her bucket of buffalo skin and her buffalo-horn ladle and went to the river. As soon as he dipped the ladle in the water, an enormous monster reared up, opened its gaping mouth, and sucked him down.

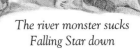

The river monster sucks Falling Star down

BUFFALO HUNTING
The Cheyenne depended on the buffalo (above) that once roamed the plains for food, tools, and hides. Before the Cheyenne acquired horses, they used to sneak up on a herd by disguising themselves as animals – as Falling Star does in this story.

Disguised as a buffalo, Falling Star catches the white crow

The fast runners

Inside the creature's stomach, crouched in fear at the back, Falling Star found all the other people the monster had swallowed alive.

Falling Star's mother was a Cheyenne girl, but his father was a star, and he was made of star-stone. He punched a hole in the monster's side and killed it. The people crawled out, and Falling Star took them back to the camp.

Falling Star punches a hole in the monster's side

Then Falling Star went to the old woman and said, "Grandmother, I am hungry."

She replied, "I cannot give you any food. Whenever the men go out to hunt, a white crow warns the buffalo that they are coming."

"Do not worry about that," said Falling Star. "Bring me a buffalo skin and two fast runners."

He said to the fast runners, "You must pretend to shoot me."

Falling Star put on the old buffalo skin and joined the buffalo herd. When the two runners approached, the white crow flew up, calling, "Run! Hunters are coming!" The buffalo herd ran away, with Falling Star in his shabby old skin following behind. The runners shot their arrows, and Falling Star fell down as if he were dead. The white crow circled above him, calling, "Why were you so slow?" The crow flew closer and closer. Falling Star reached out from beneath the buffalo skin and caught it by the legs.

He carried the bird back to the camp in triumph and presented it to the chief, who announced, "I will take this bird to my tepee, tie him to the smoke hole, and smoke him to death."

From that day on, the Cheyennes were able to kill as many buffalo as they needed, and never went hungry.

The people were so grateful that they gave Falling Star a fine tepee of his own and the prettiest girl in the tribe for his bride.

And every night, Brightest Star, Falling Star's father, shone down from the sky, and blessed them with his light.

❧ The Snow Wife ❧

LONG AGO there was a young man who had never found a girl he wanted to marry, so he lived alone. One winter night, during a violent snowstorm, he heard a knock at his door. When he opened it, he found a young woman lying in a heap outside.

He brought her into the house, and soon she began to revive, though her face remained as pale as snow. She was so beautiful that he asked her to become his wife.

They lived happily together all that winter, but as the spring thaws approached and the weather grew warmer, the young wife began to lose her strength. She grew thinner and weaker every day.

The young man carries the girl inside, and she revives

The young man thought that perhaps his wife was pining for company, so he asked some friends to a party to celebrate the coming of spring. In the middle of the party, while the guests were eating and drinking, the young man called out to his wife in the kitchen. When she did not answer, he went to look for her.

She was nowhere to be seen. There was only her kimono, lying in a pool of water in front of the stove.

To his dismay, he finds only her kimono and a pool of water

LAND OF SNOW
The story of the Snow Wife is very popular in various versions in Japan, particularly in the west, where the snow often lies three metres deep and may remain on the ground for up to six months.

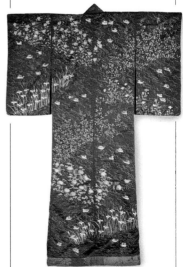

SILK KIMONO
When spring comes, the Snow Wife melts away, leaving only her beautiful kimono behind. This traditional robe, like the one shown above, would have been made of embroidered silk.

The Sleeping Prince

A KING HAD A DAUGHTER who was his heart's delight. When he had to go to war, he worried what would become of her. "Go well, father, and return well," she said. "I shall be waiting."

Every day she sat at her window, watching for her father's return, and embroidering a handkerchief to give him. One day, a golden eagle wheeled across the sky, calling, "Embroider away, embroider away; you shall marry a dead man one day."

"What do you mean?" asked the princess.

"Climb on my back and you shall see," the eagle replied.

The eagle carried her far away, to a courtyard where stood a well. The princess looked into the well; at the bottom was a palace.

There she found a prince lying as if dead. A note by his side read, "If you pity me, watch over me for three months, three weeks, three hours, and three minutes. When I sneeze, say 'Bless you, my prince, may you live for ever.' I shall wake and claim you as my bride."

The princess sat by the sleeping prince for three months and three weeks. Food was brought to her, but she never saw anyone bring it and she had no one to talk to. So when she heard a girl calling "Serving maid for hire!" from outside the well, she called back, "Look down the well!"

The girl looked pretty and kind and the princess hired her as her maid. She told her all about the sleeping prince. The maid said, "Go to sleep. I will keep watch and wake you if the prince sneezes."

As soon as the princess fell asleep, the prince sneezed. Quick as a flash the maid said, "Bless you, my prince, may you live for ever."

The prince awoke and embraced the maid.

An eagle carries the princess far away – to a palace at the bottom of a well

BIG BIRDS
Fairy-tale eagles, like the one in this story, are often hugely powerful – none more so than the rocs of *The Arabian Nights*, illustrated above by J. D. Batten in 1895.

The maid

For months the princess watches over the sleeping prince – then she hears a voice calling "Serving maid for hire!"

"You have freed me from a magic spell," he said. "You shall be my bride." Then he noticed the princess asleep on the floor.

"That's my maid," said the maid.

"Let the poor thing sleep," smiled the prince. "Then send her out to mind the geese."

When the princess awoke, her maid told her, "The prince woke up, and said he wanted me, not you, and you were to mind the geese."

There was nothing the princess could do.

The prince asked the maid what gift she would like. "A crown of diamonds," she replied. He asked the goose girl what she would like. She replied, "The millstone of patience, the hangman's rope, and the butcher's knife." He gave each girl what she asked for.

That night the prince heard sad murmurings coming from the goose girl's room. The princess was

The princess is unfairly sent to mind the geese

As soon as the princess falls asleep, the prince sneezes and finds the maid

The princess

The prince

The maid Crown

Millstone

Knife

Rope

The prince bursts into the room, just in time to stop the lovelorn princess killing herself out of grief

telling the millstone of patience her troubles. She asked, "Millstone, what should I do?"

"Have patience," the millstone replied.

Then she asked the knife, "Knife, what should I do?"

"Stab yourself!" the knife replied.

Then she asked the rope, "Rope, what should I do?"

"Hang yourself!" the rope replied.

The prince burst in. "Don't do it!" he shouted. "You are my true bride and that other girl is a liar. It is she who should hang!"

"No," said the princess. "Though she tried to do me harm, let her go free. Just take me home to my father and marry me."

GOODNIGHT, PRINCE! The story of the sleeping prince is particularly popular in Greece, and is also found in Italy and Armenia.

Ivan & the Firebird

DANCE OF FIRE
Russian folklore has many other Firebird tales, one of which formed the basis of the world-famous ballet with music by Igor Stravinsky. It was first performed in Paris in 1910 with costumes designed by Leon Bakst.

GOLDEN ORIOLE
A glittering yellow feather from the golden oriole, a shy bird that inhabits woodland across Europe and central Asia, may have helped inspire the legend of the magical Firebird.

Ivan spies the Firebird's golden feather

ONCE THERE LIVED a mighty tsar, who had in his service a brave young huntsman named Ivan, the owner of a magic talking horse. One day when Ivan was riding through the forest, he spied a golden feather, shining like a flame, lying on the path. It was a feather from the Firebird.

"Leave that feather alone!" said Ivan's horse. "If you pick it up, you'll pick up trouble with it." But Ivan was not afraid of trouble, so he picked up the feather and gave it to the tsar.

"This feather is so lovely," the tsar declared, "that I must have the whole bird. If I can't have the Firebird, you shall lose your head."

Ivan went to his horse and wept bitter tears. The horse said, "I told you so. But don't cry yet. The *real* trouble is still to come. Go to the tsar and ask to have a hundred sacks of corn scattered over a field."

Ivan did so, and the next day at dawn he rode out to the field and hid behind a tree. As the sun rose, he heard a rustling like the waves of the sea. It was the Firebird's wings. As it alighted on the corn, the horse came forward and stepped on its wing. Ivan bound it tightly with cords and brought it to the tsar.

The tsar was delighted with this gift and made Ivan a nobleman. But then he said, "Since you were so clever at catching the Firebird, you shall fetch me a bride. Beyond three times nine lands, at the edge of the world, lives the princess Vasilisa. Bring her to me and I will make you rich. Fail and you will lose your head!"

The Firebird alights on the scattered corn; Ivan catches it for the tsar

Ivan

Ivan's magic talking horse

Ivan went back to the horse, weeping bitter tears. The horse said, "I told you so. But don't cry yet. The *real* trouble is still to come. Go to the king and ask him for a tent with a golden roof and provisions for the journey."

After that, Ivan mounted his magic horse and rode off across three times nine lands to the edge of the world, where the red sun rises in flames from the deep blue sea. He stopped on the golden sand and looked out to sea. There he saw Princess Vasilisa rowing a silver boat with golden oars.

Where the grasslands met the sand, Ivan set up his golden-roofed tent, laid out a feast from the wonderful provisions the tsar had given him, and settled down to wait for the the princess.

When Princess Vasilisa saw the golden roof of the tent, she rowed towards the shore. As she stepped from her boat, Ivan said, "Welcome! Please be my guest and taste the fine wines I have brought from foreign lands."

The princess entered the tent, and soon she and Ivan were deep in talk and laughter as they ate and drank the tsar's wonderful food and wine. After a while, she became sleepy. As soon as she had fallen asleep, Ivan folded up the tent, mounted the magic horse, and, with the sleeping princess lying across the saddle, set off for home like an arrow shot from a bow.

The tsar was overjoyed to see the princess. He rewarded Ivan with gold and silver and made him even more noble than before. But when Princess Vasilisa awoke, and found that she was pledged in marriage to the wicked old tsar, she was grief-stricken.

EDGE OF THE WORLD
Ivan's journey to the "edge of the world" might have taken him to Provideniya Bay at sunrise (above) on Russia's east coast.

When Ivan first sees Princess Vasilisa, she is rowing a silver boat with golden oars

Obeying the tsar's orders, Ivan carries off the sleepy princess

The cruel, greedy tsar is overjoyed to see the princess, but she is grief-stricken

THE TSARS
The word tsar or czar comes from Caesar, the name adopted by the Roman emperors. The tsars ruled the Russian Empire from 1547 to the Russian Revolution of 1917. Among the most ruthless were Ivan the Terrible and Peter the Great (above). They were absolute rulers, with total power over their subjects, like the tsar in this tale.

CUNNING CRAB
The crab has a reputation for deviousness in many cultures – perhaps because of its sideways, scuttling walk. In this story, however, a well-placed hoof prevents any sneaky crab tricks!

Nothing the tsar could say would bring back her smile. She said, "I will never marry except in my wedding gown, and that is hidden beneath a stone in the middle of the deep blue sea."

The tsar said to Ivan, "Fetch Princess Vasilisa's wedding gown. Or you shall lose your head."

Ivan went to his horse and wept bitter tears. The horse said, "I told you so. But don't cry yet. The *real* trouble is still to come. Climb up and I will take you to the sea."

When they reached the sea, the horse stepped on a huge crab that was crawling out of the ocean. The crab said, "Spare me, please! I will do whatever you want."

Ivan said, "Fetch me the wedding gown of Princess Vasilisa, which is underneath a stone in the middle of the deep blue sea."

The crab gave a harsh cry and the sea began to heave. From it crawled thousands of crabs, ready to do their king's bidding. He sent them down into the depths of the ocean. In an hour they returned with the princess's wedding gown.

Ivan brought the gown to the tsar, who said, "Now, Princess Vasilisa, will you marry me?"

The crab king

Ivan asks the king of the crabs to fetch Princess Vasilisa's wedding gown from the depths of the sea. Thousands of little crabs do their king's bidding

"I will only marry you," said the princess, "if you order Ivan to jump into a vat of boiling water."

The tsar was so eager to marry the princess that, despite everything Ivan had done for him, he ordered a cauldron of water to be set over a fire and brought to the boil. And when it was boiling, he ordered it to be brought forward.

This is the trouble my horse warned me of, thought Ivan. If only I had listened to him! Then Ivan said to the tsar, "Please let me say farewell to my faithful horse." The tsar nodded, and Ivan went to the magic horse and flung his arms around its neck.

"Why are you crying?" asked the horse.

"The tsar wants to have me boiled alive," wept Ivan.

"Do not cry yet. There are worse troubles than this," said the horse,

The princess says she will only marry the tsar if Ivan is boiled alive

By his horse's magic, the boiling water makes Ivan even more handsome!

HUBBLE BUBBLE
The cauldron is a powerful symbol of magical transformation, fertility, and rebirth. In past times, a cauldron was an essential part of a witch or wizard's equipment. The one in this tale has magic powers of renewal – but only for the hero.

Ivan says farewell to his faithful steed

Believing the boiling water will make him young and good-looking, the old tsar jumps in the cauldron

WICKED WIZARD
The villain of other Firebird stories, replacing this tale's greedy tsar, is an evil wizard named Koschei the Deathless, here illustrated by A. Alexeiff. Koschei can only be killed if an egg containing the secret of his power is broken.

and it wove a spell of protection over Ivan, so that the water could not harm him. In fact, when Ivan was thrown into the boiling water, he came out stronger and more handsome than ever.

When the tsar saw what a power of good the water had done Ivan, he thought, if I get into the cauldron, I will become young and strong again. So he jumped into the water and boiled to death.

Ivan was crowned tsar in his place, married Princess Vasilisa, and they lived happily ever after.

The Black Bull of Norroway

I N NORROWAY, long ago, there lived a lady who had three daughters. One day, the oldest daughter said to her mother, "Mother, bake me a bannock and roast me a collop, for I'm going away to seek my fortune."

Her mother did so, and the girl went away to an old witch washerwife and told her that she had come to seek her fortune. The witch told her that if she kept watch out of the back door, her fortune would come. On the third day came a handsome man in a coach and six. "This one's for you!" said the witch.

So the girl got into the coach, which sped away.

The bull's brother's castle

The witch

The bull and the girl

A coach and six comes for the oldest girl

HOME COOKING
The daughters ask for food traditionally eaten by Scottish travellers. A collop is a slice of meat and a bannock is an unsweetened cake made of oats. Bannocks were cooked on an iron hot-plate called a griddle, shown above.

A coach and four comes for the second girl. But for the youngest comes a fearsome black bull that carries her off

The next day the second daughter arrived at the witch's house. When she looked out of the witch's back door, she saw a handsome man in a coach and four. "This one's for you!" said the witch.

Then the third daughter said to her mother, "Mother, bake me a bannock and roast me a collop, for I'm going away to seek my fortune." She went to the old witch washerwife and, like her sisters before her, kept watch from the back door for her fortune to come to her. Nothing came on the first day and nothing on the second. On the third, she saw a great black bull come bellowing down the road.

"This one's for you!" said the witch. The girl screamed in grief and fright. But the witch set her on the bull's back and away they went.

On and on they went, until the girl was faint with hunger. The black bull said, "Eat out of my right ear and drink out of my left ear." She did as he said, and was wonderfully refreshed.

Then the bull went on again, until they came to a splendid castle. "This castle belongs to my brother," said the bull. "We can rest here tonight." When they came to the castle, the bull's bother and his wife took the girl in and turned the bull out to graze in the park.

THE MIGHTY BULL
For farming peoples all over the world, the bull was (or is still) the major symbol of strength and fertility. This belief in the power of the bull was strong among the Celtic peoples of Europe. The black bull of this tale has many god-like qualities, including magically providing the girl with food and drink and fighting the devil.

In the morning, they fetched the girl into a shining parlour, and gave her a fine apple, warning her not to bite into it until she was in the greatest trouble anyone had ever known.

After another long day's ride, they came to a second castle. "This castle belongs to my second brother," said the bull. "We can rest here tonight." In the morning, the people of the castle gave the girl a fine pear, warning her not to bite into it until she was in the greatest trouble anyone had ever known.

At the end of the third day they came to another castle, the biggest one yet. "My youngest brother lives

The bull's brother and his wife give the girl a magic apple

here," said the bull. At that castle, they gave the girl a fine plum, warning her not to bite into it until she was in the greatest trouble anyone had ever known.

The next morning, the bull and the girl rode on, until they came to a dark glen. The bull set the girl down and said, "Now I must go and fight the devil. Sit on that stone and do not move hand or foot until I return. If you move, I will never be able to find you again. If all about you turns blue, you will know I have beaten the devil. But if all about you turns red, the devil will have beaten me."

THE HIGH ROAD
The heroine of this Lowland tale seems to be journeying north, past castles like Dundarave on Loch Fyne, towards the snow-capped mountains of the Highlands.

By the blue light, she realizes the bull has defeated the devil. She makes a fatal movement.

BEATING THE DEVIL
The devil, here pictured by Frank C. Papé in *The Book of Psalms* (1914), may be beaten in this story, but he is never far away in British folklore. A dropped fork, spilt water, or salt all attract him, although you may drive him away if you throw a pinch of spilt salt over your left shoulder and thus into his eyes. Yawning can be dangerous, for if you do not place your hand over your mouth, the devil may fly in.

The girl sat on the stone and didn't move a muscle. After a long time, everything around her turned blue and, in her joy at the bull's victory, she crossed one leg over the other.

Now the bull was really the Duke of Norroway, who had been enchanted into the shape of a black bull until he defeated the devil. Because the girl had moved, he could not find her when he came back from the fight.

The girl climbs the hill of glass

The girl sat for a long time, weeping all alone. At last she got up and set off, she didn't know where to.

On she wandered, until she came to a great hill of glass. She tried to climb it, but she couldn't. She tried to walk around it, but she couldn't. At last she came to a smithy, and the smith promised her that if she would serve him for seven years, he would make her a pair of iron shoes with which she could climb the glass hill. And at the end of seven years he was as good as his word, and the girl climbed the glass hill in her iron shoes.

When she reached the top, she found herself back in the witch washerwife's hut! "Wash these shirts," the witch said, "and I'll help you find your true love." The witch did not tell her that the shirts, which were stained with the devil's blood, belonged to the Duke of Norroway, who had sworn to marry the girl who could wash them clean. The witch had tried, her daughter had tried, but neither could shift the stains. But when the girl tried, the shirts were spotlessly clean.

The shirts come out spotless

The witch took the shirts to the duke, and told him that her daughter had washed them clean. So the Duke of Norroway and the witch's daughter were to be married.

When the girl realized she had been tricked, she thought of the beautiful apple she had been given and, biting into it, discovered it was filled with gold and silver jewellery. She went to the witch's daughter and said, "If you will delay your wedding one day, and allow me to go to the duke's room tonight, you can have these jewels."

The witch's daughter agreed, but the witch prepared a sleeping drink for the duke, so the girl could not awaken him.

The next day, the girl opened the pear, and found it full of jewels even more magnificent than those in the apple. She made her bargain again with the witch's daughter, but once more the witch gave the duke a sleeping draught, and she could not awaken him.

On the third day, the duke went hunting. His friends asked him about the crying and sighing coming from his bedroom the past two nights. The puzzled duke replied that he hadn't heard a thing.

Meanwhile, the girl opened the plum, and found jewellery even richer than that in the pear. She bargained as before, and the witch prepared another sleeping drink for the duke; but this time the duke, suspecting a trick, threw the drink away without tasting it.

Cunning Witch
The witch washerwife, also known as the "henwife", is the traditional witch of Scottish storytelling. She is more of a wise woman, cunning in the arts of medicine and magic, than an out and out villainess.

The duke is made to think that the witch's daughter cleaned the shirts

The sleeping duke

The jewels persuade the witch's daughter to let the girl spend time with the duke

The duke had just dozed off to sleep when the girl came into his room, sat by his side, and sang:

"Seven long years I served for thee,
The glassy hill I climbed for thee,
The bloody shirt I wrang for thee,
Will you not waken and turn to me?"

The duke awoke and turned to her. She told him all that had befallen her since they had parted, and he told her all that had befallen him. And he cast off the witch and her daughter and married the girl, and maybe they are still happily together today.

On the third night, the duke hearkens to the girl's sad song

Index to Part One

Numbers in **bold** refer to an entry in Who's Who in Mythology.

A

Achilles, 132
Acrisius, King of Argos, 148
Adapa, 38-39
Aegeus, King, 109
Aeneas, 154-155, **180**
Aeschere, 106
African myths: East, 76; West, 70-71, 77, 173
Ahriman, 30-31, 176, **180**
Ahura Mazda, 30-31, 176-177, **180**
Aido-Hwedo, 173
Ailill, King of Connaught, 128
Aino, 54
Ainu, 25
Aioina, 25, **180**
air-girl, 54
Alchera, 28
Alcmene, 130, 131
Ale, 77
Algonquin myths, 92-93
All-Father, *see* Odin
Amaterasu, 27, 84-85, **180**
Amazons, 132
Amphitrite, 110
Amphitryon, 130
Amulius, 138
Anchises, 154, 155
Anglo-Saxon myths, 106-107
Angra Mainyu, *see* Ahriman
An, *see* Anu
Andromeda, 148
Antum, 45
Anu, 38-39, 45, **180**
Anubis, 81, **180**

Apep, 16, 146
Aphrodite, 60, 108, **180**
Apollo, 104, **180**; and Cadmus, 96; and King Midas, 104, 105; and Orpheus, 166; and Pandora, 60; and the Sibyl, 154
apples, 73; golden, 133
Apples of Youth, 72-73
Ares, 180; *see also* Mars
Ariadne, 110, 111
Aristaeus, 166
Artemis, **180**
Arthur, King, 86-88, 89-91, 116, 156-158, **180**
Aruru, 44, **181**
Ascalaphus, 83
Asgard, 21, 62-63, 64-65, 72-73, 118
Ashanti myths, 70-71
Ask, 21
Aso, 70-71
Athena, 60, 61, **181**; and Bellerophon, 149; and Cadmus, 96-97; and Heracles, 130; and Perseus, 148
Athens, 96, 109
Atlantis, 170-171
Atlas, 134
Audhumla, 19
Augean stables, 132-133
Augeus, King, 132-133
Australian Aboriginal myths, 28-29, 69
Avagddu, 114
Avalon, 157, 158
Az, 176
Aztec myths, 140-143

B

Bacchus, *see* Dionysus
Baganda myths, 76
Balder, 162-165, 175, **181**
Bamapama, 69, **181**
Baron Samedi, *see* Ghede
Bast, *see* Bastet
Bastet, 146, **181**
Bedivere, Sir, 157, 158
Being, 62
Bellerophon, 149
Benten, 150, **181**
Beowulf, 106-107, **181**
Bors, Sir, 90, 91
Bran, 159-161, **181**
Bran the Blessed, 160
Bergelmir, 20
Bestla, 19
Bifrost, 21
Bor, 19
Bubastis, 146
Buddha, 147
Bull of Heaven, 45
Buri, 19

C

Cadmus, 96-97, **182**
Calliope, 166
Camlann, 156
Cap of Invisibility, 148
cat, 146
Cathbad, 129
Cattle of Geryon, 132

Celtic myths, 86-88, 89-91, 156-158
Cerberus, 135
Ceres, *see* Demeter
Ceridwen, 114-115
Cerynean hind, 132
Changing Woman, 36
Charon, 154, 166, **182**
Child of Water, 36-37
Chimaera, 149, **182**
Chinese myths, 22-23, 52, 151
Chuku, 77, **182**
Cinvat Bridge, 177
Clito, 170
Cold, 37
Conchubar, King of Ulster, 125-127
Core, 82
cosmic egg, 22-23
Coyote, 74-75, **182**
coyote, 74, 141
Creiwry, 114
Cretan bull, 132
Crete, 108, 112
Cronus, 58
Cuchulain, 125-129, **182**
Cumae, 154
Cupid, *see* Eros

D

Daedalus, **182**; and fall of Icarus, 112-113; and the Labyrinth, 108-109; and the temple at Cumae, 154
Danae, 148, 149
Delphi, 96
Demeter, 82-83, **182**
demigods, 132
Devi, 98, 99, 144, **182**
devil, 25
Diana, *see* Artemis
Dido, Queen of Carthage, 154
Dionysus, 102, 103,167, **182**
Dis, *see* Hades, King of the Underworld
Divine Mother, 98
dog, 35, 77, 168, 177

dragon, 23
Draupnir, 163, 164
Dreamtime, 28-29, 69
duck, 53, 54, 147
Durga, 98, 99
dwarfs, 20, 67

E

Ea, **182**; and Adapa, 38, 39; and Enkidu, 45; and the flood, 47, 48
Earth-maker, 74-75, **182**
East, 20
Ebisu, 26
Ector, Sir, 86-88
Egyptian myths, 16, 80-81, 146, 151, 172
Eisteddfod, 115
elephant, 144, 145
Elli, 123, 124
Elphin, 115-116
Elysium, 154
Embla, 21
Emer, 126-127
Emperor of Heaven, 52
Enkidu, 44-45, **182**
Enlil, 45, 47, 48, **182**
Epimetheus, 60
Eridu, 38
Erlik, 34-35, **182**
Eros, **182**
Erymanthian boar, 132
Estsánatlehi, 36, **182**
Europa, 96, 108
Eurydice, 166-167
Eurystheus, 130, 131, 135
Evenor, 170
Excalibur, 157

F

Fate, 62
Faunus, *see* Pan
Faustulus, 138
Fenris-wolf, 66, 67, 174, **182**
Finnish myths, 54-57
fire-priest, 30, 177

First Creator, 53, **183**
Flame, 124
floating world, 24-25
Fon myths, 173
Forgall Manach the Wily, 126-127
Freyja, 64, 65, **183**
Freyr, **183**
Friday, 164, 187
Frigg, 162, 163, 164, **183**
frost giants, 18, 19, **183**

G

Gaia, 58, 133
Galahad, Sir, 89-91
Ganesha, 144-145, **183**
Gawain, Sir, 156
Gayomart, 30-31, 177
Geb, 16, 80, **183**
Ghede, the Lord of Death, 117, **183**
giants, *see* frost giants
Gilgamesh, Lord of Uruk, 44-48, **183**
Ginnungagap, 18
Gleipnir, 67
Glooskap, 92-93, **183**
God, 17, 49, 50, 51
Good Mind, 30
Gorgons, the, 148, **183**
Greek: and apples, 73; myths, 58-61, 82-83, 96-97, 102-103, 104-105, 108-111, 112-113, 130-135, 148-149, 166-167, 170-171, 172; pantheon, **181**; and phoenix, 151
Grendel, 106-107
Guinevere, Queen, 88, 90, 156
Gwion, 114

H

Hades, 135; *see also* Underworld
Hades, King of the Underworld, **183**; and Heracles, 135; and Orpheus, 166, 167; and Persephone, 82-83; and Perseus, 148
Haitian myths, 117

Hannahanna, 94
Hare, *see* Coyote
Hastseyalti, 36
Hebrus, River, 167
Heimdall, 21, 174, **183**
Heinin, 116
Hel, 66, 162, 164
Helios, 82
Heorot, 106
Hephaestus, 60, 61, **183**
Hera, 58, 130, **183**; and golden
    apples, 133; and Heracles,
    130-131
Heracles, 61, 130-135, **183**
Hercules, 130; *see also* Heracles
Hermes, 60, 148, **184**
Hermod, 164,
Hesperides, Garden of the, 133-134
Hian, 42-43
Hina, 68
Hippolyta, 132
Hiruko, 26
Hittite myths, 94-95
Hoder, 162, 163, 175
Holy Grail, the, 89-91
Holy People, 36
Hope, 60
Horus, 81, **184**
House of Death, 33
Hrothgar, 106
Hugi, 122
Huginn, 62
Hunger, 37
Hydra, 132

I

Icarus, 112-113
Idun, 72-73
Ilmarinen, 55-56, **184**
Inanna, *see* Ishtar
Indian myths, 98-99, 144-145, 147
Indonesian myths, 42-43
Inspiration, 114
Inuit myths, 168, 169
Iranian myths, 30-31, 176-177
Irish myths, 125-129, 159-161

Ishtar, 44-45, 47, **184**
Isis, 80-81, **184**
Isle of Joy, 160
Isle of Women, 160
Izanagi, 24, 26-27, 84, **184**
Izanami, 24, 26-27, 84, **184**

J

Japanese myths, 24-25, 26-27,
    84-85, 150
Jataka tales, 147
Jormungand, *see* Midgard serpent
Jotunheim, 62, 63
Juno, *see* Hera
Jupiter, 139; *see also* Zeus

K

Kalevala, 54, 57
Kali, 98, 99
Kama, 99
Kamrusepas, 95, **184**
Kamui 24-25, **184**
kangaroo, 69
Kay, Sir, 86, 87
Killer of Enemies, 36-37
Knights of the Round Table, 88,
    89, 156
Knowledge, 114
Kojiki, 27
Kranyatz, 49-51
Kumush, 32-33, **184**
Kunitokotatchi, 26, **184**
Kurent, 49-51, **184**
Kwaku-Ananse, 70-71, **184**

L

Labyrinth, 109-111
Lady of the Lake, 157
Lancelot, Sir, 89-91, 156

Land of Gloom, 26, 27
Land of the Dead, *see* Niflheim
Lemminkainen, 56, **184**
Lethe, River, 155
Leucippe, 170
Lif, 175
Lifthrasir, 175
Lisa, 173
Logi, 121
Loki the Trickster, **184**;
    and Apples of Youth, 72-73;
    his children, 66; and death
    of Balder, 163-165; and
    Freyja, 64-65; in the land of
    giants, 118-124; and
    Ragnarok, 174
Lone Man, 53
Lord of Men and Beasts, 92
Lord of the Dawn, 143
Lord of the Dead, 142
Louhi, 55-57, **185**
Love, 30
Lucan, Sir, 157
Lugaid, 129

M

Maelgwyn, King, 115-116
Maenads, 167
Maeve, Queen of Connaught,
    128
Mahisha, 98, 99
Maidu myths, 74-75
Manannan, 159
Mandan myths, 53
Mares of Diomedes, 132
Mars, 138, 139; *see also* Ares
Mashu, 46
Mashya, 31, 176, 177
Mashyoi, 31, 176, 177
Maui-of-a-Thousand-Tricks, 68,
    185
Mawu, 173
Medusa, 148
Mercury, *see* Hermes
Merlin, 86, 88, 89, 90, **185**
Mexican myths, 140-143

Mictlantecuhtli, 142, **185**
Midas, King, 102-103, 104-105
Midgard: kingdom of, 21, 62;
    serpent, 66, 124, 174, **185**
Mimir, 62
Minerva, *see* Athena
Minos, King of Crete, 96,
    108-111, 112
Minotaur, the, 108-111, **185**
Miollnir, 65, 118
mistletoe, 163
Mmoatia, 70, 71
Mmoboro, 70, 71
Modoc myths, 32-33
Morda, 114
Mordred, 156, 157
Morgan le Fay, Queen, 158
Morrigan, 129, **185**
Mother of Sea Beasts, 168
Munnin, 62
Muspell, 18, 20, 174

N

Nana-Buluku, 173, **185**
Native American myths, 32-33,
    36-37, 53, 74-75, 92-93
Navajo myths, 36-37
Necessity, 62
Nemean lion, 131, 133
Nepthys, 80
Neptune, *see* Poseidon
Nereus, 134
Nidhogg, 62
Niflheim: creation of, 18, 21;
    and death of Balder, 162; and
    Hel, 66; and Yggdrasil, 62, 63
nightingale, 167
Nine Muses, 166, 167
Nsir, Mount, 48
Norns, the, 62, **185**
Norse: myths, 18-21, 62-63,
    64-67, 72-73, 118-124, 162-
    165, 174-175; pantheon, **187**
North, 20
Nsia, 70, 71
Numitor, 138

Nut, 16, 80, **185**
Nyankonpon, 70, **185**
Nymphs of the North Wind, 148

O

Odin, **185**; and creation, 18-21;
    and death of Balder, 162-165;
    and Fenris-wolf, 67; and
    Loki/Freyja, 64-65; and
    Ragnarok, 174; and Thiassi,
    72-73; and Yggdrasil, 62-63
Old Age, 37, 124
Old Man, 54, 56
Old Man of the Ancients, 32
Old Man of the Sea, 134
Old Woman, 54
Olympians, 58, **181**
Olympus, Mount, 58, 59, 167
Onini, 70, 71
Onokoro, 26
Orpheus, 102, 166-167, **185**
Osebo, 70, 71
Osiris, 80-81, **185**
Otherworld, 160
ox, 52
Ox star, 52

P

Pactolus, River, 102, 103
Pan, 104-105, 172, **185**
Pandora, 60
P'an-ku, 22-23, **185**
Parpara, 42-43
Parvati, 98, 99, 144-145
Pasiphae, 108, 109
peacock, 147
Pegasus, 148, 149
Pellervoinen, 54
Pelles, King, 89, 90, 91
Perceval, Sir, 90, 91
Persephone, 82-83, 135, 166, **185**
Perseus, 132, 148-149, **185**
Persian, *see* Iranian

phoenix, 23, 151
Polycaste, 112
Polydectes, 148, 149
Polynesian myths, 68
pomegranate, 83
Poseidon, 108, 109, **185**; and
    Atlantis, 170, 171
Prometheus, 56-61, **186**
Proserpina, 154; *see also*
    Persephone

Q

Queen of the Underworld, 82
Quetzal bird, 141, 142
Quetzalcoatl, 140-143, **186**
Quetzalpetatl, 141

R

Ra, *see* Re
Ragnarok, 165, 174-175
Raktabija, 99
rat, 145
Ratatosk, 62
Re, 16, 146, **186**
Remus, 138-139
Rhea, 58
Rhea Silvia, 138
Roman myths, 138-139, 154-155
Rome, 138
Romulus, 138-139
runes, 62
Roskva, 119-124
Ryu-wo, 150

S

Sabines, 139
Sampo, 55-57
sandpainting, 36
Saoshyant, 176, 177, **186**
satyrs, 102
Scathach, 127

Scorpions, 46
Sedna, 168, **186**
Sekhmet, 146
Serbian myths, 17, 49-51
Seriphos, 148
Set, 80, 81, **186**
Seth, *see* Set
shaman, 168
Shamash, 45, 46
sheep, 77
Shinto, 27, 150
Shiva, 98, 99, 144-145, **186**
Shu, 16, 80
Siberian myths, 34-35
Sibyl, 154, 155
Sidhe, 129
Siduri, 46
Siege Perilous, 89, 90
Sigyn, 165
Silenus, 102
Skrymir, 119-124
sky world, 42-43
Sleipnir, 65, 162, 164
snakes, 48
South, 20
South Wind, 38
sown men, 97
Spider Woman, 36
Stymphalian birds, 132
Styx, River, 154, 166
Sumerian myths, 38-39, 44-48
Surt, 174
Susanowo, 27, 84-85, **186**
Syrinx, 172

T

Taliesin, 114-116, 186
Talos, 112
Tammuz, 39
Taranga, 68
Tartarus, 154
Teelget, 37
Tefnut, 16
Telepinu, 94-95, **186**
Tezcatlipoca, 140-143, **186**
Thebes, 96

Theseus, 108-111, 132, **186**
Thetis, 61
Thialfi, 118-124
Thiassi, 72-73
Thor, 65, 118-124, 174, **187**
Thought, 124
Thursday, 119, 187
Titans, the, 58, 134, **181**
Tmolus, 104-105
torque, 126
tortoise, 23
tree: of life, *see* Yggdrasil;
    mythical, 35
Tsenhale, 37
Tsohanoai, 36-37
Tsuki-yomi, 27, 84
Tuatha de Danann, 126, **187**
Tuesday, 67, 187
Tuntu, *see* Kamui
Tyr, 67, **187**

U

Ulgan, 34-35, **187**
Ulster Cycle, 125
Uma, 98
Underworld, 154-155, 166, 168;
    see also Hades
Unferth, 106-107
Ungambikula, 28-29
unicorn, 23
Uranus, 58, **187**
Ure, *see* Bamapama
Urshanabi, 46
Uruk, 44, 45
Utgard, 21, 120, 121
Utgard-Loki, 121-124
Uther Pendragon, King, 86, 88
Utnapishtim, 46-48, **187**
Uzume, 84, 85, **187**

V

Vainamoinen, 54-57
Valhalla, 63
Valkyries, the, 179, **187**

Ve, 19, 21
Venus, 154; *see also* Aphrodite
Vidar, 174
Vili, 19, 21
Vinadhara, 144
Vishnu, 98
Vodu, the, 173
Voodoo, 117
Vulcan, *see* Hephaestus

W

wagtail, 24, 25
Walukaga, 76
Wasis, 92-93
Wednesday, 187
Welsh myths, 114-116, 160
West, 20
White Corn Boy, 36

X, Y, Z

Xolotl, 141-143
Yang, 22
Yeitso, 37
Yellow Corn Girl, 36
Yggdrasil, 21, 62-63, 175, 187
Yin, 22
Ymir, 18, 19, 20
Yryn-ai-tojon, *see* Ulgan
Zeus, **187**; and Alcmene, 130;
    and Atlantis, 171; and Danae,
    148; and Europa, 96, 108; and
    Hades, King of the Underworld,
    83; and Prometheus, 58-61
Zoroaster, 30

INDEX TO PART TWO

A

Alfonsus, Petrus, 243
Anancy, 282-283
Andersen, Hans Christian, 199, 216
angel, 240, 286
apple, 211, 308
Apuleius, 225
Arabian Nights, The, 211, 286, 332
Asbjørnsen, Peter Christen, 304
Ash Lad, 195, 197, 246-247, 304-305
Australian fairy tale, 296

B

Baal Shem Tov, 286, 287
"Baba Yaga", 195, 288-289
Baba Yaga Bonylegs, 288-289
ballets from fairy tales, 204, 314, 334
Beast, 221-225
Beaumont, Mme de, 220
Beauty, 220-225
"Beauty & the Beast", 201, 220-225
Bible stories, 279, 293, 295
"Black Bull of Norroway, The", 311, 338-341
"Bluebeard", 298-301
Bluebeard, 298-301
   real-life Bluebeards, 299
"Boat That Sailed on Land, The", 248-249

Brazilian fairy tale, 231
Brightest Star, 328, 330

C

Cape Verdean fairy tale, 256
Carrière, Joseph Médard, 248
castle, 202, 215, 221, 252, 269, 319
changeling, 237
Chief Nzambi, 302
Chinese fairy tale, 258
"Cinderella", 312-315
Cinderella, 311, 312-315
Costa Rican fairy tale, 226
Cricket, 235, 239
"Cricket, the Fortune-Teller", 239
Cupid, 225
Czech fairy tale, 210

D

Damper, 296-297
"Dancing Water, The", 274-277
"Demon in the Jug, The", 286-287
devil, 340
"Doctor Know-All", 239
Dona Labismina, 230-233
dragon, 196, 279
Duke of Norroway, 340-341
Dutch fairy tale, 262

E

"Easy Come, Easy Go", 235, 262-263
"Eating Match With a Troll, An", 304-305
Ellis, Elsie Spicer, 233
"Endless Tale, The", 255
English fairy tales, 250, 255, 290
eventyr, 304

F

fairy, 197, 202, 213-215, 237, 260, 284, 304
   sea, 322
fairy godmother, 314
fairy tale
   collectors of, 198-199
   history of, 194-197
"Falling Star", 328-330
Falling Star, 329-330
False Faces, 290
Fet-Fruners, Prince, 279-281
films from fairy tales, 224, 273, 307, 314
Finnish fairy tale, 319
Firebird, 334-337
First Girl, 328-329
"Fisherman & His Wife", The", 235, 264-266
"Fly, The", 254
Flying Head, 290
"Flying Head, The", 290

French fairy tales, 202, 220, 272, 298, 312
"Frog Prince, The", 195, 208-209

G

German fairy tales, 208, 236, 264, 306, 316
giant killer, 295, 305
"Girl Who Combed Pearls, The", 244-245
"Girl who Pretended to Be a Boy, The", 195, 271, 278-281
golden apples, 211
golden donkey, 294
golden hen, 294
"Golden Goose, The", 251
"Goldilocks & the Three Bears", 306
good luck charms, 264
"Goodman of Wastness, The", 322-323
Greek fairy tale, 332
Grey, Sir George, 285
Grimm, the Brothers, 199, 204, 209, 211, 251, 267, 294, 306, 315

H

"Heart's Door, The", 319-321
Hungarian fairy tale, 252

I

"I Ate the Loaf", 243
Iliane, Princess, 280-281
Indian fairy tale, 324
Inuit fairy tale, 218
Iranian fairy tale, 240
Irish fairy tales, 213, 267
Italian fairy tale, 274
Ivan, 334-337
"Ivan & the Firebird", 334-337

J

Jack, 195, 291-295
  Lazy, 235, 250-251
"Jack & the Beanstalk", 195, 291-295
"Jack the Giant Killer", 305
Jamaican fairy tale, 282
Jamie Freel, 213
"Jamie Freel & the Young Lady", 213-215
Japanese fairy tales, 207, 331
Jewish fairy tale, 287
jinn, 286

K

Kahukura, 284-285
"Kahukura & the Net-Makers", 284-285
Kenyan fairy tale, 206
Koschei the Deathless, 337

L

La Fontaine, 212
"Lame Fox, The", 195, 210-212
"Lazy Jack", 250-251
"Little One Inch", 207
Little One Inch, 207
"Little Red Riding Hood", 272-273
Little Red Riding Hood, 192, 272-273
love, 308, 311
luck, 235, 239, 242, 264, 292, 302
Luemba, 302-303

M

"Magic Whistle, A", 296-297
"Man-Crow", 282-283
Man-Crow, 282-283

Maori fairy tale, 284
Maria, 230-233
Mavungu, 302-303
Mbokothe, 206
Mecca, 243
mermaid, 322
Milky-White, 291
Moe, Jørgen, 304
"Mushkil Gusha", 240-242
Mushkil Gusha, 240-242

N

naga, 327
Native American fairy tales, 290, 328
nature spirit, 260
Nihon Shoki, 228
North American fairy tale, 248
Norwegian fairy tales, 246, 304
Nzambi's daughter, 302-303

O

ogre, 207,
ogress, 205, 280
Oisin, 228
oni, 207
operas from fairy tales, 224, 227
Otohime, Princess, 228

P

patupaiarehe, 284
"Peasant's Wise Daughter, The", 267
Perrault, Charles, 198, 202, 253, 272, 298, 299, 312, 314
Pinocchio, 245
"Poor Girl Who Became Queen, The", 235, 267-269
Portuguese fairy tale, 244
"Prince Nettles", 252-253
Psyche, 225
"Puss in Boots", 195, 253

R

"Rapunzel", 316-318
Rapunzel, 311, 316-318
Romanian fairy tale, 278
Romero, Silvio, 230
"Rumpelstiltskin", 236-238
Rumpelstiltskin, 236-238
Russian fairy tales, 288, 334

S

St George, 196
Scottish fairy tales, 322, 338
selkie, 322
Severi, 319-321
"Shape-Changer, The", 206
"Shoes That Were Danced to
  Pieces", 256-257
"Sleeping Beauty, The", 202-205
"Sleeping Prince, The", 332-333
"Snake Prince, The", 311,
  324-327
"Snow White", 306-309
Snow White, 196, 306-309
"Snow Wife, The", 331
Soliday, 282-283
Spanish fairy tale, 243
Speaking Bird, The, 277

spinning, 199, 203, 236
Sunlight, 279-281
Surinamese fairy tale, 214
swagman, 296

T, U

"That's a Lie!", 246-247
"Three Magic Oranges",
  226-227
Tir nan-Og, 228
Tom Thumb, 207
transformations, 195, 201, 212,
  337
Trinidadian fairy tale, 239
troll, 197, 304
"Twin Brothers, The", 302-303
"Unknown Sister, The", 216-217
Urashima, 228-229
"Urashima & the Turtle", 201,
  228-229

V

Vappu, 320-321
Vasilisa, Princess, 334-337
Vietnamese fairy tale, 254

W

Walt Disney, 199, 307, 308,
  314
"Waltzing Matilda", 296
weaving, 258
"Whale's Soul & Its Burning
  Heart, A", 201, 218-219
"Why the Sea Moans", 230-233
wishing well, 208
witch, 196, 288, 341
witchdoctor, 302
wolf, 272-273, 278-279
"Wonderful Brocade, The", 235,
  258-261

Y, Z

Yeats, W. B., 197
"Yeh-hsien", 312
Zaïrian fairy tale, 302

Acknowledgements to Part One

Photographic Credits
t=top, b=bottom, c=centre, l=left, r=right

AKG London/Erich Lessing: 130tl.
American Museum of Natural History 53br, 75tr;
Courtesy Department Library Services (neg. no. 14471)
37tr.
Ancient Art & Architecture Collection/Ronald Sheridan
30bl, 45br, 98tl, 109br, 147tr, 154tl, 177tr; B. Wilson
front cover, 96tl.
Antikensammlungen und Glyptothek, Munich 104tl.
Ardea London 59tl.
Ashmolean Museum, Oxford 23b.
The Bridgeman Art Library/Bibliothèque Nationale
157tr; British Museum, London, front cover, 8, 140tl;
Bernard Cox/Archaeological Museum 170tl.
The British Library (Add. 10,294 f.94) 158bl.
The British Museum 16l, 29tr, 46bl, back cover, 84bl,
80tl, 87br, 102, 103tr, 105tr, 110bl, 112tl, 145br, 149tr,
150tl, 151br, front cover, 168tl.
Bruce Coleman Ltd /Mr R. V. Bryant: 124b; Thomas
Buchholz 20bl; Gerald Cubitt 43tr; Stephen J. Krasemann
74t; Hans Reinhard 72tl.
Michael Diggin 161tr.
C.M Dixon 94bl, 96bl, 119tl, 138bl, 175tr.
Ecoscene/Whitty 92tl.
Finnish Tourist Board 54br.
Michael & Patricia Fogden 142tl.
Werner Forman Archive /Arhus Kunst Museum,
Denmark 165tr; National Museum of Ireland: 126b;
Schindler Collection, New York: 36tl; Statens Historiska
Museum, Stockholm, front cover, 18tl, front cover, 64tl;
Fortean Picture Library/Allen Kennedy 128bl.
Germanisches National Museum, Nürnberg 88tl.
Sonia Halliday Photographs 166cl.
Hamburgisches Museum für Völkerkunde 68l.
Robert Harding Picture Library 42bl, 108tl, 113tr, 146bl,
157br; Michael Jenner back cover, 127tr; Robert McLeod
25tr.

Michael Holford 38tl, 45tr, 48tl, 60tl, 61tr, 81tr, 84tl,
99tr, 107br, 144l, 146tl, 174tl.
Neil Holmes 88bl, 107tr.
The Hutchison Library 42tl, 31tr, 77r, 117tr, 177br.
Instituto Nacional de Antropologia e Historia, Mexico
141cr.
Japan National Tourist Organization 26tl.
La Belle Aurore/Steve Davey & Juliet Coombe 29br.
Collection Musée de l'Homme, Paris 76tl.
National Museum of Denmark, Copenhagen 63cr, 120tl,
122cl, 164cl.
National Museum of Ireland front cover, 90bl.
National Museum of Scotland 159tr.
NHPA/Orion Press 24tl.
Oslo Ship Museum 65tl, 118bl.
OSF /Animals Animals/Roger Brown 28tl; Richard Kolar
35tr;   Martin Chillmaid 19tr; Jeff Foott 152-153; Breck P.
Kent 33tr; John Netherton 100-101; Ben Osborne 51tr.
Planet Earth Pictures/David Redfern: 66bl.
Pitt Rivers Museum, Oxford 56bl, 69tr, 169tr.
Poseidon Pictures/Peter J. Terry: 138tl.
Rijksmuseum voor Volkenkunde, Leiden/Ben Grishaauer
93tr.
© photo RMN 44tl, 52tl, 154bl.
Royal Geographical Society/Paul Harris 34tl.
Matti Ruotsalainen 56tl.
Scala 148tl.
Harry Smith Collection/Polunin Collection 131tr.
Statens Historiska Museum, Stockholm 62tl, 162bl.
Turkish Tourist Office 170bl.
**University Museum of Archaeology and Anthropology,
Cambridge** back cover, 127br.
Universitäts und Landesbibliothek, Bonn 89tr.
Jerry Young 14-15, 22tl, 40-41, 78-79, 136-137, 178-179.
Wales Tourist Board 114tl, 115br.
Michel Zabé 143tr.
Zefa Pictures/Konrad Helbig 95cr.

Dorling Kindersley would like to thank:
Mr G. Bates; the Corbally Stourton Art Gallery, London;
Sheila Dignen; Felicity Devlin of the National Museum of
Ireland; Lucy Godman; Jim Hamill of the Museum of
Mankind, London; Mr Hamim of the Indonesian Embassy,
London; Robin Hunter; The Keeper's Secretary, Pre-
history and Romano-British Dept, the British Museum,
London; Kew Gardens; Barbara Ann Kipfer, Ph. D.;
Father M. Kostic; Dr Kuniholm of the Malcolm &

Carolyn Einer Laboratory for Aegean and Near Eastern
Archaeology, New York; Meg McCulloch of the Australian
Tourist Commission, London; and Erja Tikka of the Finnish
Embassy, London, for their help in producing this book.

Illustrations pp. 180-187: Fiona Bell Currie

Index: Lynn Bresler

Acknowledgements to Part Two

Key: l=left, r=right, t=top, c=centre, a=above, b=below

The publisher would like to thank the following for their kind permission to reproduce the photographs:

AKG Photo: 334tl; British Museum, London 316b ; Dresden Gemäldegalerie, Alte Meister: *Im Wirtshaus*, David Teniers (1610–1690) 263; from *The Fisherman and His Wife*, P. Hey (1867–1952) 265tr ; *Suleiman the Magnificent*, 1530–40 Titian School, © Erich Lessing 280tl; *Peter I, the Great*, I. M. Nikitin (1690–1741) 336tl; *Trat ein Bursche in den Reigen*, 1902, A.P. Rabuschkin 298clb; *The Witch*, 1870, Hans Thoma 196br; *The Village of Thy Nguyen, 1958* 254; *Wilhelm IV of Bavaria, Tournament Vienna 1515* 278
American Museum of Natural History: 290bl; 329
© Bildarchiv Preussischer Kulturbesitz, Berlin: 199tl
Bildhuset, Ake Eison Lindman: 246
BFI Stills, Posters and Designs: United Artists (1942) 275
The Bridgeman Art Library, London: Chris Beetles Ltd., London: *Trinidad*, by Albert Goodwin (1845–1932) 239 ; Bible Society, London: *Seven-headed Serpent* , from the Book of Revelations, Luther Bible (c.1530) 279; Bonhams, London: *Indian seven-jewelled necklace* 324; British Library, London: *Arabian Nights, "He Saw a Genie of Monstrous Bulk"*, by René Bull (d. 1942) 197tr, 286; British Library, London: *Border Detail of a Mermaid and a Tinker* 322bl; Christie's Images: *The Alchemist at Work*, by David Teniers the Elder (1582–1649) 236b; The Maas Gallery, London: *The Stuff That Dreams Are Made Of*, by John Anster Fitzgerald (1832–1906) 194; Manchester City Art Galleries: *Cupid & Psyche* by Sir Edward Burne-Jones 225tr; Private collection: *Duleep Singh, Maharajah of Lahore*, 1854 by Franz Xavier Winterhalter (1806–73) 325; private collection: Genesis 28: *10 Jacob's Ladder*, Nuremberg Bible (1483) 293
By Permission of the British Library, London: *Shelfmark G17758* 272tl; *Shelfmark C57.a.20* 298
The British Museum, London: 6
© Neil Campbell-Sharpe: 222tl
Jean Loup Charmet: 198tc ; 288tl
Bruce Coleman Ltd.: Alain Compost 277; M. Diggin 267; Christer Fredriksson 304; Stephen J. Krasemann 328clb; Gordon Langsbury 262cl; Claudio Marigo 231br; William S. Paton 339tr; Mary Plage 226; Staffan Widstrand 218
Sue Cunningham Photographics: 232tl ; 232bl
Michael Diggin Photography: 267
Ecoscene: James Marchington 322tl
E.T. Archive: 253 ; 256tl
Mary Evans Picture Library: 195br; 197tl; 199cla; 202tl; 207; 216tl; 240bl; 245br 258bl; 283; 305; 306tl; 306bl; 309; 312; 340cl; 345br
Chris Fairclough Colour Library : 260bl
Ffotograff: © Patricia Aithie 259
The Finnish Tourist Board: 320
Werner Forman Archive: Metropolitan Museum of Art, New York 258tl ; Museum für Volkenkunde 302tl
Fortean Picture Library/Janet & Colin Bord: 208
Garden Picture Library: Brian Carter 238
Ronald Grant Archive: 224tl, 301, 314bl; © Disney Enterprises, Inc. 199crb; © Disney Enterprises, Inc.308
Guildhall Art Gallery, Corporation of London: 341

Robert Harding Picture Library: 202bl, 229tr, 233, 319; Kathy Collins 262bl; © Carol Jopp 331tr; Mike Newton 276; Ellen Rooney 339br; Bildagentur Schuster, Schmied 290tl
Michael Holford: 260tl; 327tr
Hulton Getty: 268clb
Hutchison Library: © A. Eames 284
Images Colour Library/Charles Walker Collection: 196bl
Palace/NFFC/ITC (courtesy Kobal) 273
Magnum: H. Gruyaert 321
Manchester City Art Galleries: *A Winter Night'sTale*, D. Maclise 198bl
© Musées Royaux des Beaux Art de Belgique, Bruxelles/ © Koninklijke Musea voor Schone Kunsten van Belgie, Brussel: *Anthropomorphic Landscape, Portrait of a Man*, Dutch School 16th century 195ca
Museum of London: 300
Reproduced by courtesy of the Trustees of the National Gallery, London: *A Grotesque Old Woman*, Quinten Massys (1465–1530) 280bl ; *The Vision of the Blessed Gabriel*, detail, Carlo Crivelli (c. 1430/1435–94) 211
Det Nationalhistoriske Museum på Frederiksborg, Hillerod: *Portrait of Hans Christian Andersen*, 1834 Albert Küchler 199tr
National Maritime Museum: 245tr
Natural History Photographic Agency : E. A. Jones 266
Peter Newark's American Pictures: 249
Peter Newark's Western Americana: 328tl; 330
Opie Collection. Bodleian Library, Oxford: 291tr
Oxford Scientific Films: © Paul Franklin 206; © David Curl 296bl; © Jorge Sierra Antinolo 334cl
Panos Pictures: J. C. Callow 302bl
Photostage: © Donald Cooper 227
Real Academia de San Fernando, Madrid: 295br
Rex Features: Michael Friedel 256bl; © Ross Bray, Wildtrek Media 296tl
Royal Albert Memorial Museum: 303
Scala: 196tr
Science & Society Picture Library: 275tr
The Slide File: 213 ; 214 ; 215
Sotheby's Picture Library: 222cl
South American Pictures/Tony Morrison: 231tr
Leslie E. Spatt: 204
Tony Stone Images: 243; Darryl Torckler 285; Hans Peter Huber 265crb; Paul Harris 326; Robert Frerck 327br
Tate Gallery, London: *Oberon, Titania, and Puck*, c.1785 William Blake (1757–1827) 197br
Topham Picture Source: 297
Tokyo National Museum: 229br
Trip: Ibrahim 241; W. Jacobs 252; N. Price 335; H. Rogers 240tl
Reproduced by courtesy of the Trustees of the Victoria and Albert Museum: 331crb
Rex Whistler: *Reversable Head of Cinderella and the Godmother*, c. 1935, Estate of Rex Whistler 1996, all rights reserved, DACS 314tl
Rodney Wilson: 200-201c; 234-235c; 269 ; 270-271c; 310-311c
Zefa: 282, 318

Dorling Kindersley would like to thank:
Lynn Bresler for the index, and Janet Allis for design assistance.